SMART SOLUTIONS

Skills, Problem Solving, Tools, and Applications

Algebra and Geometry

Jerry Howett

New Readers Press

Acknowledgments

Advisers to the Series

Connie Eichhorn
Supervisor of Transitional Services
Omaha Public Schools
Omaha, NE

Mary B. Puleo
Assistant Director
Sarasota County Adult and
Community Education
Sarasota, FL

Lois Kasper
Instructional Facilitator
N.Y. Board of Education
New York, NY

Margaret Rogers
Coordinator
San Juan Unified Adult Education
Sacramento, CA

Jan Phillips
Assistant Professor
William Rainey Harper College
Palatine, IL

Consultant/Field-tester

Connie Eichhorn
Supervisor of Transitional Services
Omaha Public Schools
Omaha, NE

Library of Congress Cataloging-in-Publication Data

Howett, Jerry.
Algebra and geometry / Jerry Howett.
p. cm. — (Smart solutions)
ISBN 1-56420-124-4 (pbk.)
1. Algebra. 2. Geometry. I. Title. II. Series.
QA152.2.H69   1996
512' . 12—dc20   96-4930
                                                           CIP

ISBN 1-56420-124-4

Copyright © 1996
New Readers Press
Publishing Division of Laubach Literacy International
Box 131, Syracuse, New York 13210-0131

Printed in the United States of America

Director of Acquisitions and Development: Christina Jagger
Photo Illustrations: Mary McConnell
Developer: Learning Unlimited, Oak Park, IL
Developmental Editor: Kathy Osmus

9 8 7 6 5 4 3 2

Contents

5   **Introduction**

6   **Skill Preview**

12 Unit 1: The Basics of Algebra

14   Writing Expressions

16   Powers and Roots

18   Order of Operations

20   Perimeter and Area   Application

22   The Number Line   Tools

24   Adding and Subtracting Signed Numbers

26   Multiplying and Dividing Signed Numbers

28   Expressions and Variables

30   Substitution

32   Finding Patterns in Algebra   Problem Solver

34   Mixed Review

36   Simple Formulas and Substitution

38   Using a Calculator   Tools

40   The Distributive Property

42   Simplifying Expressions

44   Scientific Notation   Application

46   Celsius and Fahrenheit Thermometers   Tools

48   Writing a Number Sentence   Problem Solver

50   Unit 1 Review

52 Unit 2: Putting Algebra to Use

54   Solving Equations

56   Addition and Subtraction Equations

58   Multiplication and Division Equations

60   Equations and Multiple Operations

62   Simplifying Equations

64   Using Substitution

66   Using Formulas   Tools

68   Solving Inequalities

70   Mixed Review

72   Lists and Diagrams   Tools

74   Algebra Word Problems   Problem Solver

78   Percents and Equations   Application

80   Using Ratio   Application

82   Using Proportion   Application

84   Different Ways to Solve Problems   Problem Solver

86   Unit 2 Review

88 Unit 3: The Basics of Geometry

90   Points, Lines, and Angles

92   Protractors   Tools

94   Pairs of Angles

96   Rulers, Yardsticks, and Tape Measures   Tools

98   Changing Units of Measure   Problem Solver

100 Mixed Review

102 Properties of Quadrilaterals

104 Properties of Circles

106 Properties of Triangles

108 The Pythagorean Theorem

110 Understanding Maps   Application

112 Unit 3 Review

114 Unit 4: Using Geometry

116	Perimeter and Circumference Formulas	Tools
118	Solving Complex Perimeter Problems	
120	Area Formulas	Tools
122	Solving Complex Area Problems	
124	Solid Figures	
126	Volume Formulas	Tools
128	Surface Area	
130	Mixed Review	
132	Seeing Geometric Figures	Application
134	Choosing Perimeter, Area, or Volume	Problem Solver
136	Drawing a Picture	Problem Solver
138	Renovating a Room	Application
140	Using the Cost Formula	Application
142	Unit 4 Review	

144 Unit 5: Combining Algebra and Geometry

146	Similar Figures	
148	Using Proportion with Similar Figures	
150	Finding Missing Dimensions	Application
152	Equations and Geometric Figures	
154	Setting Up Solutions	Problem Solver
156	Mixed Review	
158	The Coordinate System	Tools
160	Distances on the Coordinate System	
162	Making a Table of Patterns	Tools
164	Graphing Multistep Linear Equations	
166	Slope and Intercept	
168	Linear Equations and Graphs	Application
170	Unit 5 Review	

172	**Posttest**
178	**Answer Key**
217	**Glossary**
221	**Tool Kit**

Powers, Square Roots, and Order of Operations
Units of Linear Measurement and Rounding
Formulas and Calculators

Introduction

Math skills play an increasingly vital role in today's world. Everyone needs to work confidently with numbers to solve problems on the job and in other areas of daily life.

This book and the others in the *Smart Solutions* series can help you meet your everyday math needs. Each unit is organized around four key areas that will build your competence and self-confidence:

- **Skills** pages present instruction and practice with both computation and word problems.

- **Tools** pages provide insight into how to use objects (such as rulers or calculators) or apply ideas (such as estimates or equations) to a wide variety of math situations.

- **Problem Solver** pages provide key strategies to help you become a successful problem solver.

- **Application** pages are real-life topics that require mathematics.

Key Features

Skill Preview: You can use the Skill Preview to determine what skills you already have and what you need to concentrate on.

Talk About It: At the beginning of each unit, you will have a topic to discuss with classmates. Talking about mathematics is key to building your understanding.

Key Concepts: Throughout the book, you will see this symbol ▶, which indicates key math concepts and rules.

Making Connections: Throughout each unit, you will work with topics that connect math ideas to various interest areas and to other math concepts.

Special Problems: These specially labeled problems require an in-depth exploration of math ideas. You may be asked to explain or draw or to do something else that demonstrates your math skills.

Working Together: At the end of each unit, you will work with a partner or small group to apply your math skills.

Mixed and Unit Reviews: Periodic checkups will help you see how well you understand the material and can apply what you have learned.

Posttest: At the end of the book, you will find a test that combines all of the book's topics. You can use this final review to judge how well you have mastered the book's skills and strategies.

Glossary: Use this list of terms to learn or review key math words and ideas.

Tool Kit: You can refer to these resource pages as you work through the book.

Skill Preview

This survey of math skills will help you and your teacher decide what you need to study to get the most out of this book. It will show you how much you already know and what you need to learn in the areas of algebra and geometry.

Do as much as you can in each section below. If you can't do all of the problems in a section, go ahead to the next section and do all of the problems that you can.

Note: Use any of the following formulas that you need.

- cost (*c*): $c = nr$ where n = number of items and r = rate
- distance (*d*): $d = rt$ where r = rate and t = time
- perimeter (*P*) of a rectangle: $P = 2l + 2w$ where l = length and w = width
- perimeter (*P*) of a square: $P = 4s$ where s = side
- circumference (*C*) of a circle: $C = \pi d$ where $\pi \approx 3.14$ and d = diameter
- area (*A*) of a rectangle: $A = lw$ where l = length and w = width
- area (*A*) of a triangle: $A = \frac{1}{2}bh$ where b = base and h = height
- area (*A*) of a circle: $A = \pi r^2$ where $\pi \approx 3.14$ and r = radius
- surface area of a cube: $6s^2$ where s = side
- volume (*V*) of a rectangular solid: $V = lwh$ where l = length, w = width, and h = height
- Pythagorean theorem: $c^2 = a^2 + b^2$ where c is the hypotenuse of a right triangle and a and b are the legs
- slope (*m*) of a line: $m = \frac{y_2 - y_1}{x_2 - x_1}$ where (x_1, y_1) and (x_2, y_2) are two points on the coordinate system

Part 1: The Basics of Algebra

1. $7^2 =$

2. $\sqrt{400} =$

3. $8 - 13 =$

4. $5(-12) =$

5. $19 + (-4) =$

6. $\frac{-45}{-15} =$

7. What is the value of $7m - 3$ when $m = 2$?

8. Write and simplify an expression for the perimeter of the rectangle shown here.

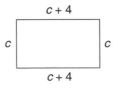

6

9. The formula $a = \frac{1}{2}(x + y)$ expresses the average (a) of two items, x and y. Use the formula to find the average of the two weights shown below.

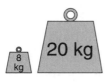

10. Write a number sentence that describes the relationship between these two line segments.

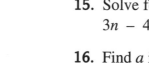

Part 2: Putting Algebra to Use

11. Solve for y in
$$24 = y - 17$$

12. Find r in
$$4r + 9 = 11$$

13. Solve for x in
$$9 = \frac{x}{5} - 3$$

14. Solve for c in
$$8c - 5 = 2c + 13$$

15. Solve for n in
$$3n - 4 < 17$$

16. Find a in
$$\frac{9}{10} = \frac{a}{6}$$

17. Tomás and José start driving at the same time and the same place. Tomás drives west at an average speed of 48 miles per hour, and José drives east at an average speed of 52 miles per hour. How far apart will they be in two hours?

18. Simplify the ratio of the length to the width of the rectangle below.

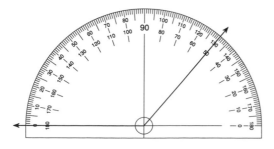

19. The ratio of men to women in Mr. Mikal's car repair class is 3:2. There are 20 students in the class. How many of the students are women?

20. The scale shown below is for a map. Find the distance between two towns if they are 1.5 inches apart on the map.

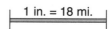

Part 3: The Basics of Geometry

21. What is the measurement of the angle?

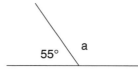

22. Find the measurement of $\angle$a.

55°   a

Skill Preview

Use the illustration at right to answer questions 23–24.

23. If ∠b = 109°, what is the measurement of ∠a?

24. Which angle is vertical to ∠a?

25. What is the length of the line segment in centimeters? (1 in. = 2.54 cm)

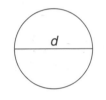

28. If ∠a and ∠c below are equal, what is the measurement of ∠a?

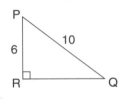

26. If the circle's diameter is 12.4 centimeters, what is the radius?

29. What is the length of side QR?

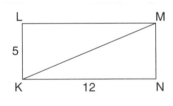

27. What is the measurement of the vertex angle?

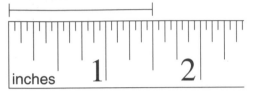

30. What is the diagonal distance from K to M?

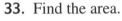

Part 4: Putting Geometry to Use

31. Find the perimeter.

$s = 9$ cm

32. Find the circumference.

10 cm

33. Find the area.

8 m

16 m

34. Find the area.

$s = 30$ m

35. Find the volume.

$s = 3$ in.

36. What is the volume of the rectangular container?

2 ft.

5 ft.   8 ft.

37. What is the surface area of the shipping container?

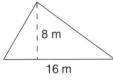

$s = 10$ ft.

8

The drawing below shows the floor plan of a carpentry shop and an adjoining storage room. Use the drawing to answer questions 38–40.

38. What is the perimeter of the space?

39. What is the floor area of the space?

40. At the price of $4 per square foot, what is the cost of putting a wood floor on the total space?

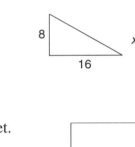

Part 5: Combining Algebra and Geometry

41. What measurement of the side labeled x will make the two triangles similar?

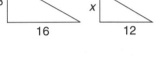

42. The area of the rectangle shown here is 180 square feet. What is the width?

43. The two rectangles are similar. Which of the following represents the side labeled x?

(1) $6 \cdot 12 \cdot 9$ (2) $6 + 12 + 9$ (3) $\frac{6 \cdot 12}{9}$

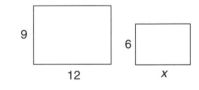

Use the illustration below to answer questions 44–46.

44. What are the coordinates of point A?

45. What is the distance from point A to point B?

46. What is the area of figure ABC?

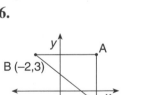

47. What are the coordinates of the y-intercept of the equation $y = x + 6$?

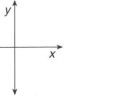

48. What is the slope of the line that passes through points P and Q?

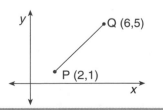

1. $7^2 = 7 \cdot 7 = \textbf{49}$

2. $\sqrt{400} = \textbf{20}$

3. $8 - 13 = \textbf{–5}$

4. $5(-12) = \textbf{–60}$

5. $19 + (-4) = 19 - 4 = \textbf{15}$

6. $\frac{-45}{-15} = 3 \; or \; \textbf{+3}$

7. $7(2) - 3 = 14 - 3 = \textbf{11}$

8. $P = 2(c + 4) + 2c$

   $P = 2c + 8 + 2c$

   $\boldsymbol{P = 4c + 8}$

9. $a = \frac{1}{2}(8 + 20)$

   $a = \frac{1}{2}(28)$

   $a = \textbf{14 kg}$

10. $3m + 4 = 19$

11. $24 = y - 17$

    $\textbf{41} = y$

12. $4r + 9 = 11$

    $4r = 2$

    $r = \frac{1}{2}$

13. $9 = \frac{x}{5} - 3$

    $12 = \frac{x}{5}$

    $\textbf{60} = x$

14. $8c - 5 = 2c + 13$

    $6c = 18$

    $c = \textbf{3}$

15. $3n - 4 < 17$

    $3n < 21$

    $n < \textbf{7}$

16. $\frac{9}{10} = \frac{a}{6}$

    $10a = 54$

    $a = \frac{54}{10} = \textbf{5}\frac{2}{5}$

17. $d = rt = 48 \cdot 2 = 96$

    $d = rt = 52 \cdot 2 = 104$

    distance apart $= 96 + 104 = \textbf{200 mi.}$

18. $15:9 = \textbf{5:3}$

19. $3x + 2x = 20$

    $5x = 20$

    $x = 4$

    number of women $= 2(4) = \textbf{8}$

20. $\frac{\text{inches}}{\text{miles}} \; \frac{1}{18} = \frac{1.5}{x}$

    $x = \textbf{27 mi.}$

21. $130°$

22. $180° - 55° = \textbf{125°}$

23. $180° - 109° = \textbf{71°}$

24. $\angle c$

25. $1.5(2.54) = \textbf{3.81 cm}$

26. $r = \frac{12.4}{2} = \textbf{6.2 cm}$

27. $60° + 40° = 100°$

    $180° - 100° = \textbf{80°}$

28. $180° - 112° = 68°$

    $\frac{68°}{2} = \textbf{34°}$

29. $10^2 = 6^2 + b^2$

    $100 = 36 + b^2$

    $\textbf{8} = b$

30. $c^2 = 5^2 + 12^2$

    $c^2 = 25 + 144$

    $c = \textbf{13}$

31. $P = 4s = 4(9) = \textbf{36 cm}$

32. $C = \pi d = 3.14(10) = \textbf{31.4 cm}$

33. $A = \frac{1}{2}bh = \frac{1}{2} \cdot 16 \cdot 8 = \textbf{64 m}^2$

34. $A = s^2 = 30^2 = \textbf{900 m}^2$

35. $V = s^3 = 3^3 = \textbf{27 in.}^3$

36. $V = lwh = 8 \cdot 5 \cdot 2 = \textbf{80 ft.}^3$

37. $A = 6s^2 = 6(10)^2 = \textbf{600 ft.}^2$

38. $P = 2(25) + 2(30) = \textbf{110 ft.}$

39. $A = 25 \cdot 20 + 15 \cdot 10$

    $A = 500 + 150 = \textbf{650 ft.}^2$

40. $c = 650(4) = \textbf{\$2,600}$

41. $\frac{8}{16} = \frac{x}{12}$

    $16x = 96$

    $x = \textbf{6}$

42. $w = \frac{180}{20} = \textbf{9 ft.}$

43. (3) $\frac{6 \cdot 12}{9}$

44. $(3,3)$

45. 5

46. $\frac{1}{2} \cdot 5 \cdot 4 = \textbf{10}$

47. $(0,6)$

48. $\frac{5 - 1}{6 - 2} = \frac{4}{4} = \textbf{1}$

Skill Preview Diagnostic Chart

Make note of any problems you answered incorrectly. Notice the skill area for each problem you missed. As you work through this book, be sure to focus on these skill areas.

Problem Number	Skill Area	Unit
1	Finding powers	1
2	Finding square roots	1
3, 5	Adding and subtracting signed numbers	1
4, 6	Multiplying and dividing signed numbers	1
7	Substituting	1
8	Simplifying expressions	1
9	Using formulas	1
10	Writing a number sentence	1
11	Solving one-step equations	2
12, 13	Solving two-step equations	2
14	Simplifying equations	2
15	Solving inequalities	2
17	Solving motion problems	2
18, 19	Using ratio	2
16, 20	Using proportion	2
21, 22	Measuring angles	3
23, 24	Identifying pairs of angles	3
25	Converting measurements	3
26	Using the properties of circles	3
27, 28	Using the properties of triangles	3
29, 30	Using the Pythagorean theorem	3
31, 38	Finding perimeter	4
32	Finding circumference	4
33, 34, 39	Finding area	4
35, 36	Finding volume	4
37	Finding surface area	4
40	Using the cost formula with area	4
41	Using proportion with similar figures	5
42	Finding missing dimensions	5
43	Setting up solutions	5
44	Identifying points on the coordinate system	5
45	Finding distance on the coordinate system	5
46	Finding area on the coordinate system	5
47, 48	Graphing linear equations	5

Unit 1

The Basics of Algebra

Skills

Writing expressions

Powers and roots

Order of operations

Signed numbers

Expressions and variables

Substitution

Using formulas

Distributive property

Simplifying expressions

Tools

Number line

Calculators

Thermometers

Problem Solvers

Finding patterns in algebra

Writing a number sentence

Applications

Perimeter and area

Scientific notation

Algebra is a branch of mathematics that builds on the arithmetic you already know. Algebra introduces the expressions, equations, and formulas that you need to extend your problem-solving abilities.

Let's compare arithmetic and algebra. Arithmetic applies to specific numbers and situations. For example, you can find the sum of 9 and 17. Algebra is more general. With algebra, you can show the sum of 9 and *any* number.

In this unit, you will learn how to describe situations using algebra.

When Do I Use Algebra?

"Does anybody really use algebra? When am I ever going to use it?" Have you thought or heard those questions? In fact, people often use algebra without knowing it. Read through the brief survey below.

Check the situations that apply to you.

☐ You know that the sales tax in your area adds a certain percent to everything you buy.

☐ You have doubled the ingredients in a recipe to make twice as much.

☐ You pay almost 25% of any money you earn in taxes.

☐ A bus stops at a corner near your house every 15 minutes. You want to know when the next bus should arrive.

☐ You know how many miles you can drive on 1 gallon of gas, so you know how far you can drive on a full tank.

How many statements did you put a check next to? Would you be surprised to find that algebra could help you in the situations above?

Tell whether you would use arithmetic (specific) or algebra (general) to solve each of the following.

_____ 1. Find the sum of Addie's rent of $380 a month and her car payment of $119 a month.

_____ 2. Write an expression for the maximum amount of rent Carlos can pay if rent is no more than $\frac{1}{4}$ of his monthly salary.

_____ 3. Saria usually leaves a 15% tip in restaurants. Express the amount of tip she leaves for any restaurant bill.

_____ 4. André wrote a check for $48.95. Find his new checking account balance if he started with $220.73.

Throughout this unit, you may use a calculator wherever that would be useful. Information about using a calculator appears on page 224.

Talk About It

Discuss problems 1 through 4 above. For each problem, explain why you would use either arithmetic or algebra to solve it.

Writing Expressions

An **expression** is a mathematical amount written with symbols. Expressions are written using the four operations—addition (+), subtraction (−), multiplication (×), and division (÷).

Addition and Subtraction

Addition and subtraction are easy to recognize. Addition combines amounts, and subtraction separates amounts. Review the following characteristics of addition and subtraction.

Addition

$5 + 4 = 9$

└ sum

In addition, the order of the numbers being added doesn't matter.

Example: $3 + 2$ *is the same as* $2 + 3$

When you add 0 to a number, you get the original number.

Example: $7 + 0 = 7$

Subtraction

$9 - 4 = 5$

└ difference

In subtraction, the order of the numbers *is* important.

Example: $8 - 6$ *is not the same as* $6 - 8$

When you subtract 0 from a number, you get the original number.

Example: $9 - 0 = 9$

Addition and subtraction are *opposites* of each other. When operations are opposites, they are called **inverse operations.** If you add 4 to a number, you can *undo* the result by subtracting 4.

Example: $17 + 4 = 21$ and $21 - 4 = 17$

A. Write an expression for each problem. Do not solve the problem. The first one is done as an example.

___$9 + $2___ **1.** Marta's hourly wage of $9 increased by $2.

_____ **2.** Henry's weight of 220 pounds went down 15 pounds.

_____ **3.** The 6:00 A.M. temperature of 12° went up 8° by noon.

_____ **4.** The visiting baseball team had 3 runs going into the last inning. The team then scored 6 more runs.

_____ **5.** The television that originally sold for $299 was marked down $50.

Multiplication and Division

To help you recognize when multiplication or division is needed, keep the following principles in mind. Multiplication combines equal amounts, and division separates equal amounts. Several symbols that show multiplication or division are shown below.

Multiplication

$5 \times 4 = 20$

           ⌐ product

In multiplication, the order of the numbers being multiplied doesn't matter.

Example: 5×4 *is the same as* 4×5

Other ways to show multiplication:

raised dot $5 \cdot 4$

parentheses $5(4)$ or $(5)(4)$

Division

      ⌐ dividend

$20 \div 4 = 5$ ◄——— quotient

      ⌐ divisor

In division, the order of the numbers is important.

Example: $20 \div 4$ *is not the same as* $4 \div 20$. In fact, $20 \div 4 = 5$ and $4 \div 20 = \frac{1}{5}$

Other ways to show division:

division bracket $4\overline{)20}$

fraction bar $\frac{20}{4}$

slash $20/4$

Multiplication and division are opposites, or inverse operations. If you multiply 4 by 3, you can *undo* the result by dividing by 3.

Example: $4(3) = 12$ and $12 \div 3 = 4$

B. **For each problem, write the same expression three different ways, using a different symbol for multiplication or division in each. Do not solve.**

6. Janice saved $25 each month for 5 months.

7. Celia has to take medicine for 28 days. How many weeks is that?

8. Half of the $240 belongs to Maurice.

9. Three friends agreed to share $36 equally.

10. I bought 10 gallons of gas for $1.149 per gallon.

C. **Use the drawing below to write *two* expressions for each problem: one using numbers and one using the letters A and B. The first one is started for you.**

11. the sum of A and B $36 +$ _____ $A +$ _____

12. the difference between A and B

13. the product of A and B

14. the quotient found when B is divided by A

A [   ] 36

B [   ] 12

Powers and Roots

In mathematics, a **power** shows repeated multiplication, or a number multiplied by itself. The expression 4^2 means "4 to the second power." In this expression, 4 is the **base** and 2 is the **exponent.** To solve a power, multiply the base by itself the number of times shown by the exponent. $4^2 = 4 \cdot 4 = \mathbf{16}$

A number raised to the second power is called a **square.** $4^2 = 16$ can be read as "4 **squared** equals 16." An expression showing a number raised to the third power is called a **cube.** $6^3 = 216$ can be read as "6 **cubed** equals 216."

Solving Powers

Examples: $6^3 = 6 \cdot 6 \cdot 6 = \mathbf{216}$

$$36 \cdot 6$$

$$5^4 = 5 \cdot 5 \cdot 5 \cdot 5 = \mathbf{625}$$

$$10^5 = 10 \cdot 10 \cdot 10 \cdot 10 \cdot 10 = \mathbf{100,000}$$

A. Calculate each power. The first one is started for you.

1. 8^2 $8 \cdot 8 =$ _____

2. 12^2 _____

3. 3^2 _____

4. 20^2 _____

5. 2^3 _____

6. 4^3 _____

7. 10^3 _____

8. 1^4 _____

9. 2^4 _____

10. 15^2 _____

11. 7^2 _____

12. 9^3 _____

In part A, some of the powers you calculated were numbers to the second power. A whole number squared results in a **perfect square.** In the problem $4^2 = 16$, 16 is a perfect square.

B. Complete the table showing some common perfect squares.

$2^2 =$ _____	$5^2 =$ _____	$8^2 =$ _____	$11^2 =$ _____	$14^2 =$ _____
$3^2 =$ _____	$6^2 =$ _____	$9^2 =$ _____	$12^2 =$ _____	$15^2 =$ _____
$4^2 =$ _____	$7^2 =$ _____	$10^2 =$ _____	$13^2 =$ _____	$20^2 =$ _____

Square Roots

The opposite of raising a number to the second power is finding the **square root.**
The symbol for this operation is called a **radical sign** $\sqrt{}$.

Example: $\sqrt{36}$ **Check**

Ask yourself, "What number multiplied   To check a square root, multiply the number
by itself equals 36?"   by itself.

The square root of 36 is 6. $\sqrt{36} = \mathbf{6}$ $6 \cdot 6 = 36$ so $\sqrt{36} = 6$

C. Find the value of each square root. Ask yourself, "What number multiplied by itself equals this number?"

13. $\sqrt{64}$ = _____   15. $\sqrt{25}$ = _____   17. $\sqrt{49}$ = _____   19. $\sqrt{4}$ = _____

14. $\sqrt{100}$ = _____   16. $\sqrt{81}$ = _____   18. $\sqrt{144}$ = _____   20. $\sqrt{9}$ = _____

Most numbers do not have a whole number as a square root. To find the square root of
a number, you can use a calculator. Just enter the number and then press the square
root key $\boxed{\sqrt{}}$. But what happens if you don't have a calculator handy? You can use
your knowledge of perfect squares to *estimate* a square root.

Example: $\sqrt{52}$

You know that $\sqrt{49} = 7$ and that $\sqrt{64} = 8$. You can conclude that $\sqrt{52}$ is between, or
within the **range** of, 7 and 8.

D. Use your knowledge of perfect squares and the answer choices to find the
range for each square root.

21. $\sqrt{40}$ is between   22. $\sqrt{5}$ is between   23. $\sqrt{105}$ is between
   (1) 6 and 7   **(1)** 1 and 2   **(1)** 9 and 10
   (2) 7 and 8   **(2)** 2 and 3   **(2)** 10 and 11
   (3) 8 and 9   **(3)** 3 and 4   **(3)** 11 and 12

24. **Discuss** Talk about how you could use your knowledge of perfect squares to find
   the square root or an estimated square root of large numbers such as 4,900 or
   4,000. Think about the perfect squares you already know.

Order of Operations

Look at the expression $3 + 2 \cdot 4$. To **evaluate** the expression means to solve the expression. You must decide what to do first: add $3 + 2$ or multiply $2 \cdot 4$. If you add first, you get $5 \cdot 4 = 20$. If you multiply first, you get $3 + 8 = 11$. Both answers cannot be right.

To make sure that everyone solving an expression gets the same answer, mathematicians agreed on an order of operations to follow.

Order of Operations

To evaluate expressions, perform the given operations in the following order. Within each level, work from *left to right*.

1. Grouping symbols: parentheses, fraction bars
2. Powers and roots
3. Multiplication and division
4. Addition and subtraction

$$(4 + 5)^2 - 7 \cdot 3$$
$$9^2 - 7 \cdot 3$$
$$81 - 7 \cdot 3$$
$$81 - 21$$
$$\mathbf{60}$$

Notice how the numbers are brought down in each line of work in this example. The 9 is under $4 + 5$, and 81 is under 9^2. You may find it useful to line up evaluation problems in this way.

Following Order of Operations

Example 1: Evaluate the expression $\frac{5 + 7}{2}$. (*Note:* When working with fraction bars, do all of the work above and below the fraction bar before dividing the top by the bottom.)

Step 1. Copy the expression.

$$\frac{5 + 7}{2}$$

Step 2. Do the operation above the fraction bar.

$$\frac{12}{2}$$

Step 3. Divide 12 by 2. The solution is 6.

$$\mathbf{6}$$

Example 2: To avoid arguments, Angela gives each of her children the same amount of candy. She had 3 pieces left over after giving 2 pieces to each of her 4 children. Write and evaluate an expression to find how many pieces of candy she had to start with.

Step 1. Write the expression.

$$3 + 2 \cdot 4$$

Step 2. Since multiplication comes before addition in the order of operations, multiply first.

$$3 + 8$$

Step 3. Add $3 + 8$. The solution is 11.

$$\mathbf{11}$$

A. Evaluate (solve) each expression.

1. $3 \cdot 10 + 5 \cdot 2$

2. $8 + 3 - 5$

3. $\sqrt{36} - 3$

4. $\frac{12}{2} - \frac{10}{2}$

5. $(9 + 6)^2$

6. $\frac{8 + 12}{5 - 3}$

7. $4(7 - 1)$

8. $2 \cdot 7^2$

9. $\frac{20 - 4}{8}$

10. $5(6 + 3) - 12$

11. $3 \cdot 5^2 + 10$

12. $10(3 + 9)^2$

13. $3 \cdot 8 - (5 + 7)$

14. $\frac{15}{12 - 7}$

15. $6(5 - 1)^2$

B. Choose the expression that shows what each expression should look like after the first step is completed.

16. $8 \cdot 5 - 3 \cdot 4$
   (*Hint:* Multiplication before subtraction)
   (1) $8 - 2 - 4$
   (2) $40 - 12$
   (3) $8 + 2 - 4$

17. $6 + \frac{21}{7} + 8$
   (1) $27 - 1$
   (2) $6 + 3 + 8$
   (3) $9 - 8$

18. $9(5 - 1)$
   (1) $9(4)$
   (2) $45 - 1$
   (3) $9(6)$

19. $(5 + 2)(5 - 2)$
   (1) $5 + 7 - 4$
   (2) $(5)(3)$
   (3) $(7)(3)$

20. $\frac{12 + 9}{3}$
   (1) $\frac{21}{3}$
   (2) $\frac{12}{3}$
   (3) $\frac{9}{3}$

21. $4 + \sqrt{9}$
   (1) $4 + 3$
   (2) $4 + 9$
   (3) $2 + 9$

Making Connections: Counting Money

Carlo counted the money in his wallet. He had three $1 bills, two $5 bills, and four $10 bills.

1. Write an expression for the total amount of money in Carlo's wallet.

2. Evaluate (solve) the expression. Compare your expression and answer with those of other students.

Perimeter and Area

The distance around a flat figure is the **perimeter.** To find the perimeter of a figure, write an expression to add the length of each side. Perimeter is measured in units including inches, feet, meters.

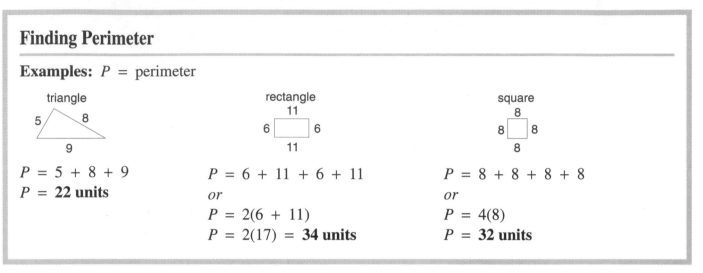

Finding Perimeter

Examples: P = perimeter

triangle

$P = 5 + 8 + 9$
$P =$ **22 units**

rectangle

$P = 6 + 11 + 6 + 11$
or
$P = 2(6 + 11)$
$P = 2(17) =$ **34 units**

square

$P = 8 + 8 + 8 + 8$
or
$P = 4(8)$
$P =$ **32 units**

A. Write an expression to find the perimeter of each of the following figures. Evaluate (solve) the expressions.

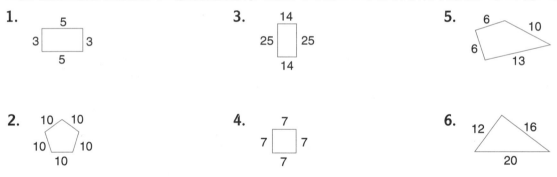

1.

3.

5.

2.

4.

6.

Area is a measure of the amount of surface on a flat figure. In the figure on the right, each square is 1 square unit. The figure is made up of how many units altogether?

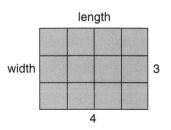

You could find the area by counting the number of square units on the figure's surface. However, with larger figures, this method would take too long. Also, not all figures will be divided into square units.

Another way to find the area is to multiply the length by the width. Do you get the same answer by counting the squares in the figure as you do when multiplying 3 by 4? You should have an answer of **12 square units** using either method.

B. Write *P* beside the items below that describe perimeter and *A* beside the items that describe area.

_____ 7. The amount of carpet needed to cover a bedroom floor

_____ 8. The length of fencing required to enclose a play yard

_____ 9. The amount of wood framing material to go around a picture

_____ 10. The number of ceramic tiles to cover the walls around a bathtub

_____ 11. The amount of paint needed to cover four garage walls

_____ 12. The length of pine trim required to go around a window

_____ 13. The amount of grass seed required to start a new lawn

---

Finding Area

A **rectangle** is a flat figure with four sides. Its opposite sides have equal lengths. To find the area of a rectangle, write an expression that multiplies the length by the width. Then evaluate the expression.

$A = lw$ where A = area, l = length, w = width
$A = 10 \cdot 4 = 40 =$ **40 square units**

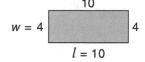

A **square** is a rectangle with four equal sides. To find the area of a square, write an expression that multiplies a side by a side or (side)^2. Then evaluate the expression.

$A = s^2$ where A = area, s = side
$A = 5^2 =$ **25 square units**

Note: Area is always expressed in **square units**—square inches, square feet, and so on.

C. Find the area of each of the following figures. Be sure to label your answers in square units.

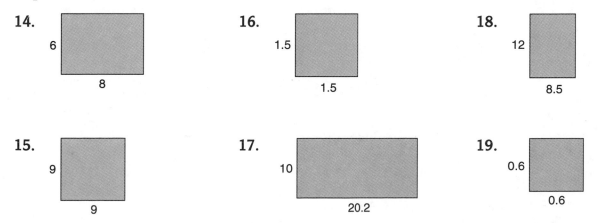

14. 6, 8

16. 1.5, 1.5

18. 12, 8.5

15. 9, 9

17. 10, 20.2

19. 0.6, 0.6

The Number Line

One way to show numbers and their relationship to each other is on a **number line.**
The spaces on a number line represent regular intervals such as units (1, 2, 3, . . .) or
tens (10, 20, 30, . . .) or fractions ($\frac{1}{4}, \frac{1}{2}, \frac{3}{4}, \ldots$).

The number line on the right shows the whole numbers
from 0 to 10. Whole numbers are also called **integers.**
The arrows at the ends mean that the numbers continue
in both directions.

Do values increase or decrease as you move to the right along the number line?
You would be correct to say values **increase** as you move to the right.

Positive and Negative Numbers

In algebra we use **negative** and **positive** numbers. A negative number has a value
less than 0, while a positive number is greater than 0.

Positive numbers, to the right of 0, can be written with
or without a + sign, for example, +5 or just 5. The
values on a number line increase as you move to the
right. +5 is larger than +3.

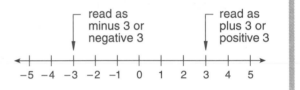

Negative numbers, to the left of 0, are written with a − sign, for example, –5. Because
the values on the number line increase as you move to the right, –3 is larger than –5.
Which has a greater value, –5 or +4? You're right if you chose **+4.**

Note: 0 is neither positive nor negative.

We use different forms of number lines in everyday life.
For example, look at the two thermometers.
The thermometer on the left shows a temperature of 50°.
The one on the right shows a temperature of –10°.

To compare the values of numbers, we use
the symbols shown here.

Symbol	Meaning	Example
=	is equal to	7 = 7
<	is less than	−4 < +6
>	is greater than	5 > 2

22

A. Fill in each blank with a symbol (=, <, or >) that makes the statement true. The first one is done as an example.

1.   8 _<_ 15

2. −10 _____ −12

3. −3 _____ −4

4. 2 _____ −6

5. −1 _____ −1

6. 9 _____ −3

7.   5 _____ 5

8. −11 _____ −12

9. −8 _____ −6

Absolute Value

Absolute value is a measure of the distance of a number from 0 on the number line. Absolute value has no positive or negative sign. The absolute value of +6 is 6, and the absolute value of −9 is 9. The symbol for absolute value is | |. Both |9| and |−9| equal 9.

B. Use the number line below for problems 10–12.

```
      A     B   C            D   E   F
  ←+—+—+—+—+—+—+—+—+—+—+—+—+—+—+—+—+—+—+→
    −5  −4  −3  −2  −1   0   1   2   3   4   5   6
```

10. Find the absolute value of each point. Point A is done as an example.

    A|−5| = _5_   C ___ = ___   E ___ = ___

    B ___ = ___   D ___ = ___   F ___ = ___

11. **a.** Which two points are the same distance from 0?

    b. Which two points have the same absolute value?

12. **Discuss** Talk about different ways to find the total distance from point A to point D. Which way would you use to find the distance between a point at 160 and a point at −100?

Making Connections: Keeping Score

A game show gives 200 points for every correct answer and −100 points for every wrong answer. Fill in the scores for each of the contestants. Which contestant won?

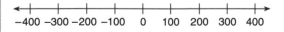

```
  ←+——+——+——+——+——+——+——+——+——+→
 −400 −300 −200 −100  0  100  200  300  400
```

Contestant: Answer	A	B
A: correct		
B: correct		
B: wrong		
A: wrong		
B: correct		
A: wrong		
Score		

Adding and Subtracting Signed Numbers

Algebra stretches arithmetic. In algebra the basic operations of arithmetic include both positive and negative numbers.

Study the patterns below. Each addition problem is written two ways and shown on a number line. When adding a number with a $+$ sign, move to the right. To add a number with a $-$ sign, move to the left.

A. Fill in the blanks for the last example in each set on this page.

Adding two positive numbers

1. $+3 + (+1) = 4$ *or* $3 + 1 = 4$

    $+3 + (+2) = 5$ *or* $3 + 2 = 5$

    $+3 + (+3) = 6$ *or* $3 + 3 = 6$

    $+3 + (\underline{}) = \underline{}$ *or* $3 + \underline{} = \underline{}$

Adding two negative numbers

2. $-3 + (-1) = -4$ *or* $-3 - 1 = -4$

    $-3 + (-2) = -5$ *or* $-3 - 2 = -5$

    $-3 + (-3) = -6$ *or* $-3 - 3 = -6$

    $-3 + (-\underline{}) = \underline{}$ *or* $-3 - \underline{} = \underline{}$

Adding Numbers with the Same Sign

The patterns above suggest that you should

- add two positive numbers and give the sum a positive sign
- add two negative numbers and give the sum a negative sign

Adding a positive number and a negative number

3. $+7 + (-3) = 4$ *or* $7 - 3 = 4$

    $+7 + (-4) = 3$ *or* $7 - 4 = 3$

    $+7 + (-5) = 2$ *or* $7 - 5 = 2$

    $+7 + (-\underline{}) = \underline{}$ *or* $7 - \underline{} = \underline{}$

4. $-7 + (+2) = -5$ *or* $-7 + 2 = -5$

    $-7 + (+3) = -4$ *or* $-7 + 3 = -4$

    $-7 + (+4) = -3$ *or* $-7 + 4 = -3$

    $-7 + (+\underline{}) = \underline{}$ *or* $-7 + \underline{} = \underline{}$

Adding Numbers with Different Signs

The last two sets of patterns suggest that you should
- find the difference between the absolute values (see page 23) of the two numbers
- give the answer the sign of the number with the larger absolute value

Examples: $-7 + 2$ The difference between $|-7|$ and $|2|$ is 5. Since -7 has the larger absolute value, give the answer a negative sign: $-7 + 2 = \textbf{--5}$

             $-2 + 7$ The difference between $|-2|$ and $|7|$ is 5. Since 7 has the larger absolute value, give the answer a positive sign: $-2 + 7 = \textbf{+5}$

B. Decide to add or find the difference. Then solve.

5. $(+7) + (+4) =$

6. $(-8) + (-6) =$

7. $-10 + (-5) =$

8. $+9 + (-3) =$

9. $(+7) + (-10) =$

10. $-14 + (+3) =$

11. $(-6) + (+11) =$

12. $-13 + (-6) =$

13. $17 + (-4) =$

14. $(-15) + (-8) =$

15. $2 + (+22) =$

16. $(-20) + (+6) =$

Subtracting Signed Numbers

When subtracting, change the sign of the number being subtracted to the opposite sign and add the number. Follow the rules for adding signed numbers.

Examples: $6 - (+7) \longrightarrow 6 + (-7) = \textbf{--1}$
                    $or\ 6 - 7 = \textbf{--1}$
      $-5 - (-3) \longrightarrow -5 + (+3) = \textbf{--2}$
                    $or\ -5 + 3 = \textbf{--2}$

C. Solve each problem. The first two are started for you.

17. $8 - (+2) = 8 + (-2) =$

18. $-3 - (-4) = -3 + (+4) =$

19. $-12 - (+9) =$

20. $(+7) - (-8) =$

21. $(-2) - (+3) =$

22. $5 - (-17) =$

23. $14 - (-1) =$

24. $(-1) - (+8) =$

25. $(+10) - (+9) =$

26. Write Create a problem to represent the problem pictured here.

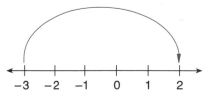

Multiplying and Dividing Signed Numbers

Study the pattern in these examples to see if you can discover the rules for multiplying signed numbers. Remember, 0 is neither positive nor negative.

Examples

$4 \cdot 1 = 4$

$4 \cdot 0 = 0$

$4(-1) = -4$

$-3(1) = -3$

$-3(0) = 0$

$-3(-1) = 3$

Use the examples to name two combinations of signs that result in a positive answer.

positive · _____ = positive

negative · _____ = positive

Use the examples to name two combinations of signs that result in a negative answer.

positive · _____ = negative

negative · _____ = negative

Your answers should match the rules shown below.

Rules for Multiplying Signed Numbers

► positive · positive = positive $3(9) = +27$

+ · + = +

► negative · negative = positive $-3(-9) = +27$

− · − = +

► positive · negative = negative $3(-9) = -27$

+ · − = −

► negative · positive = negative $-3(9) = -27$

− · + = −

A. Solve each problem.

1. $8 \cdot 4 =$ **4.** $10 \cdot 80 =$ **7.** $17(-2) =$

2. $-9 \cdot 7 =$ **5.** $(-4)(12) =$ **8.** $(-5)(-25) =$

3. $(-6)(-9) =$ **6.** $-3(-20) =$ **9.** $3(-45) =$

The **reciprocal** of a number is the inverse of a number. If you multiply a number by its reciprocal, the product is 1.

Example: The reciprocal of 5 is $\frac{1}{5}$. $5 \cdot \frac{1}{5} = \frac{5}{5} = 1$

Rules for Dividing Signed Numbers

The rules for dividing signed numbers are the same as the rules for multiplying signed numbers.

► positive ÷ positive = positive $15 \div 3 = 5$

► negative ÷ negative = positive $-15 \div -3 = 5$

► positive ÷ negative = negative $15 \div -3 = -5$

► negative ÷ positive = negative $-15 \div 3 = -5$

Note: Remember that $\frac{15}{3}$ and 15/3 mean $15 \div 3$.

B. Solve each problem.

10. $\frac{-9}{3} =$

11. $20/-5 =$

12. $-64/-8 =$

13. $-50/2 =$

14. $\frac{-7}{-7} =$

15. $-60/20 =$

16. $-100/-4 =$

17. $\frac{-32}{-16} =$

18. $\frac{50}{-5} =$

C. Use the order of operations to evaluate (solve) each expression.

19. $3(5) - 2(4) =$

20. $-8(12 - 7) =$

21. $\frac{-12}{2} + \frac{30}{6} =$

22. $-2(8 - 2)^2 =$

23. $(9 - 2)(-8 + 1) =$

24. $\frac{10 - 15}{14 - 9} =$

For another look at order of operations, turn to page 221.

Making Connections: Gains and Losses

Write a multiplication sentence using positive numbers to show weight gain or time in the future. Use negative numbers to show weight loss or time in the past. The first one is done as an example.

1. If Paul gains 4 pounds a week, his weight in 2 weeks will be $\underline{+4} \cdot \underline{+2} = \underline{+8}$ or _8_ pounds _more_ than now.

2. If Maria loses 4 pounds a week, her weight in 2 weeks will be ____ · ____ = ____ or ____ pounds ____ than now.

3. Carla gained 4 pounds a week. Her weight 2 weeks ago was ____ · ____ = ____ or ____ pounds ____ than now.

Expressions and Variables

You know that an expression is an amount written using numbers and operation signs. A symbol that represents an unknown number or value is called a **variable.** Letters are commonly used as variables.

Look at the line shown here. The unknown length from A to B is shown using a variable called x. The length from B to C is 3. What expression represents the length from A to C?

The length from A to C is the sum of x and 3. An expression for the length is $x + 3$.

Below are examples of verbal expressions written using algebra. Study them carefully. Note that any letter can be used as a variable.

Verbal Expression	Algebraic Expression
nine less than a number	$w - 9$
a number increased by seven	$t + 7$
the product of eight and a number (Notice that you do not need a raised dot or parentheses.)	$8y$
a number divided by six	$\frac{z}{6}$ or $z/6$
twice the quantity of a number increased by five	$2(n + 5)$
one less than twice a number, all divided by four	$\frac{2r - 1}{4}$

A. Write an expression for each length.

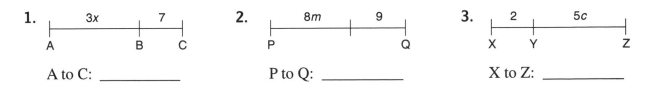

1. A to C: _____

2. P to Q: _____

3. X to Z: _____

B. Choose the correct expression for each problem.

4. seven less than a number
   - **(1)** $y - 7$
   - **(2)** $7 - y$
   - **(3)** $-7y$

5. twice a number increased by eight
   - **(1)** $2p - 8$
   - **(2)** $2p + 8$
   - **(3)** $8p + 2$

6. three times the square root of a number
   - **(1)** $3\sqrt{c}$
   - **(2)** $c\sqrt{3}$
   - **(3)** $\sqrt{3c}$

7. nine times a number, all divided by five
   - **(1)** $\frac{5m}{9}$
   - **(2)** $\frac{9m}{5}$
   - **(3)** $\frac{5}{9m}$

8. the quantity of one less than a number, all multiplied by ten
   - **(1)** $10(y - 1)$
   - **(2)** $10(y + 1)$
   - **(3)** $\frac{y - 1}{10}$

9. the quantity of six times a number, all raised to the second power
   - **(1)** $(6 + n)^2$
   - **(2)** $(n - 6)^2$
   - **(3)** $(6n)^2$

C. For problems 10–12, write an algebraic expression for each area and perimeter.

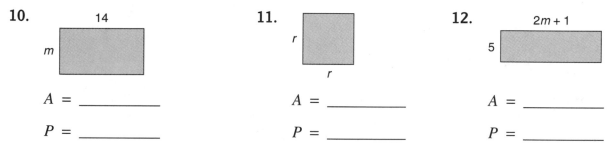

10.
   14
   m

$A =$ _____

$P =$ _____

11.
   r
   r

$A =$ _____

$P =$ _____

12.
   $2m + 1$
   5

$A =$ _____

$P =$ _____

D. Write an algebraic expression for each practical situation.

13. Sally makes w dollars an hour. Write an expression for her hourly wage if she gets a raise of $2 an hour.

14. Phil and Jorge divided the profit from their business equally. Let p represent the profit. Write an expression for the amount each of them received.

15. Let e stand for Elena's age this year. Write an expression for her age in 5 years.

16. **Multiple Solutions** Let v stand for the value of the Gómez family's house when they bought it. The house is now worth twice as much. Write two expressions for the current value of the house.

Substitution

To solve some problems, you **substitute** a number for the variable. When you combine the numbers in an expression, you evaluate (solve) the expression.

Using Substitution

Example 1: Celia owes her sister $8. Find how much money she'll have left after paying her sister. Let n equal the amount of money Celia has now. Find the value of $n - \$8$ when $n = \$12$ and when $n = \$21$.

Step 1. Write the expression.	$n - \$8$	$n - \$8$
Step 2. Substitute the value for n.	$\$12 - \$8$	$\$21 - \$8$
Step 3. Subtract.	**$4**	**$13**

If Celia starts with $12, she'll have $4 left. If she starts with $21, she'll have $13 left.

Remember to follow the order of operations when using substitution.

Example 2: Find the value of $ac - ad$ when $a = 5$, $c = 4$, and $d = 3$.

Step 1. Write the expression.	$ac - ad$
Step 2. Substitute 5 for a, 4 for c, and 3 for d.	$5 \cdot 4 - 5 \cdot 3$
Step 3. Do the multiplication from left to right.	$20 - 15$
Step 4. Subtract.	**5**

A. Evaluate each expression for the given values of the variables.

1. $2c$
   a. when $c = 6$
   b. when $c = 15$

2. $\frac{n}{2}$
   a. when $n = 8$
   b. when $n = 12$

3. $(y + 4)^2$
   a. when $y = 6$
   b. when $y = 11$

4. $w + \frac{1}{2}w - 6$
   a. when $w = 18$
   b. when $w = 24$

5. $\sqrt{r} + 2r$
   a. when $r = 16$
   b. when $r = 25$

6. $9(x - 2)$
   a. when $x = -5$
   b. when $x = -9$

B. **Write an expression and find each perimeter using the given values of the variables. Remember, perimeter is the distance around a figure.**

For another look at perimeter and area, turn to page 223.

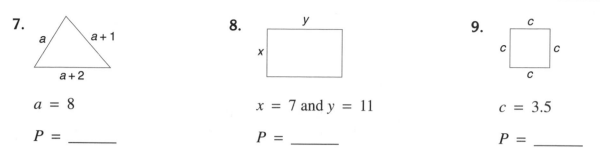

7.
$a = 8$

$P =$ _____

8.
$x = 7$ and $y = 11$

$P =$ _____

9.
$c = 3.5$

$P =$ _____

C. **Write an expression and solve to find the area using the given values of the variables.**

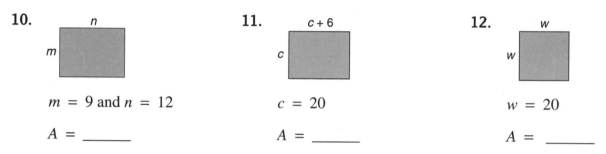

10.
$m = 9$ and $n = 12$

$A =$ _____

11.
$c = 20$

$A =$ _____

12.
$w = 20$

$A =$ _____

D. **Evaluate (solve) each expression.**

13. If $a = 7$ and $c = 4$, what is the value of $ac - 5$? _____

14. Find the value of $\frac{m}{3} - \frac{n}{2}$ when $m = 24$ and $n = 8$. _____

15. If $c = 8$ and $d = 3$, what is the value of cd^2? _____

16. If $s = 10$ and $t = 5$, what is the value of $\frac{s + t}{s - t}$? _____

Making Connections: Sales Tax

Sales tax is one application of substitution. For example, in a state with 5% tax, you can represent the sales tax as $.05p$ where $5\% = .05$ and $p =$ price (or cost). Use the expression $.05p$ to find the sales tax on a sweater that costs $25. (Remember that $.05p$ means $.05 \times p$.)

Finding Patterns in Algebra

You have already looked at patterns in this book. You saw the patterns that established the rules for adding, subtracting, multiplying, and dividing signed numbers. In this lesson, you will see a variety of patterns.

One example of patterns in mathematics is the number series. A **number series** is a set of numbers that continue according to a rule.

The counting numbers (1, 2, 3, . . .) are a number series in which each number is 1 larger than the number before it. In the series 1, 4, 7, 10, . . . each number is 3 more than the preceding number.

A. Find the next term in each of the following number series.

   1. 1, 3, 5, 7, _____

   2. 2, 4, 8, 16, _____

   3. 12, 7, 2, −3, −8, _____

   4. −9, −5, −1, 3, _____

   5. 20, 10, 5, $2\frac{1}{2}$, _____

   6. −100, −200, −300, _____

B. Draw the next figure in each of the following series.

7. △, ▢, ⬠, _____   **8.** (figures) _____

C. Multiply the numbers in the left-hand column by the numbers in the top row. The table has been started for you. After you complete the table, describe the patterns you see.

×	−2	−1	0	+1	+2
−1	+2	+1			
−2					
−3					
−4					
−5					

D. The table below shows different lengths for one side of a square. Complete the table for the corresponding perimeter and area. The first one is done as an example.

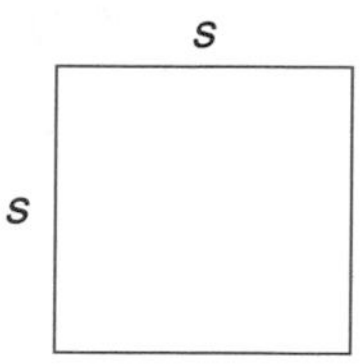

Squares						
length of one side	1	2	3	4	5	6
perimeter	4	___	___	___	___	___
area	1	___	___	___	___	___

For another look at squares, turn to page 221.

E. The chart below shows rates for mailing packages with Pete's Prompt Package Service. Use the table to solve problems 9–11.

Pete's Prompt Package Service						
Weight (in pounds) up to but not over	1	2	3	4	5	6
Cost (in dollars)	1.00	1.75	2.50	3.25	4.00	4.75

9. What is the cost of sending a package that weighs 2 pounds?

10. What would be the cost of sending a package that weighs 7 pounds? Explain your answer.

11. What would be the cost of sending a package that weighs 4.5 pounds? Explain your answer.

F. Solve each problem.

12. A souvenir T-shirt from Adventure Farm costs $20.00. Each additional T-shirt costs $17.50. What is the cost of 3 T-shirts?

13. **Discover** You know that $(-3)(+4)$ is -12. If you multiply -12 by -2 you get $+24$. In other words, $(-3)(+4)(-2) = +24$.

Try to discover a pattern for multiplying more than two signed numbers.
Hint: Try multiplying several combinations of signs. Look for a connection between the number of negative signs in the problem and the sign of the final answer.

$(-2)(+2) = -4$

$(-2)(+2)(-2) = +8$

$(-2)(+2)(-2)(+2) = +16$

$(-2)(+2)(-2)(+2)(-2) =$

$(-2)(+2)(-2)(+2)(-2)(+2) =$

Mixed Review

A. Use the figure at the right to solve problems 1 and 2.

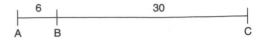

1. Which of the following expresses the length from A to C?

    (1) $30 - 6$ **(2)** $\frac{30}{6}$ **(3)** $6 + 30$

2. Which expresses length BC divided by length AB?

    (1) $\frac{30}{6}$ **(2)** $\frac{36}{6}$ **(3)** $\frac{6}{30}$

B. Evaluate each problem.

3. $(14)^2 =$ 4. $2^5 =$ 5. $3^4 =$

C. Choose the correct solution to each problem.

6. $\sqrt{289}$
    (1) 13   **(2)** 15   **(3)** 17

7. $\sqrt{529}$
    (1) 13   **(2)** 23   **(3)** 33

8. $\sqrt{10,000}$
    (1) 10   **(2)** 100   **(3)** 1,000

D. Find the perimeter for each of the following figures.

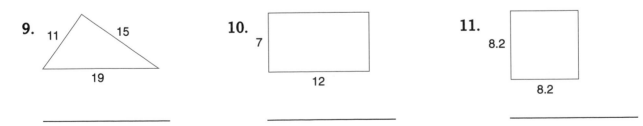

9. 11   15   19   _____

10. 7   12   _____

11. 8.2   8.2   _____

E. Fill in each blank with a symbol (<, >, or =) that makes the statement true.

12. 5 ___ 25

13. 6 ___ −6

14. 14 ___ +14

F. Solve each of the following.

15. (+18) + (−12) =

16. (−16) + (−3) =

17. 4 + (−12) =

18. (−20) − (−6) =

19. (−19) − (+3) =

20. (+7) − (−2) =

21. −5(−6) =

22. $\frac{1}{2}$(30) =

23. (7)(−1) =

24. $\frac{-39}{-3}$ =

25. $\frac{14}{-21}$ =

26. $\frac{-81}{+9}$ =

G. Write an algebraic expression for each area below.

27.

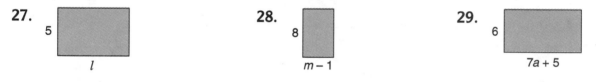

5

l

28.

8

m − 1

29.

6

7*a* + 5

H. Evaluate each expression for the given values of the variables.

30. 4*a* − 3 when *a* = 7

31. $\frac{c}{6}$ + 5 when *c* = 120

32. *mn* + *n*^{2} when *m* = −2 and *n* = 5

33. 5(*x* − *y*) when *x* = 1 and *y* = 4

I. Find the next number in each series.

34. 1, 3, 9, 27, 81, _____

35. 14, 8, 2, −4, −10, _____

J. Solve the problems.

36. Ming thinks she'll get a raise of $.50 an hour. Write an expression to show her new hourly wage if her old hourly wage equals *w*.

37. If a customer buys 6 or more energy-saving lightbulbs, C.J.'s Hardware takes $.50 off the original price for each bulb. Write two expressions: one showing the cost of *n* lightbulbs at the original price and another showing the cost when *n* is 6 or more. Let *p* = original price.

Simple Formulas and Substitution

A **formula** is a standard rule that shows a constant relationship between variables. Formulas are practical applications of substitution. Formulas are frequently used in business and science.

▶ For example, the cost formula is
cost = number of items × rate (price)
$c = nr$

As the formula is set up, you can use known values for n and r to find the cost c.

Example: Use the cost formula to find the cost of 3 cassettes at the price of $6.99 each (before tax).

Step 1. Copy the cost formula. $c = nr$

Step 2. Substitute 3 for n and $6.99 for r. $c = 3 \cdot \$6.99$

Step 3. Multiply. The cost is $20.97. $c = \mathbf{\$20.97}$

A. Use the cost formula to solve the problems. You may use a calculator.

1. Find the cost of 6 gallons of gasoline.

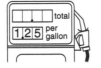

3. Find the cost of 2 T-shirts at the price of $7.80 each.

2. What is the cost of 4 gallons of paint at the rate of $13.20 each?

4. What is the price of $\frac{1}{2}$ pound of cheese?

A formula can be written in terms of any of its variables.

▶ To find the number of items when you know the total cost and the rate: $n = \frac{c}{r}$

Example: Use the formula to find the number of gallons: $n = \dfrac{\$10.00}{\$1.25}$ ◀——— total cost
◀——— price per gallon

▶ To find the rate when you know the total cost and the number of items: $r = \frac{c}{n}$

Example: Use the formula to find the price per gallon: $r = \dfrac{\$10.00}{9}$ ◀——— total cost
◀——— number of gallons

B. Use the correct form of the cost formula to solve the problems. *Hint:* Identify which values are given and which value is unknown. You may use a calculator.

5. Alfonso paid $8.94 for 6 cans of spray paint. What was the price per can?

6. Alma paid $6.95 for apple juice that sold for $1.39 per can. How many cans did she buy?

▶ The distance formula is
distance = rate (speed) × time
$d = rt$
To find the rate when you know the distance and time: $r = \frac{d}{t}$
To find the time when you know the distance and rate: $t = \frac{d}{r}$

For another look
at the distance formula, turn to page 224.

C. Use the correct form of the distance formula for the problems. You may use a calculator.

7. Find the distance a driver travels in 3 hours by maintaining a steady rate of 55 miles per hour.

8. What distance could a hiker travel by walking for 5 hours at an average rate of 2.5 miles per hour?

9. A plane flew 1,275 miles at an average rate of 425 miles per hour. For how many hours did the plane fly?

10. A driver went 180 miles in 4 hours. What was his average rate of speed?

D. Below are three figures and the formulas for finding their areas. Use substitution to find the area of each figure.

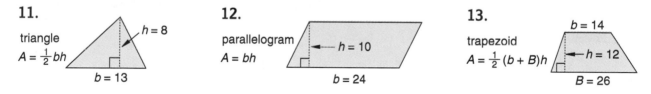

11.
triangle
$A = \frac{1}{2}bh$
$h = 8$
$b = 13$

12.
parallelogram
$A = bh$
$h = 10$
$b = 24$

13.
trapezoid
$A = \frac{1}{2}(b + B)h$
$b = 14$
$h = 12$
$B = 26$

E. Solve each problem.

14. The formula for changing square feet to square yards is $y = \frac{x}{9}$ where y is the number of square yards and x is the number of square feet. The floor of Bettina's room has 180 square feet. How many square yards of carpet does she need to buy to cover the floor?

15. **Explain** Show how the cost formula $c = nr$ is the same as $n = \frac{c}{r}$ or $r = \frac{c}{n}$. Pick sample numbers to support your argument.

Using a Calculator

A calculator is a convenient tool for solving problems quickly and accurately.

A typical calculator is shown here. Yours may look slightly different.

To evaluate expressions in this book, you will use the number keys (0 to 9), the decimal point key, the four operation keys ($\boxed{+}$, $\boxed{-}$, $\boxed{\times}$, and $\boxed{\div}$), the $\boxed{=}$ key, and occasionally the $\boxed{\sqrt{}}$ key.

As you use a calculator, you will find many other uses for it too.

> If you have a calculator, use it to solve problems or to check your answers in other exercises in this book.

A. Use a calculator to evaluate (solve) each of these expressions. Problems 1–5 show which keys to press and in what order.

1. 7(12)

   $\boxed{7}\boxed{\times}\boxed{1}\boxed{2}\boxed{=}$

2. $\frac{18}{3}$

   $\boxed{1}\boxed{8}\boxed{\div}\boxed{3}\boxed{=}$

3. 15 − 6

   $\boxed{1}\boxed{5}\boxed{-}\boxed{6}\boxed{=}$

4. $(23)^2$

   $\boxed{2}\boxed{3}\boxed{\times}\boxed{2}\boxed{3}\boxed{=}$
   or $\boxed{2}\boxed{3}\boxed{x^2}$ ⌐

   Some calculators have an
   x^2 key for squares.

5. $\sqrt{1,764}$

   $\boxed{1}\boxed{7}\boxed{6}\boxed{4}\boxed{\sqrt{}}$

6. $x + y$

   when $x = 9$
   and $y = 25$

7. $a - c$

   when $a = 18$
   and $c = 11$

8. mn

   when $m = 16$
   and $n = 2$

9. pqr

   when $p = 10$,
   $q = 0.9$, and
   $r = 250$

10. b^2

    when $b = 0.15$

11. $\sqrt{w}$

    when $w = 7,396$

38

B. Use a calculator to find the perimeter of each figure.

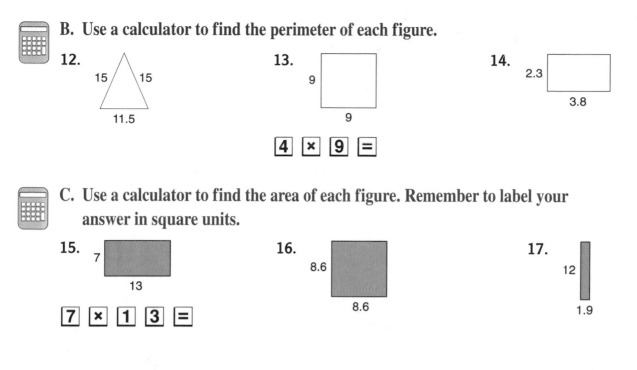

12.

15 15

11.5

13.

9

9

$\boxed{4}\ \boxed{\times}\ \boxed{9}\ \boxed{=}$

14.

2.3

3.8

C. Use a calculator to find the area of each figure. Remember to label your answer in square units.

15.

7

13

$\boxed{7}\ \boxed{\times}\ \boxed{1}\ \boxed{3}\ \boxed{=}$

16.

8.6

8.6

17.

12

1.9

Multistep Problems

To evaluate expressions with two or more steps, you can use the memory key (if your calculator has one). Or use a calculator to get partial answers to problems. Then combine the partial answers. Some calculators perform operations following the order of operations.

D. Use a calculator to evaluate each multioperation expression.

18. $5 \cdot 6 - 4 \cdot 3$

$\boxed{5}\ \boxed{\times}\ \boxed{6}\ \boxed{=}$ [30.]

$\boxed{4}\ \boxed{\times}\ \boxed{3}\ \boxed{=}$ [12.]

19. $3a + 4b$

when $a = 7$ and $b = 9$

20. $7 + 9(20)$

21. $5m - 12$

when $m = 13$

22. $(6.8 - 4.3)^2$

23. $9c - 2d$

when $c = 6$
and $d = 7$

E. Use a calculator to solve these formula problems.

24. Find the distance a train travels in 3.5 hours if it maintains an average speed of 92 miles per hour.

25. Find the cost of 2.8 pounds of beef at $2.69 a pound.

26. **Investigate** Test your calculator to see if it follows the order of operations. Enter $\boxed{5}\ \boxed{\times}\ \boxed{6}\ \boxed{-}\ \boxed{4}\ \boxed{\times}\ \boxed{3}\ \boxed{=}$. Did you get the same answer as in problem 18? Try entering problems 19–23 in your calculator. Compare your answers.

The Distributive Property

If you look closely at this rectangle, you'll notice that the total length is not given. There are two ways to find the total area of this rectangle.

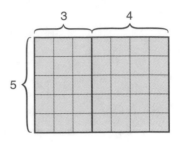

Method 1. First find the total length. $3 + 4 = 7$
Then multiply the total length by the width. $7 \cdot 5 = $ **35 square units**

Method 2. First find the area of each rectangle. $5 \cdot 3 = 15$ and $5 \cdot 4 = 20$
Then add the two areas. $15 + 20 = $ **35 square units**

Each method gives an answer of 35 square units.

You have already learned that parentheses are grouping symbols. In the expression $5(3 + 4)$, the sum of $3 + 4$ is grouped inside parentheses. Everything within the parentheses will be multiplied by 5.

Using the Distributive Property

The problem $5(3 + 4)$ can be evaluated two ways.

Method 1. First find the sum inside the parentheses.
Then multiply the sum by 5.

$5(3 + 4)$
$5(7)$
35

Method 2. First multiply each number inside the parentheses by 5.

Then find the sum of the two products.

$5(3 + 4)$
$(5)(3) + (5)(4)$
$15 + 20$
35

In both cases the answer is 35.

▶ This example demonstrates the **distributive property.** We say that multiplication is *distributive over addition and subtraction.* In the example, 5 is distributed over the sum of 3 and 4. We can show the distributive property using variables.

Addition

$a(x + y) = ax + ay$
$5(4 + 3) = 5(4) + 5(3)$
$5(7) = 5(4) + 5(3)$
$35 = 20 + 15$
$35 = 35$

In these examples,
$a = 5$, $x = 4$, and $y = 3$

Note: The left side of each equation shows Method 1, and the right side shows Method 2. Both are correct and equal.

Subtraction

$a(x - y) = ax - ay$
$5(4 - 3) = 5(4) - 5(3)$
$5(1) = 5(4) - 5(3)$
$5 = 20 - 15$
$5 = 5$

A. For each problem, use the expression 9(7 + 3).

1. What is the sum inside the parentheses?

2. What is the product of 9 and the sum inside the parentheses?

3. What is the product of 9 and 7?

4. What is the product of 9 and 3?

5. What is the sum of the answers to problems 3 and 4?

6. Are the answers to problems 2 and 5 the same?

7. Together, problems 1 and 2 are one method of evaluating the expression 9(7 + 3). Together, problems 3, 4, and 5 are another method. Which method do you like better? Why?

B. Choose the solution that correctly applies the distributive property.

8. $4(7 + 11)$
   (1) $4 \cdot 7 + 11$
   (2) $4 \cdot 7 + 4 \cdot 11$
   (3) $4 + 7 \cdot 11$

9. $9(8 - 3)$
   (1) $9 \cdot 8 - 9 \cdot 3$
   (2) $9 - 9 \cdot 3$
   (3) $9 \cdot 8 - 3$

10. $2(a + 13)$
    (1) $2a + 13$
    (2) $2 + 13a$
    (3) $2a + 2 \cdot 13$

11. $8 \cdot 3 + 8 \cdot 6$
    (1) $8(8 + 3)$
    (2) $3(8 + 6)$
    (3) $8(3 + 6)$

12. $15 \cdot 9 - 15 \cdot 4$
    (1) $15 + 9 - 4$
    (2) $15(9 - 4)$
    (3) $15(9)(4)$

C. Write _two different_ expressions for the area of each figure. Do not solve the expressions.

13.

14.

15.

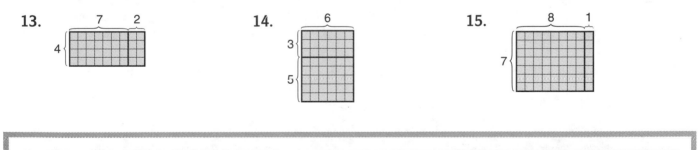

The formula for the average (or mean) for two items is $a = \frac{1}{2}(x + y)$ where a is the average, and x and y are the two items. Use two methods to find the average of two test scores of 78 and 86.

Test Scores	
Test	78
Test	86

Simplifying Expressions

Compare these two expressions:

Expression 1: $4x + 9 + 3x - 1$

When $x = 2$, the expression is
$4(2) + 9 + 3(2) - 1 =$
$8 + 9 + 6 - 1 = $ **22**

Expression 2: $7x + 8$

When $x = 2$, the expression is
$7(2) + 8 = $ **22**

When $x = 2$, these two expressions have the same value. In fact, the expressions are equal for any value of the variable. The two expressions are called **equivalent expressions.** Expression 2 is a **simplified** form of Expression 1.

Simplifying Expressions

Example 1: Simplify $2x + 2 + x - 4$.

Step 1. Group **like terms.** These are terms that have the same variable. *Note:* x means the same as $1x$.

$$2x + 2 + x - 4$$

Step 2. Group the numbers. Use the rules for adding signed numbers.

$$3x + 2 - 4$$

Step 3. Write the simplified expression.

$$\mathbf{3x - 2}$$

Example 2: Simplify $-6k + 3 + 2k - 7$.

Step 1. Group the variables. Use the rules for adding signed numbers with the **coefficients** (the number multiplying the variable).

$$-6k + 3 + 2k - 7$$

Step 2. Group the numbers.

$$-4k + 3 - 7$$

Step 3. Write the simplified expression.

$$\mathbf{-4k - 4}$$

A. Simplify each expression.

1. $5x - 2x$

2. $-6k + k$
   (*Hint: k* is the same as 1*k*.)

3. $7t + 5 - 9t$

4. $2a + 9a - 9 + 6$

5. $10 + 7m - m + 3$

6. $12 - 6y - 5 + 18$

7. $k + m - 2k - 9m$

8. $8c + 3d - 2c + 5d$

9. $-2s - 8t + 9t - 6s$

B. Use the triangle to solve each problem.

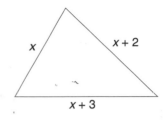

10. Which side is the longest? How could you tell that it's the longest side besides how it looks?

11. Write an expression for the perimeter of the figure.

12. Simplify the expression.

13. Find the value of the expression when $x = 8$.

14. What is the value of the perimeter when $x = 25$?

C. Use the rectangle to solve each problem.

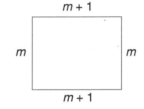

15. Write an expression for the perimeter of the figure.

16. Simplify the expression.

17. What is the value of the expression when $m = 4.5$?

18. Find the value of the perimeter when $m = 18$.

D. Use the square to solve each problem.

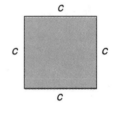

19. Write an expression for the perimeter of the figure.

20. Simplify the expression.

21. Find the value of c when the perimeter equals 24. (*Hint:* Use the expression you found in problem 20.)

22. Use the value for c from problem 21 to find the area of the square. Remember to label your answer in square units.

Scientific Notation

To write long numbers, mathematicians and scientists use **scientific notation.** This system is based on powers of ten.

Our number system is also based on powers of ten. The place value chart shows the names of the first 10 whole number places in our number system.

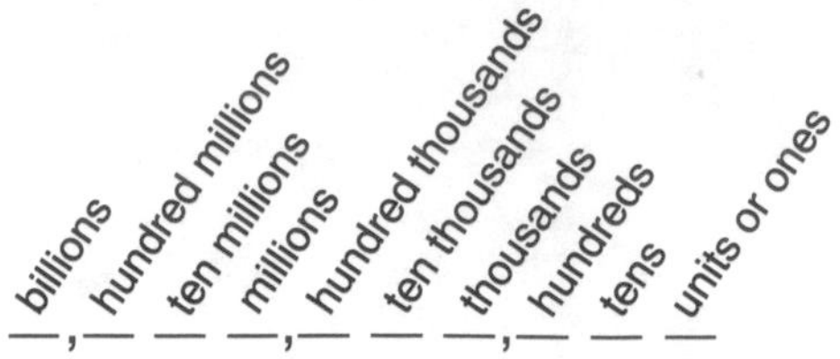

billions, hundred millions, ten millions, millions, hundred thousands, ten thousands, thousands, hundreds, tens, units or ones

—,— — —,— — —,— — —

Place Values

Look at these three ways of writing large numbers.

Words	Digits	Scientific Notation
two hundred sixty thousand	260,000 5 places	2.6×10^5 5 places
five million	5,000,000	5×10^6
ten million four hundred thousand	10,400,000	1.04×10^7
three billion	3,000,000,000	3×10^9

To write a number in scientific notation, express the number as the product of

- a number from 1 to 10
- a power of 10

power of 10

2.6×10^5

number from 1 to 10

Compare the number of places the decimal point moves to the left to the exponent. In each case, the exponent shows the number of digits *after* the first digit.

Using Scientific Notation

Example: Write 2,800,000 in scientific notation.

- Choose the decimal number 2.8 as the number from 1 to 10.
- Since the decimal point moves 6 places to a position between the 2 and 8, the exponent is 6.

$2,800,000 = \mathbf{2.8 \times 10^6}$

6 places

A. Choose the correct expression for each number.

1. 19,000
  (1) 19×10^3
  (2) 1.9×10^4
  (3) 190×10^2

2. 735,000
  (1) 7.35×10^5
  (2) 7.35×10^6
  (3) 7.35×10^7

3. 6,400,000
  (1) 0.64×10^6
  (2) 64×10^6
  (3) 6.4×10^6

B. For each problem, write the number in scientific notation.

4. 3,500,000

5. 485,000

6. 56,000,000

7. 75,000

8. 920,000

9. 130,000,000

C. Write out each number shown in scientific notation.

10. 8.1×10^4

11. 9.3×10^8

12. 4×10^7

13. 2.5×10^6

14. 6×10^9

15. 3.8×10^5

Making Connections: Earth Measurements

Listed below are various measurements of distance, area, and speed for the Earth.
Write each number in scientific notation.

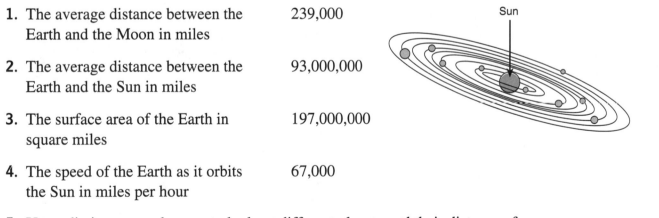

1. The average distance between the Earth and the Moon in miles   239,000

2. The average distance between the Earth and the Sun in miles   93,000,000

3. The surface area of the Earth in square miles   197,000,000

4. The speed of the Earth as it orbits the Sun in miles per hour   67,000

5. Use a dictionary or almanac to look up different planets and their distances from the Sun. Make a table, and list each distance, using scientific notation.

Celsius and Fahrenheit Thermometers

The two most commonly used temperature scales are **Fahrenheit** and **Celsius** (sometimes called **Centigrade**). The United States has traditionally used the Fahrenheit scale, but today it is becoming common to see Celsius temperatures posted as well.

Shown at the right are illustrations of the two thermometers. Temperatures on both scales are measured in **degrees** (°). The thermometers look a lot like number lines with different scales.

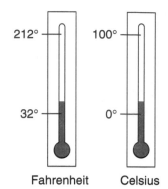

To change a Celsius temperature into the corresponding Fahrenheit temperature, use the formula $F = \frac{9}{5}C + 32$ where C is the temperature in Celsius degrees and F is the temperature in Fahrenheit degrees.

Remember to apply the rules for combining signed numbers.

Changing Celsius to Fahrenheit

Example: Convert −5° Celsius to Fahrenheit.

- Copy the formula.
- Substitute −5° for C.

$$F = \frac{9}{5}C + 32$$
$$F = \frac{9}{5}(-5) + 32$$
$$F = -9 + 32 = \mathbf{23°F}$$

A. **Convert each of the following Celsius temperatures into the corresponding Fahrenheit temperature. Use the formula above.**

1. 10°C

2. 35°C

3. −15°C

4. −50°C

5. 40°C

6. 100°C

A formula for finding the approximate Fahrenheit temperature for a Celsius temperature is $F \approx 2C + 30$ where $\approx$ means "is approximately equal to" and C is the temperature in Celsius.

B. Use the formula for approximating Fahrenheit temperatures to estimate each of the following.

7. 14°C   **8.** −20°C   **9.** 24°C

Changing Fahrenheit to Celsius

To change a Fahrenheit temperature into the corresponding Celsius temperature, use the formula $C = \frac{5}{9}(F - 32)$ where F is the Fahrenheit temperature and C is the Celsius temperature.

Example: Convert −13° Fahrenheit to Celsius.

- Copy the formula. $C = \frac{5}{9}(F - 32)$
- Substitute −13° for F. $C = \frac{5}{9}(-13 - 32)$

$$C = \frac{5}{9}(-45) = -25°C$$

C. Convert each of the following Fahrenheit temperatures into the corresponding Celsius temperature. Use the formula above.

10. 59°F   **12.** −4°F   **14.** 95°F

11. 113°F   **13.** −22°F   **15.** 14°F

D. Below is a chart of specific temperatures. Use the two exact Celsius and Fahrenheit conversion formulas to fill in the missing temperatures.

Specific Temperatures	Fahrenheit	Celsius
Boiling point of water (at sea level)	212°F	_____
Healthy body temperature	_____	37°C
Comfortable room temperature	68°F	_____
Freezing point of water (at sea level)	_____	0°C
Temperature at which scales are equal	_____	−40°C
The coldest temperature recorded in the United States outside Alaska	−70°F	_____

Writing a Number Sentence

Mathematics is a language for expressing relationships among numbers. The example below shows a sentence translated from words into mathematical symbols. The seven words in the verbal expression can be translated into five mathematical symbols.

Example: A number increased by four is nine.

$$x \quad + \quad 4 = 9$$

Study the next examples carefully. Watch for the differences between sentences that express equalities (the $=$ sign) and those that express inequalities ($<$ or $>$).

Verbal Expression	Algebra
The product of three and a number <u>is</u> twenty-four.	$3w = 24$
Eight less than a number <u>is</u> five.	$y - 8 = 5$
Eight <u>is less than</u> five times a number.	$8 < 5c$
The quotient of a number divided by four <u>is</u> six.	$\frac{c}{4} = 6$
A number increased by nine <u>is</u> sixteen.	$x + 9 = 16$
A number <u>is greater than</u> nine.	$n > 9$
Two times a number decreased by seven <u>is</u> twenty-three.	$2a - 7 = 23$

Remember that the verb *is* often corresponds to the $=$ sign, but phrases such as *is more than* or *is less than* correspond to inequalities.

A. Choose the correct mathematical sentence for each of the following.

  1. The product of six and a number is thirty.
     (1) $6 + n = 30$ (2) $6n = 30$ (3) $n - 6 = 30$

  2. Twelve less than a number is nineteen.
     (1) $12 < 19$ (2) $12 - y = 19$ (3) $y - 12 = 19$

  3. The quotient of a number divided by five is greater than fourteen.
     (1) $\frac{c}{5} > 14$ (2) $\frac{c}{5} = 14$ (3) $5c > 14$

4. A number decreased by eight is twenty.

   (1) $8p < 20$ **(2)** $8 < p - 20$ **(3)** $p - 8 = 20$

5. One less than two times a number is fifteen.

   (1) $2r - 1 = 15$ **(2)** $2r < 15 - 1$ **(3)** $2r = 15 - 1$

6. Three more than ten times a number is thirty-nine.

   (1) $3a + 10 = 39$ **(2)** $10a + 3 = 39$ **(3)** $3 > 10a + 39$

B. Write a verbal expression for each mathematical sentence.

7. $12 - x = 5$ _____

8. $5x > 12$ _____

9. $12x - 5 = 1$ _____

C. Below each of the following pairs of lines are three mathematical sentences. Choose the sentence that does *not* describe the relationship between the lines in each pair.

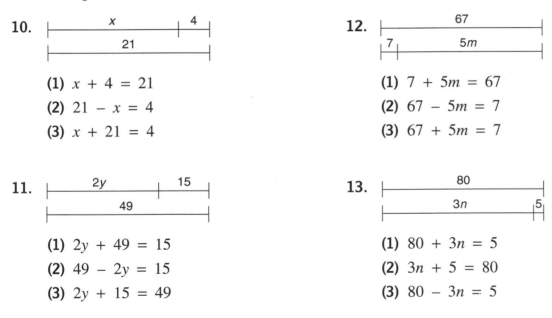

10.

   (1) $x + 4 = 21$
   (2) $21 - x = 4$
   (3) $x + 21 = 4$

11.

   (1) $2y + 49 = 15$
   (2) $49 - 2y = 15$
   (3) $2y + 15 = 49$

12.

   (1) $7 + 5m = 67$
   (2) $67 - 5m = 7$
   (3) $67 + 5m = 7$

13.

   (1) $80 + 3n = 5$
   (2) $3n + 5 = 80$
   (3) $80 - 3n = 5$

14. Discuss Small word changes can make big mathematical changes. Explain the difference between the phrases "seven less than" and "seven is less than." Make up examples that show the difference.

Unit 1 Review

A. Evaluate each of the following expressions.

1. $7(-12) =$

2. $-13 + (-8) =$

3. $\frac{-9}{-30} =$

4. $\sqrt{121} =$

5. $(6 - 10)^2 =$

6. $5(1 - 8) =$

B. Choose an expression that is equal to each of the expressions given.

7. $8(9 - 1) =$

(1) $8 \cdot 9 - 1$ (2) $8 - 1 \cdot 8$ (3) $8 \cdot 9 - 8 \cdot 1$

8. $10(c + 3) =$

(1) $10c + 30$ (2) $10c + 3$ (3) $c + 30$

C. Write and simplify an expression for the perimeter of each figure.

9.

$n - 6$

$n - 6$

10.

a

$a + 4$

D. Find the area for each figure. Label your answers in square units.

11.

$m + 5$

$m + 5$

when $m = 16$

12.

x

$x + 8$

when $x = 15$

E. Solve each problem.

13. At the 1990 census, the population of the People's Republic of China was 1,130,000,000. Write this number in scientific notation.

14. The average distance from Mars to the Sun is 1.42×10^8 miles. Write the number in digits.

F. Use the formula $F = \frac{9}{5}C + 32$ or $C = \frac{5}{9}(F - 32)$ to convert each of the following temperatures.

15. 15°C = ____ °F

16. −30°C = ____ °F

17. 50°F = ____ °C

18. 23°F = ____ °C

G. Write a number sentence that describes the relationship between the lines in each pair.

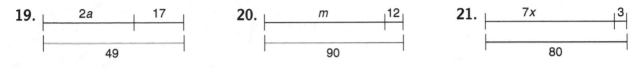

19.

20.

21.

Working Together

Do the following activities with a partner or with a group of other students.

1. Draw a rectangle that represents the floor plan of a room that you can measure. Write an expression that shows the length in terms of the width. For example, if the width is 12 feet and the length is 15 feet, the width is w and the length is $w + 3$. Calculate both the perimeter and the floor area of the room.

   Discuss times you might need to know the perimeter and area of a room.

2. Use a newspaper to look up the highest and lowest temperatures in your area. Represent the temperatures in both Fahrenheit and Celsius degrees. Compare your answers.

3. Discuss ways to calculate the cost of a restaurant meal. Make up a formula to show the total cost. Include the local sales tax rate (if there is one) and a 15% tip. Compare your formulas.

4. Use an almanac or encyclopedia to look up the population of several countries. Round each population so it can be written using scientific notation. Make a table listing each country and its population in digits and scientific notation.

Putting Algebra to Use

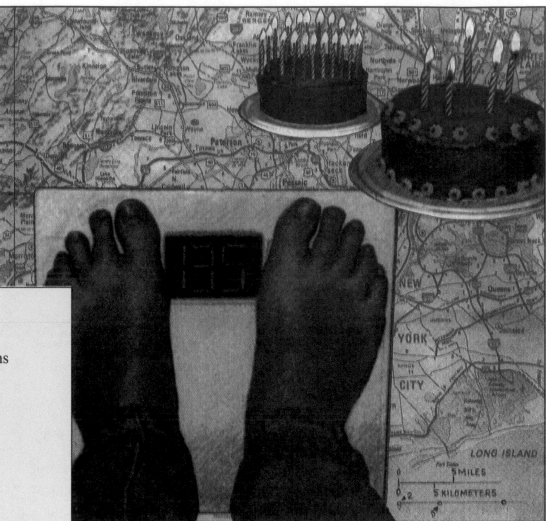

Skills

Solving equations

Simplifying equations

Using substitution

Solving inequalities

Tools

Formulas

Diagrams

Problem Solvers

Number puzzles and age problems

Motion and money problems

Word problem approaches

Applications

Relating percents and equations

Ratios

Proportions

An **equation** is a statement that two amounts are equal. Equations are easy to recognize. Every equation has a left side and a right side. The sides are separated by an equal sign (=). For example, $4 + 2 = 6$ and $x = 1x$ are both equations.

You wrote equations in the last unit. Equations are one of the most useful tools in algebra.

In this unit you will learn to solve equations and to use equations to solve word problems.

How Do I Use Algebra?

With algebra you can write statements about the relationships between numbers. For example, the terms x and $3x$ show a constant relationship between the two expressions. No matter what value you give x, the value of $3x$ will always be three times as much.

If you also know that the sum of those terms is 20, you can find one exact value for each term. You can write the equation $x + 3x = 20$.

Check each item that you can solve with the information provided. Write an expression or equation for each item to help you see if you have enough information to solve it.

   □ **1.** the length of a rectangle whose area is 24

   □ **2.** John's weight when he loses 15 pounds

   □ **3.** Silvia's age 10 years from now

   □ **4.** a rectangle's length that is 5 more than its width

   □ **5.** a number that is subtracted from 17 to equal 10

   □ **6.** Janina's age now if she was 32 ten years ago

Your expressions and equations may look similar to these:

1. $24 = lw$

2. $w - 15$

3. $a + 10$

4. $l = w + 5$

5. $17 - n = 10$

6. $a = 32 + 10$

Examine each of the algebraic statements carefully. Only items 5 and 6 can be solved for a specific value.

___

Throughout this unit, you may use a calculator wherever that would be useful. Information about using a calculator appears on page 224.

Talk About It

Compare the expressions and equations that you wrote with those of other students in the class. How are they the same? How are they different? Why could items 5 and 6 be solved for a specific value, while the others could not? Share your reasons.

Solving Equations

In Unit 1 (p. 48), you learned to write number sentences—both equations and inequalities. This lesson explains how to solve equations.

Solving Equations Mentally

Example: Write two equations to express the relationship between the two lines shown here.

- Write an addition equation. $x + 4 = 21$

  Think: What number added to 4 equals 21?

- Write a subtraction equation. $21 - 4 = x$

  Think: 21 minus 4 equals what number?

The solution to both equations is $x = \mathbf{17}$.

You can use your knowledge of arithmetic to solve the equations in this lesson. In other words, write an equation, and ask yourself questions like the ones in the example above to find an answer.

A. Write addition and subtraction equations to express the relationship between the lines in each pair. Then solve the equations.

1.

2.

3.

Equation: _____	Equation: _____	Equation: _____
Equation: _____	Equation: _____	Equation: _____
Solution: _____	Solution: _____	Solution: _____

The unknown can be on either side of the $=$ sign. For example, $12 = 2 + m$ can also be written $2 + m = 12$.

B. Solve each equation by finding the unknown value of the variable. The first one is completed for you.

4. $a + 7 = 9$

   $a = 2$

5. $y - 4 = 13$

6. $3p = -36$

   Think: $3 \times$ what $= -36$?

7. $5 = \frac{r}{10}$

   Think: What $\div 10 = 5$?

8. $8 = m - 1$

9. $4 = s + 6$

10. $\frac{v}{3} = 16$

11. $13 = \frac{1}{2}c$

12. $n - 8 = 0$

54

You can also use equations to find unknown quantities, such as measurements.

Writing and Solving Equations

Example: The area of a rectangle can be expressed with the formula $A = lw$. According to the figure, 9 times the width equals an area of 54 square units.

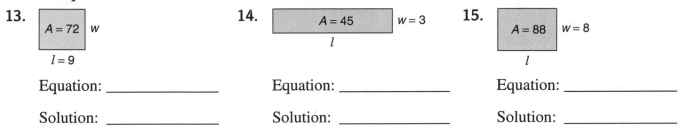

Use the area formula to write an equation based on the figure.

$$A = lw$$

Think, "9 times what number is 54?"

Equation: $54 = 9w$

You know that 9 times 6 is 54.

Solution: $6 = w \; or \; w = 6$

C. For each figure below, write an equation that expresses the area. Then solve each equation for the unknown measurement.

13.

$A = 72$ w

$l = 9$

Equation: _____

Solution: _____

14.

$A = 45$ $w = 3$

l

Equation: _____

Solution: _____

15.

$A = 88$ $w = 8$

l

Equation: _____

Solution: _____

D. For problems 16–18, write an equation. Then find the solution to each equation.

16. The total length of the line is 20. What is the value of x?

17. The total length of the line is 24. What is the value of y?

18. This figure's perimeter is 32. Find the length of the missing side.

19. **Draw** Both $x + 12 = 29$ and $29 - x = 12$ express the relationship between the two lines shown here. Draw two different lines and label them to create a problem similar to the one shown here. Ask another student to write both an addition and a subtraction equation to show the relationship between the two lines that you drew.

Addition and Subtraction Equations

As you saw in the last lesson, it is not difficult to solve an equation with small, easy whole numbers and one operation. To solve more complicated equations, we need a method to calculate solutions.

To solve equations, we use **inverse operations.** An inverse operation does the reverse or opposite of another operation.

Think about addition. If you gain (add) 5 pounds, how do you get back to your original weight? You must lose (subtract) 5 pounds.

► To keep an equation equal and balanced, you must perform the same operation to both sides.

Example: Alicia gained 5 pounds over the holidays and now weighs 135 pounds. What was her original weight? Let x represent the original weight.

Get back to the original weight. Subtract 5 from each side.

The equation remains equal. The solution is $x = 130$. The original weight was **130 pounds.**

$$x + 5 = 135$$

original weight — weight gain — current weight

$$
\begin{aligned}
x + 5 &= 135 \\
-5 \quad &\quad -5 \\
x &= 130
\end{aligned}
$$

Addition and subtraction are inverse operations. If you add 5 to a number, you can *undo* this operation by subtracting 5.

Using Inverse Operations

Example: Solve for m in the equation $315 = m - 78$.

Step 1. Write the problem.

Step 2. Choose the inverse operation to subtraction. Add 78 to both sides. This leaves the variable m alone on one side of the equation.

$$
\begin{aligned}
315 &= m - 78 \\
+\,78 &\quad\quad +\,78 \\
\hline
393 &= m + 0
\end{aligned}
$$

Step 3. Find the solution.

$$393 = m$$

Check. Substitute 393 for m.

$$315 = 393 - 78$$
$$315 = 315$$

A. Solve each equation for the unknown. Check your answers.

1. $c - 15 = 105$

2. $w + 25 = 10$

3. $88 = u - 12$

4. $\$18 = p - \$1.65$

5. $\$50 = t - \$29.90$

6. $d + 7.6 = 8$

B. Simplify each equation by combining numerical terms. Then solve each equation.

7. $f + 23 + 71 = 284$

8. $e + 5\frac{1}{2} + 8\frac{1}{2} = 40$

C. Solve for the missing side in each triangle. $P = s_1 + s_2 + s_3$ where P = perimeter and s_1, s_2, and s_3 = sides.

9.

7.3

$P = 18.6$

$a = \underline{\hspace{1cm}}$

10.

$7\frac{1}{4}$

$P = 22$

$b = \underline{\hspace{1cm}}$

11.

c

$P = 39.4$

$c = \underline{\hspace{1cm}}$

Inverse operations are sometimes used to solve word problems.

Example: A group of coworkers has collected $25 to buy a gift. The boss is going to contribute the remaining amount. How much will the boss give if the gift costs $45?

Step 1. Write the equation for the problem.

Step 2. Use inverse operations to solve. In this case, subtract $25 from both sides of the equation.

$$
\begin{aligned}
\$25 + m &= \$45 \\
- \$25 \qquad &\quad - \$25 \\
\hline
0 + m &= \$20 \\
m &= \mathbf{\$20}
\end{aligned}
$$

D. First write an equation. Then solve the problem.

12. If Alfredo gets a raise of $1.25 an hour, his new wage will be $10 an hour. Let w represent his current hourly wage. What is Alfredo's current hourly wage?

13. The temperature at 9:00 P.M. was $t°$ Fahrenheit. If the temperature drops 6°, it will be −5°F. Find the 9:00 P.M. temperature.

14. Victor borrowed $40 from his brother. This gave him enough money to pay for a $150 car repair. How much money (m) of his own did Victor have?

15. **Discuss** To solve the equation $x + 7 = 5$, you can subtract 7 from both sides. Can you also add (−7) to both sides? Is the solution the same? Why or why not?

Multiplication and Division Equations

The method of inverse operations can also be used with multiplication and division. Follow the example below.

Example: Most of the houses in Danville are valued at 3 times their 1970 value. A $90,000 house is worth 3 times what it was in 1970. What was the house worth in 1970?

House Value	
1970	Now
?	$90,000

Let x represent the 1970 value of the house.
$3x = \$90,000$

$$3x = \$90,000$$

increase — 1970 value — current value

To solve for the 1970 value, use inverse operations. Division is the inverse of multiplication. Divide each side of the equation by 3.

$$\frac{3x}{3} = \frac{\$90,000}{3}$$

The equation remains equal. The solution is $x = \$30,000$. The house was worth **$30,000** in 1970.

$$x = \$30,000$$

Multiplication and division are inverse operations. If you multiply a number by 3, you can *undo* it by dividing by 3.

Using Inverse Operations

Example: Solve for c in the equation $12 = \frac{c}{3}$.

The operation in the equation is division. The inverse of division is multiplication.
Multiply both sides by 3. $\quad 3 \cdot 12 = \frac{c}{3} \cdot 3$
The solution is $36 = c$. $\quad\quad$ **$36 = c$**

Check. Substitute 36 for c. $\quad 12 = \frac{36}{3}$

A. Solve and check each equation.

1. $4a = 36$

2. $\frac{c}{5} = 9$

3. $7d = -56$

4. $\frac{1}{2}a = 37$

5. $\frac{e}{-2} = 15$

6. $50 = 100g$

7. $\frac{n}{12} = -6$

8. $-3w = 36$

9. $1.1r = 4.4$

10. $\frac{r}{10} = 5$

11. $15s = -15$

12. $12 = 2t$

B. Find the missing length or width for each of the figures.

13.
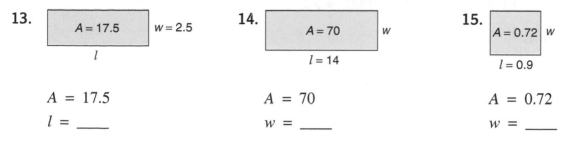

$A = 17.5$ $w = 2.5$ l

$A = 17.5$
$l =$ _____

14.

$A = 70$ w $l = 14$

$A = 70$
$w =$ _____

15.

$A = 0.72$ w $l = 0.9$

$A = 0.72$
$w =$ _____

C. Simplify each equation by combining the unknowns. Then solve.

16. $4a + 5a = 90$

17. $7m + m - 3m = 45$

18. $48 = 9c + 8c - c$

19. $10 = 12x - 5x + 13x$

Making Connections: Unit Pricing

When comparing items for sale, you sometimes need to look at more than the total cost.

Suppose you are comparing cereal prices. If you know the total cost and the number of ounces in a box, you can find the rate. The rate in this case is the *price per ounce*. The rate is often called **unit price.**

Use the cost formula to find the unit price (the price per ounce) for each of the following breakfast cereals. Decide which cereal has the lowest unit price.

Hint: Use a calculator, and round off each price to the nearest penny. For example, 0.116 rounds up to $0.12.

For another look
at rounding, turn to page 222.

Cost formula: cost = number of items · rate, or $c = nr$. To find the unit price (the rate), find $\frac{c}{n} = r$.

Cost: $1.89
Number of ounces: 16

Cost: $3.48
Number of ounces: 32

Cost: $2.99
Number of ounces: 20

Cost: $1.55
Number of ounces: 12

Equations and Multiple Operations

You have already learned how to use inverse operations to solve equations. For example, to solve $3x = 15$, divide each side by 3 to get $x = 5$.

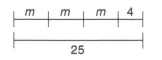

Some equations require the use of more than one inverse operation. For example, the relationship between the two lines above can be expressed with the equation $3m + 4 = 25$. In this equation the variable is multiplied by 3. Then 4 is added to the product. Multiplication and addition are used.

Which two operations do you think are needed to solve this equation? You're right if you chose **subtraction** and **division.**

When solving an equation, your goal is to get a *single variable* on one side of the equation.

Using Two Inverse Operations

Example 1: Solve the equation $3m + 4 = 25$.

Step 1. Subtract 4 from both sides.

$$3m + 4 = 25$$
$$ -4 \quad -4$$
$$3m \quad\quad = 21$$

Step 2. Divide both sides by 3.

$$\frac{3m}{3} = \frac{21}{3}$$

The solution is $m = 7$.

$$m = 7$$

Check. Substitute 7 for m.

$$3(7) + 4 = 21 + 4 = 25$$

Example 2: Solve the equation $7 = \frac{a}{4} - 3$.

Step 1. Add 3 to both sides.

$$7 = \frac{a}{4} - 3$$
$$+ 3 \quad\quad + 3$$
$$10 = \frac{a}{4}$$

Step 2. Multiply both sides by 4.

$$4 \cdot 10 = \frac{a}{4} \cdot 4$$

The solution is $a = 40$.

$$40 = a$$

Check. Substitute 40 for a.

$$7 = \frac{40}{4} - 3 = 10 - 3 = 7$$

A. Solve and check each equation.

1. $2m + 5 = 17$

2. $\frac{r}{4} - 1 = 19$

3. $7s + 2 = 30$

4. $8a - 3 = 13$

5. $19 = 6n - 5$

6. $17 = 10y - 3$

7. $25 = \frac{b}{3} + 13$

8. $11 = 2x - 9$

9. $6x - 1 = 2$

10. $\frac{t}{2} + 5 = 9$

11. $7r + 3 = -11$

12. $5 = 9a - 4$

B. Write an equation that expresses the relationship between the lines in each pair. Then solve each equation.

13.

14.

15.

C. Write an equation for each problem. Then solve. The first one has been started for you.

16. The total distance from A to C in the illustration is 87. What is *m?*

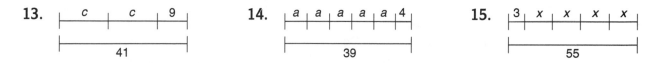

$3m - 5 + 7m + 12 = 87 \qquad m =$

17. The perimeter of this figure is 46. Solve for *x*.

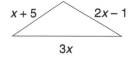

18. Four more than twice Joan's age is 60. Let $a =$ her age. What is her age?

19. Sam plans to save $60 a week to buy a new sound system. If his brother returns $140 that he borrowed from Sam, how many weeks will it take Sam to have a total of $500?

20. **Multiple Solutions** Solve to find *x* in the equation $51 - x = 20$. Is this a one-step or a two-step solution? Show more than one way to solve the equation. Is there more than one solution to the equation?

Simplifying Equations

Some unsolved equations have variables (unknowns) on both sides of the equal sign.
To solve the equation, the variables must be combined.

The lines shown here are equal. The equation $11k + 6 = 4k + 34$
expresses the relationship between the two lines.

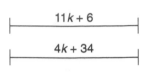

Notice that variables and numbers appear on both sides of the equal sign.
To simplify the equation, use inverse operations to combine variables on
one side of the equal sign and numbers on the other side.

Combining Terms

Example: Solve the equation $11k + 6 = 4k + 34$.

Step 1. Subtract $4k$ from both sides.
(Since $11k > 4k$, it's simpler to subtract $4k$ from
each side. That way a positive k is left.)

Step 2. Subtract 6 from both sides.

$$
\begin{array}{rcr}
11k + 6 &=& 4k + 34 \\
-\ 4k & & -\ 4k \\
\hline
7k + 6 &=& 34 \\
-\ 6 & & -\ 6 \\
\hline
7k &=& 28
\end{array}
$$

Step 3. Divide both sides by 7.

$$\frac{7k}{7} = \frac{28}{7}$$
$$k = 4$$

Check. $11(4) + 6 = 4(4) + 34 \qquad 50 = 50$

A. Solve each equation.

1. $11c = 3c - 24$

2. $7y = 2y + 20$

3. $4a = a + 18$

4. $9n = 21 + 2n$

5. $30 + 10r = 11r$

6. $15 + 5p = 20p$

7. $2s + 32 = 6s$

8. $3w + 20 = 7w$

9. $8b = 5b - 12$

10. $9z = 6 - 3z$

11. $3t = 30 - 2t$

12. $5e = 48 - e$

B. Write an equation that expresses the relationship between the lines in each
pair. Then solve each equation.

13.

14.

The equation $3(c - 4) = 15$ expresses the relationship between the two lines at the right.

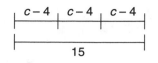

Use the distributive property to simplify equations with parentheses.

Using the Distributive Property

Example: Solve the equation $3(c - 4) = 15$.

Step 1. Multiply the terms inside the parentheses by 3.

Step 2. Add 12 to both sides.

Step 3. Divide both sides by 3.

The solution is $c = 9$.

$$3(c - 4) = 15$$
$$3c - \cancel{12} = 15$$
$$\underline{+ \ \cancel{12} \ + \ 12}$$
$$3c = 27$$
$$\frac{\cancel{3}c}{\cancel{3}} = \frac{27}{3}$$
$$\boldsymbol{c = 9}$$

C. Solve each equation.

15. $2(y + 3) = 20$

16. $5(m + 1) = 60$

17. $5(d + 2) + 3d = 58$

18. $4(s - 2) - 3s = 7$

19. $19 = 2(w + 3) + 5$

20. $3(n + 5) - 8 = 10n$

21. $2(p + 4) + 1 = 5p$

22. $4(r + 3) - 2 = 9r$

D. Solve each problem.

23. Write an equation for the area of the rectangle. Solve for x.

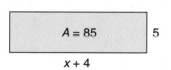

24. **Experiment** Use the methods described below to solve the equation $7a - 4 = 2a + 11$ four different ways.

   a. To each side, first add 4; then subtract $2a$; then divide by 5.

   b. From each side, first subtract 11; then subtract $7a$. Since you want to find a, not $-a$, divide each side by -5.

   c. From each side, first subtract $2a$; then add 4; then divide by 5.

   d. From each side, first subtract $7a$; then subtract 11. Since you want to find a, not $-a$, divide each side by -5.

   e. Are some methods easier than others? Explain.

Using Substitution

So far, you have used substitution to evaluate expressions and check answers. You can also use substitution to solve problems with more than one variable.

Substituting a Value in an Equation

Example: What is the value of x if $3x + 2y = 26$ and $y = 7$?

$$3x + 2y = 26$$

Step 1. Substitute 7 for y.
$$3x + 2(7) = 26$$
$$3x + 14 = 26$$

Step 2. Subtract 14 from both sides.
$$3x = 12$$

Step 3. Divide both sides by 3.
$$x = 4$$
The value of x is 4.

A. Solve each problem.

1. What is the value of a if $5a - c = 43$ and $c = 12$?

2. Find the value of s when $4s + 3t = -1$ and $t = -3$.

3. Find the length and width of the figure at right if $y = 10$ and the perimeter is 52. *Hint:* When you find the values for x and y, substitute them in $3x$ and $x + y$.

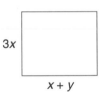

$3x$

$x + y$

Solving for a Value and Substituting It

Example: Solve for w and z if $7w - 3 = 11$ and $z = 10w$.

$$7w - 3 = 11$$

Step 1. Add 3 to both sides.
$$7w = 14$$

Step 2. Divide both sides by 7.
$$w = 2$$

Step 3. To find z, substitute 2 for w.
$$z = 10w = 10(2) = 20$$
The values are $w = 2$ and $z = 20.$

B. Solve each problem.

4. Solve for m and t if $9m - 4 = 68$ and $t = 2m$.

5. Solve for r and s if $17 = \frac{1}{2}r + 11$ and $s = 3r$.

6. Solve for n and p if $4(n - 6) = 20$ and $p = 7n$.

Substituting an Expression for a Variable

Example: Find the values of d and e if $3d + 2e = 50$ and $e = 2d - 3$.

Step 1. Substitute $2d - 3$ for e.	$3d + 2(2d - 3) = 50$
Step 2. Use the distributive property.	$3d + 4d - 6 = 50$
Step 3. Combine like terms.	$7d - 6 = 50$
Step 4. Add 6 to both sides.	$7d = 56$
Step 5. Divide both sides by 7.	$d = 8$

To find e, substitute 8 for d.

$$e = 2d - 3$$
$$e = 2(8) - 3$$
$$e = 16 - 3$$
$$e = 13$$

C. Solve the problems. Be sure to find the values of *both* variables.

7. Find the values of r and s when
$2r + 5s = 29$ and $r = 2s + 1$.

8. Solve for c and d if $3c - 2d = 14$ and
$d = c - 3$.

9. What are the values of p and t if
$5p + 4t = 98$ and $t = 2p + 5$?

10. Find the values of a and b if
$2a + 5b = -22$ and $a = b + 3$.

Making Connections: Formulas as Equations

An equation with more than one variable is called a **literal equation.** A literal equation can be solved for any of its variables. Formulas, such as those on pages 223–224, are a special kind of literal equation.

Example: On a trip, you know the distance and time it took to get to somewhere. You want to find your average rate of speed on the trip.

- Choose the distance formula. $d = rt$

- Get r (rate of speed) alone. $\frac{d}{t} = r$
  Divide both sides by t.

- Substitute your known values for d and t to find the rate.

Rewrite each equation in terms of the unknown that is asked for.

1. Solve $c = nr$ for r.

2. Solve $P = 4s$ for s.

3. Solve $A = lw$ for l.

4. Solve $A = s^2$ for s.
   Hint: What is the inverse of squaring a number?

Using Formulas

Below is a chart of formulas, many of which you have already used in this book. You will see that some of the formulas are written differently from the way they were written when you first saw them.

Description	Formula		Notes
Perimeter (P) of a triangle	$P = a + b + c$		a, b, and c are sides
Perimeter of a rectangle	$P = 2l + 2w$		l = length, w = width
Perimeter of a square	$P = 4s$		s = side
Area (A) of a rectangle	$A = lw$		l = length, w = width
Area of a square	$A = s^2$		s = side
Cost (c)	$c = nr$		n = number of items r = rate or price of one item
Distance (d)	$d = rt$		r = rate or speed t = time
Simple interest (i)	$i = prt$		p = principal r = rate of interest t = time
Mean (m) or average	$m = \dfrac{x_1 + x_2 + \ldots + x_n}{n}$		x_1 = first item x_2 = second item n = number of items
Temperature conversions			
Celsius to Fahrenheit	$F = \frac{9}{5}C + 32$		C = Celsius temperature
Fahrenheit to Celsius	$C = \frac{5}{9}(F - 32)$		F = Fahrenheit temperature

Rewriting Formulas

You can rewrite a formula in terms of its variables and substitute values into the new formula.

Example: Manolo drove 360 miles in 6 hours. At what average speed did he drive?

Choose the distance formula.	$d = rt$
Get r alone. Divide both sides by t.	$r = \frac{d}{t}$
Substitute the known values and solve for r.	$r = \frac{360}{6} = $ **60 miles per hour**

For each problem, first choose the correct formula. Then rewrite the formula to solve for the variable asked for in the problem. Finally, evaluate (solve) the equation. You may use a calculator. The first one is started for you.

1. The perimeter of the rectangle is 17. What is the length?

   $w = 3.5$

   $P = 2l + 2w$

   $P - 2w = 2l$

2. Mehmet paid $156 for 20 bundles of roofing shingles before tax. Find the cost per bundle.

3. The formula for the mean of four items can be written as $m = \frac{a + b + c + d}{4}$. Find out what score Sara needs on a quiz to have an average of 80 if her first three scores were 74, 92, and 75.

4. Serena knows that the formula for converting Celsius to Fahrenheit temperature is $F = \frac{9}{5}C + 32$. She wants to find the Celsius temperature that corresponds to 104°F. Assume she doesn't know the formula for converting Fahrenheit to Celsius. (*Hint:* First solve the Fahrenheit conversion formula for C.)

5. Tim knows that he hikes at a rate of about 3 miles per hour. He wants to hike between two villages that are 18 miles apart. Find out how long it should take Tim to hike from village to village. Add $1\frac{1}{2}$ hours to the time to account for rest breaks.

6. Steve is lending his daughter Casey $3,600 so she can buy a used car. At the end of 1 year Casey will owe simple interest of $216. Find the interest rate that Steve charges Casey.

7. The perimeter of the triangle is 22. Find the length of the missing side.

8. CDs cost $11.99 each. Find the greatest number of CDs Frank can buy for $100, not counting tax.

9. **Discover** Rewrite the formula for the area of a square to solve for s. (*Hint:* What is the inverse of squaring a number?) Then find the measurement of the side of a square with an area of 196.

Solving Inequalities

You have learned that equations compare equal amounts. **Inequalities** compare unequal amounts. The list below shows common inequality symbols.

Symbol and Meaning	$<$ is less than	**Example**	$-5 < -3$ (-5 is less than -3)
	$>$ is greater than		$1 > -4$ (1 is greater than -4)
	$\leq$ is less than or equal to		$x \leq 8$ (x is less than or equal to 8)
	$\geq$ is greater than or equal to		$x \geq 2$ (x is greater than or equal to 2)

Solving inequalities is similar to solving equations.

Solving Inequalities

Example 1: Solve the inequality $4x - 7 > 5$.

Step 1. Add 7 to both sides.
Step 2. Divide both sides by 4.

$4x - 7 + 7 > 5 + 7$
$4x > 12$
$\frac{4x}{4} > \frac{12}{4}$
$\boldsymbol{x > 3}$

The solution is $x > 3$.

Check. Choose the smallest whole number that is true for $x > 3$ to check the inequality. Use 4, since $4 > 3$. $4(4) - 7 > 5; 16 - 7 > 5; 9 > 5$.

The inequality is **true for $x = 4$.**

Example 2: Is the inequality $-9x + 8 < 26$ true for both $x = -1$ and $x = -2$?
First solve the inequality.

Step 1. Subtract 8 from both sides.
Step 2. Divide both sides by -9.

$-9x + 8 - 8 < 26 - 8$
$-9x < 18$
$\frac{-9x}{-9} > \frac{18}{-9}$
$x > -2$

The solution is $x > -2$.
Substitute the values for x in the solution.
The inequality is **true for $x = -1$.** $-1 > -2$
The inequality is **not true for $x = -2$.** $-2 = -2$ is equal to, not greater than

Check. Substitute -1 for x in the inequality. $-9(-1) + 8 < 26; 9 + 8 < 26; 17 < 26$
Substitute -2 for x. $-9(-2) + 8 < 26; 18 + 8 < 26; 26$ is not less than 26.

► When multiplying or dividing both sides of an inequality by a negative value, the inequality sign changes to the opposite inequality sign. In the case of Example 2 above, dividing by -9 changes $<$ to $>$.

A. Solve each inequality.

1. $8x - 1 < 7$

2. $\frac{1}{2}n - 1 > 9$

3. $5(a + 2) \geq 45$

4. $2(m - 3) < 20$

5. $18 > 8c + 4 - c$

6. $36 \leq 9(y - 6)$

B. Choose the values for which each inequality is true.

7. $x + 5 \leq 9$ **(1)** -3 **(2)** 0 **(3)** 2 **(4)** 4 **(5)** 5 **(6)** 8

8. $\frac{1}{3}x + 1 > 5$ **(1)** 10 **(2)** $11\frac{1}{2}$ **(3)** 12 **(4)** 14 **(5)** 20 **(6)** 25

C. Write and solve an inequality that expresses the relationship between the lines in each pair.

9.

x	x	3

13

10.

m	m	m	5

23

11.

a	7	a	4

17

D. Solve each inequality and simplify each expression.

12. $n - 3 < 40$

13. $5n < 40$

14. $5n - 3 - 40$

15. $5n - 40 + 3$

16. $5(n - 3) < 40$

17. $5(n - 3) - 40$

E. Answer each question.

18. What is the smallest whole-number value for w that makes the area of the dance floor greater than 100?

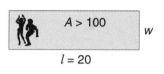

19. In the village of Philport the turnout for elections ranges from 30% to 70% of the registered voters. There are 1,200 registered voters in the village. Which of the following choices expresses the *number* of voters (x) who turned out for the last election? (*Hint:* 10% of 1,200 is 120.)

(1) $0 \leq x \leq 1{,}200$
(2) $300 \leq x \leq 700$
(3) $360 \leq x \leq 840$
(4) $400 \leq x \leq 900$

20. Investigate Perform each of the following operations on the inequality $3 < 7$, and check whether the inequality is still true.

a. Add 2 to both sides.

b. Subtract 4 from both sides.

c. Multiply both sides by 6.

d. Multiply both sides by -2.

Mixed Review

A. Write and solve an equation that expresses the relationship between the lines in each pair.

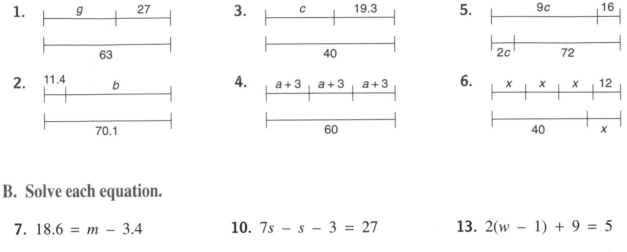

1. g | 27 ; 63

2. 11.4 | b ; 70.1

3. c | 19.3 ; 40

4. a + 3 | a + 3 | a + 3 ; 60

5. 9c | 16 ; 2c | 72

6. x | x | x | 12 ; 40 | x

B. Solve each equation.

7. $18.6 = m - 3.4$

8. $8x = -6$

9. $\frac{c}{3} = -1.1$

10. $7s - s - 3 = 27$

11. $5a - 1 = -21$

12. $19 = \frac{a}{2} + 13$

13. $2(w - 1) + 9 = 5$

14. $6e + 5 = 2e + 13$

15. $y + 9 = 5(y - 3)$

C. Solve each problem.

16. Find the length of the rectangle. The area is 216.

$w = 12$ | $A = 216$
$l = m + 8$

17. Find each side of the triangle. The perimeter is 47.

2x, x + 5, x + 6

18. What is the value of x if $9x - y = -17$ and $y = 8$?

19. Solve for d and e if $3d - 13 = 23$ and $e = \frac{2}{3}d$.

20. Find the values of m and n if $4m + 5n = 57$ and $n = 2m + 3$.

21. Jeremy charged his brother Clyde 8% simple interest to borrow $1,850. When Clyde paid off the loan, he paid Jeremy $296 in interest. Use the formula $i = prt$ to find how many years it took Clyde to pay his brother. *Hint:* 8% = .08
$$t = \frac{i}{pr}$$

22. The formula for finding the average of 3 items is $m = \frac{a + b + c}{3}$. Hank is a waiter. On Thursday night he made $74 in tips, and on Friday night he made $110. Use the formula to find out how much he has to make in tips on Saturday night in order to have an average of $100 for the 3 nights.

23. Rewrite the formula $C = \frac{5}{9}(F - 32)$ to solve for F. Then find the Fahrenheit temperature that corresponds to 60° Celsius.

24. Rewrite the cost formula $c = nr$ to solve for r. Then find the price per pound of strip steak if 2.5 pounds of the steak cost $12.25.

25. Rewrite the distance formula $d = rt$ to solve for t. Then find the time it takes Fred to hike 22 miles if he averages 4 miles per hour (not counting rest breaks).

D. Solve each inequality.

26. $\frac{1}{4}x - 7 > 3$

27. $-9 < 2x - 1$

28. $3(p - 2) \leq -30$

29. $19 \geq 10c + 3 - 2c$

E. Solve each problem.

30. Write and solve an inequality that expresses the relationship between the two lines pictured here.

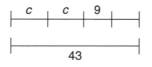

31. What is the smallest whole-number value for l that makes the area of the rectangle greater than 192 square units?

$A > 192$ $w = 12$

l

Lists and Diagrams

To use equations to solve word problems, it is sometimes helpful to break down information into parts. You can use lists and diagrams to organize these parts.

A. Problems 1 and 2 are about two numbers and their relationship to each other. Write an algebraic expression for each description. Problem 1 is started for you.

1. One number is 6 more than another.
    Let n = the smaller number.
    - **a.** the smaller number n
    - **b.** the larger number $n + 6$
    - **c.** the smaller number decreased by 3
    - **d.** twice the larger number
    - **e.** the sum of the two numbers
    - **f.** the difference between the numbers

2. One number is 4 times another.
    Let x = the smaller number.
    - **a.** the smaller number
    - **b.** the larger number
    - **c.** the sum of the two numbers
    - **d.** 5 more than the smaller number
    - **e.** 9 less than the larger number
    - **f.** 3 times the larger number

B. For each problem, let x represent the age of the person indicated. Show the other person's age in relation to x. Charts 3 and 5 are started as examples.

3. Luba is 3 years older than Anna.

	Anna	Luba
age now	x	x + 3
age last year	x − 1	(x − 1) + 3
age in 10 years		
age y years ago		

5. The sum of Tom's and Linda's ages is 40.

	Tom	Linda
age now	x	40 − x
age next year		
age 4 years ago		
age in y years		

4. Juan's age now is twice that of his daughter Sara.

	Juan	Sara
age now		x
age in 6 years		
age 2 years ago		
age y years ago		

6. Alma is 23 years older than her son Tony.

	Alma	Tony
age now		x
age 5 years ago		
age in y years		
age z years ago		

The value of money can be shown in relation to different bills and coins. For example, the value of 1 dime is 10 pennies. The value in pennies of d dimes is written as $10d$—because 3 dimes are worth $10(3)$ or 30 pennies (cents).

C. Write an expression for each of the following.

7. the value in pennies of n nickels (*Hint:* How many pennies in a nickel?)

8. the value in pennies of q quarters

9. the value in pennies of h half-dollars

10. the value in dollars of x \$10 bills

11. the value in dollars of y \$20 bills

12. the value in dollars of z \$100 bills

Using arrows is a convenient way to illustrate motion or distance problems. The arrows show the relationship between motions or distances in a problem.

For example, assume two drivers start from the same place at the same time. They head in the same direction but travel at different speeds. You could show this situation using the arrows at right.

The longer arrow represents the faster driver.

D. Match one pair of arrows with each of the situations described in problems 13–15.

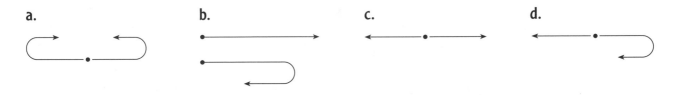

a.   b.   c.   d.

13. Two hikers start at the same spot and head off in opposite directions.

14. Two drivers start at the same spot and head in the same direction, but one of the drivers then turns around and heads back toward the starting point.

15. Two bicyclists start at the same spot and travel in opposite directions. Then one stops and heads back toward the starting point.

16. **Write** Describe a travel situation that could be represented by the pair of arrows that did *not* match one of the situations in problems 13–15.

Algebra Word Problems

On the next four pages, you will see several types of algebra word problems. You will practice using algebra to solve these problems. Some of the problems apply to everyday situations, while others often appear on tests at school and work.

Number Puzzles

Solving Number Puzzles

Example: One number is 2 less than another number. Represent the two numbers as algebraic expressions.

Let x = the larger number.
Let $x - 2$ = the smaller number.

Three times the smaller number is 30 more than the larger number. What are the two numbers?

Step 1. Write an equation using the two expressions.

$$3(x - 2) = x + 30$$

Step 2. Simplify the equation.

$$3x - 6 = x + 30$$

Step 3. Group like terms together.

$$2x = 36$$

Step 4. Solve for both numbers.

$$x = 18 \qquad x - 2 = 16$$

Check. $3(16) = 18 + 30 \qquad 48 = 48$

A. Solve the problems.

1. a. The sum of two numbers is 21. Which pair of expressions represents the two numbers?

    (1) x and $3x$ **(3)** x and $21x$
    (2) x and $21 - x$

b. Three times the smaller number is 1 less than the larger. Find the two numbers.

2. a. The sum of two numbers is 100. Which pair of expressions represents the two numbers?

    (1) x and $2x$ **(3)** x and $100 - x$
    (2) x and $100x$

b. Two times one number is the same as 3 times the other number. Find the two numbers.

3. Carlos is a carpenter. For an hour of work, he charges $1 less than 4 times as much as his assistant Rosie. For an 8-hour day, they charge their clients $232, not including materials. How much does each of them make in 1 hour?

4. Gus, Antonio, and Sam drove their cars to a lake where they like to fish. For the trip, Antonio used 1 more gallon of gas than Gus, and Sam used twice as much gas as Antonio. Together they used 39 gallons of gas. How much gas did each of them use?

Age Problems

Solving Age Problems

For age problems, first prepare a diagram that expresses the ages. Then write and solve an equation.

Example: Fred is 5 times as old as his grandson Joe. In 10 years, the sum of Fred's age and Joe's age will be 92. How old are Fred and Joe now?

	age now	age in 10 years
Joe	x	x + 10
Fred	5x	5x + 10

Step 1. Fill in the diagram.

Step 2. Write an equation to describe the problem.

$$x + 10 + 5x + 10 = 92$$

Step 3. Solve the equation.

$$6x + 20 = 92$$
$$6x = 72$$
$$x = 12$$

Joe is **12**, and Fred is **60**.

$$5x = 5(12) = 60$$

B. Solve the problems.

5. Dorothy's age is 2 more than 3 times her son Greg's age. In 9 years the sum of their ages will be 60.

	age now	age in 9 years
Greg		
Dorothy		

   a. Fill in the chart.

   b. Find their ages now.

   c. Find their ages in 9 years.

   d. As a check, find the sum of their ages in 9 years.

6. The sum of the ages of Annabel and her sister Laurie is 34. Eight years ago Annabel's age was half of Laurie's age. Find their ages now.

7. The Gordons' house is 35 years old, and the Romans' house is 25 years old. How many years ago was the Gordons' house twice as old as the Romans' house?

8. In 2 years Cal and Phil will have worked a total of 50 years in their father's car repair shop. Phil has worked there 6 years longer than Cal has. As of this year, how long has each of them worked at the shop?

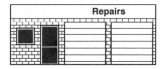

75

Motion Problems

To solve a motion or travel problem, use arrows to describe the movement in the problem. Keep in mind the question. Are you looking for distance, rate, or time?

Solving Motion Problems

Example: Two trains leave a station at the same time. One heads north at an average speed of 60 miles per hour, and the other heads south at an average speed of 75 miles per hour. How far apart will they be at the end of 2 hours?

Step 1. Draw a diagram to help you picture the movement of the trains.

Step 2. Write an equation to describe the problem.

$$60 \cdot 2 + 75 \cdot 2 = d$$

Step 3. Solve the equation.

$$120 + 150 = d$$
$$\mathbf{270 \text{ miles}} = d$$

C. Draw a picture and write an expression for each problem. Then solve.

9. Frank and Dave started driving at the same time from the same place. They went in the same direction, but Frank drove at an average speed of 45 miles per hour, and Dave drove at 55 miles per hour. How long did it take them to be 25 miles apart?

   a. Draw arrows to show the action in the problem.

   b. Write an expression showing the time it took Frank and Dave to be 25 miles apart.

   c. Solve the problem.

10. Jed and Alicia started driving at the same time. Jed drove west, and Alicia drove east at an average rate 10 miles per hour faster than Jed. At the end of 3 hours, they were 318 miles apart. Find the average speed for each of them.

11. Andreas and Udo started bicycling north at 9:00 A.M. at a speed of 16 miles per hour. After 2 hours Andreas turned around and headed back home while Udo continued on. Assuming no change in speed, how far apart were they by noon?

Money Problems

With money problems, write an algebraic expression to represent the number of each type of coin or bill. Keep the units the same. Express coin values in pennies. Express paper-money values in dollars.

Solving Money Problems

Example: Lola has a total of $1.55 in nickels and dimes. She has 5 more dimes than nickels. How many of each coin does she have?

Step 1. Write expressions to show the number of nickels and the number of dimes.

Let x = number of nickels.
Let $x + 5$ = number of dimes.

Step 2. Write an equation to describe the problem. Write the expressions in terms of pennies.

$5x + 10(x + 5) = 155$

Step 3. Solve the equation.

$5x + 10x + 50 = 155$
$15x = 105$

Lola has 7 nickels and 12 dimes.

$x = 7 \qquad x + 5 = 12$

D. Solve the problems.

12. Mark has 9 coins in his pocket. He has quarters and dimes only. The total value is $1.35.

   a. If q represents the number of quarters, which expression represents the number of dimes?

   (1) $q + 9$ **(2)** $10q$ **(3)** $25q$ **(4)** $9 - q$

   b. If q represents the number of quarters, which expression represents the value of the quarters in pennies?

   (1) $25q$ **(2)** $10q$ **(3)** 9 **(4)** $5q$

   c. Which of the following numbers represents the total value of the coins in pennies?

   (1) $1,350$ **(2)** 135 **(3)** 13.5 **(4)** $.135$

   d. How many of each coin does Mark have?

13. Ana spent $1.60 to make a call from a pay phone. She used a total of 12 coins in nickels and quarters. How many of each did she use?

14. Al has quarters, dimes, and nickels in his pocket for a total of $3.40. He has twice as many quarters as nickels and 3 times as many dimes as nickels. How many of each coin does he have?

15. Serena deposited $175 cash in her savings account. There were no $1 bills, but she had 3 times as many $5 bills as $10 bills, and the number of $20 bills was 1 less than twice the number of $10 bills. How many of each bill did she deposit?

16. **Write** Count the amount of change you have with you. Write an algebraic expression for the total change value. Use variables to represent the number of each type of coin.

Percents and Equations

Percents (%) tell how many parts out of one hundred. For example, 20% (percent) represents 20 (part) out of 100 (whole). Percents are commonly used in business. You have already used percents in this book.

To use percents in a calculation, a formula, or an equation, first convert the percent to a fraction or decimal. Before you go on, memorize the equivalents in the percent table at right.

There are several ways to write percent problems. One way is to write an equation using the model shown below:

Percent Equivalents		
percent =	decimal =	fraction
25%	.25	$\frac{1}{4}$
$33\frac{1}{3}\%$	$.33\frac{1}{3}$	$\frac{1}{3}$
50%	.5	$\frac{1}{2}$
$66\frac{2}{3}\%$	$.66\frac{2}{3}$	$\frac{2}{3}$
75%	.75	$\frac{3}{4}$
100%	1.0	1

$$50\% \quad \times 6 \quad = 3$$
percent × whole = part

Remember: Finding a percent of a whole gives you a part.

Solving Percent Problems

	Problem	**Equation**	**Solution**
Find the part.	25% of 16 = x	$.25(16) = x$ or $\frac{1}{4}(16) = x$	$4 = x$
Find the whole.	25% of y = 10	$.25y = 10$ $\frac{.25y}{.25} = \frac{10}{.25}$ or ⌐ 10 ÷ .25 $\frac{1}{4}y = 10$ $4\left(\frac{1}{4}y\right) = 10(4)$	$y = 40$
Find the percent.	z% of 50 = 5	$z(50) = 5$ $\frac{z(50)}{50} = \frac{5}{50}$	$z = \frac{1}{10} = 10\%$

A. Write and solve an equation for each of the following. Decide whether the variable represents the part, the whole, or the percent.

1. 25% of 80 = x

2. 50% of n = 16

3. p% of 300 = 120

4. $33\frac{1}{3}\%$ of 45 = y

5. p% of 64 = 48

6. 20% of c = 30

7. p% of 170 = 17

8. 6% of 400 = t

9. 30% of w = 75

B. Solve each problem. Use a calculator when indicated.

10. Which of the following expresses the total cost of an item whose list price is d dollars when the sales tax is 6%? *Note:* Sales tax is found by multiplying list price by the percent of sales tax.

    (1) $.06d$

    (2) $.94d$

    (3) $d + .06d$

    (4) $d + .06$

11. Find the list price of a shirt that cost $25.44 including a 6% sales tax. (*Hint:* Use the expression from problem 10 and a calculator.)

12. Carlo works in an electronics store. He makes $12 an hour plus a 10% commission on the items that he sells. A commission is an amount earned over the base salary. It is a percent of the price of the items sold.

    a. Complete the expression below for the amount Carlo makes in a day when he works h hours and has a total of t in sales.

    ____ h + ____ t

    b. Find the amount Carlo makes in a day when he works 8 hours and sells a total of $780 in electronic equipment.

    c. Write and solve an equation to find the total value of electronic equipment Carlo must sell in an 8-hour day in order to earn $300.

    d. One week Carlo sold a total of $5,400 in electronic equipment and made $960. Write and solve an equation to find the total number of hours he worked that week.

13. The drawing below shows the plan of the patio outside Alberto's diner. Alberto wants to increase its area by 60%. The width must remain the same. What will be the length of the extension?

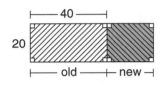

14. At Phil's Photo Shop, several items are listed at 30% off.

    a. Write an equation for the final cost c of an item whose original price is p and is now listed at 30% off.

    b. What is the sale price of a pair of binoculars that originally sold for $94?

15. Sabrina runs a dress shop. She puts a 40% markup on every item in the store. Write and solve an equation to find the most she will pay a supplier for a blouse that costs her customers $28.

16. **Investigate** What is the highest "percent off" that you can find? Do you ever see 100% off or 150% off? Why or why not?

Using Ratio

A **ratio** is a comparison of numbers by division. If Tom is 35 years old and his daughter Maggie is 5, the ratio of Tom's age to Maggie's age is $\frac{35}{5}$ or 35:5. The ratio is read as "35 to 5."

A ratio, like a fraction, can be simplified.

Simplifying Ratios

Example: Simplify the ratio of Tom's age to Maggie's age.

Divide both numbers by 5. 35:5 = **7:1** or $\frac{35}{5} = \frac{7}{1}$
Tip: A ratio is treated differently from a fraction. Always leave a denominator in a ratio, even if the denominator is 1.

A. Write and simplify a ratio for each of the following.

1. So far this season, Ben's softball team has won 8 games and lost 6. What is the ratio of the team's wins to losses?

2. For the team in problem 1, what is the ratio of the number of games won to the total number played so far?

3. Marla invested $1,000 to start a business, and her friend Sandra invested $750. What is the ratio of Marla's investment to Sandra's?

4. The Vassily family takes home $2,100 each month, and they spend $350 a month for food. What is the ratio of their monthly food bill to their take-home pay?

B. Write the ratio indicated for the sides of each figure.

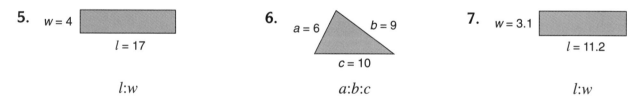

5. $w = 4$
$l = 17$

$l{:}w$

6. $a = 6$ $b = 9$
$c = 10$

$a{:}b{:}c$

7. $w = 3.1$
$l = 11.2$

$l{:}w$

Ratios and Word Problems

You can use ratios to set up equations for some word problems. For example, if the ratio of two unknowns is 2:3, the unknowns can be expressed as $2x$ and $3x$. Notice that $2x{:}3x$ simplifies to 2:3 when each side is divided by x.

Solving Ratio Word Problems

Example: The ratio of two numbers is 5:4 or $\frac{5}{4}$. The sum of the numbers is 135. What are the numbers?

Let $5x$ represent the larger number and $4x$ represent the smaller number. Solve an equation showing their sum to be 135.

$$5x + 4x = 135$$
$$9x = 135$$
$$x = 15$$

The larger number is $5(15) = $ **75,** and the smaller is $4(15) = $ **60.**
Check the sum: $75 + 60 = 135$
Check the ratio: $\frac{75}{60} = \frac{15}{12} = \frac{5}{4}$

C. Solve each problem.

8. The total enrollment in evening computer classes at Central School is 56. The ratio of men to women is 3:4. How many women are in the evening computer classes?

9. Al, Boris, and Cassidy decide to start a business. Al invests $2,000; Boris invests $5,000; Cassidy invests $8,000. They share the profit using ratios that match the ratios of the amounts of their original investments. If total profit for the first year is $4,500, how much will Boris get?

10. A rectangle has a perimeter of 200. The ratio of the length to the width is 3:2. What are the length and the width?

Making Connections: Population Density

Population density is the ratio of the number of people to the size of the area they live in. Cities have dense populations, while farming areas are less densely populated.

Place	Population	Area sq. mi.	Density pop./sq. mi.
X Town	1,200	8	1,200/8 =
Y County	58,000	600	
NY City	7,300,000	309	
U.S.	250,000,000	3,500,000	

To calculate population density, divide the population by the area in square miles where that population lives.

Calculate the population density for each of the areas described in the table above. Round off your answers to the nearest tenth. You may use a calculator. The first one is started for you.

For another look at rounding, turn to page 222.

Using Proportion

A **proportion** is an equation that shows two ratios to be equal. Two equal fractions are an example of a proportion. We can use the characteristics of equal fractions to solve a proportion with an unknown number.

Look at the equal fractions shown here. When you multiply the numerator of each fraction by the denominator of the other fraction, the products are equal. This operation is called **cross multiplication.** The products are called **cross products.**

$$\frac{6}{8} \times \frac{3}{4}$$
$$6 \cdot 4 = 3 \cdot 8$$
$$24 = 24$$

To solve a proportion that contains an unknown, write and solve an equation with the cross products.

Solving a Proportion

Example: Solve the proportion $\frac{4}{5} = \frac{x}{30}$ for x.

Step 1. Write an equation with the cross products.
$$5x = 4 \cdot 30$$
$$5x = 120$$

Step 2. Divide both sides by 5.
$$x = 24$$

A. Solve each equation.

1. $\frac{5}{6} = \frac{x}{18}$

2. $\frac{12}{a} = \frac{4}{3}$

3. $\frac{c}{8} = \frac{7}{2}$

4. $\frac{1}{9} = \frac{5}{m}$

5. $\frac{6}{5} = \frac{w}{4}$

6. $\frac{7}{y} = \frac{1}{2}$

7. $\frac{n}{5} = \frac{2}{3}$

8. $\frac{7}{8} = \frac{3}{r}$

9. $\frac{7}{10} = \frac{e}{12}$

Proportion and Word Problems

Proportion is a practical tool for solving many word problems. One application is enlargements. When a picture is enlarged, the ratio of length to width must be the same in the original picture and the enlargement.

When setting up a proportion problem, remember to keep like parts in the same position. For example, if the width is on top in the first ratio, it should also be on top in the second ratio.

Solving Proportion Word Problems

Example: A photo is 3 inches wide and 5 inches long. It is enlarged to have a length of 20 inches. What is the new width?

Let w represent the new width.

Step 1. Set up a proportion of the width to the length. $\frac{3}{5} = \frac{w}{20}$

Step 2. Write an equation with the cross products and solve.

$5w = 3 \cdot 20$
$5w = 60$

The new width is 12 inches. $w = \mathbf{12 \ inches}$

B. For each figure below, one new measurement is given for an enlargement. Find the other new measurement.

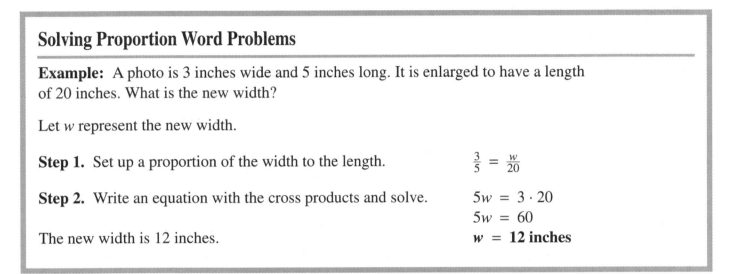

10.
$w = 9$
$l = 12$

new $w = 36$

new $l = $ _____

11.
$l = 15$
$w = 4$

new $l = 60$

new $w = $ _____

12.
$w = 10$
$l = 18$

new $w = 90$

new $l = $ _____

C. Use proportion to solve each of the following problems.

13. The ratio of sugar to flour in a certain recipe is 2:3. If Joe uses 6 cups of sugar, how much flour does he need?

14. A recent survey asked people whether they favored term limits for elected officials. The ratio of those in favor to those opposed was 5:3. If 400 people responded, how many were in favor of term limits?

15. The scale on a map is 1 inch $=$ 15 miles. How far apart are two towns that are 2.5 inches apart on the map?

16. **Investigate** Look at a road map. Find the scale on the map. Use a ruler and proportion to find the distances between towns on the map.

Different Ways to Solve Problems

There is often more than one way to solve a problem. The example below shows a solution using a simple equation and another solution using proportion.

Solving Word Problems Different Ways

Example: There are twice as many men as women in Mr. Henry's welding class. The class has 18 students. How many students are women?

Method 1. Simple equation

men $= 2x$
women $= x$
$2x + x = 18$
$3x = 18$
$x = $ **6 women**

Method 2. Proportion

men:women $= 2:1$
total $= 2 + 1 = 3$
$\frac{\text{women}}{\text{total}} \frac{1}{3} = \frac{x}{18}$
$3x = 18$
$x = $ **6 women**

Solve each problem two ways. You may use a calculator.

1. For every $1 that Bill invested in a part-time business, his partner, Fred, put in $3. They sold the business after 10 years and made a profit of $80,000. If they divide the benefits according to their investments, how much should each receive?

   a. Simple equation:

   b. Proportion:

2. Frank drives 156 miles in 3 hours. Find the distance he can go at the same rate in 10 hours.

   a. Rate per hour:

   b. Proportion:

3. If 5 pounds of salmon costs $32.50, what does 18 pounds cost?

   a. Unit cost:

   b. Proportion:

4. Mike starts riding his bike at the same time that his friend Nick starts driving. They go the same direction along the same road. Mike keeps up an average speed of 15 miles per hour, and Nick drives at an average of 55 miles per hour. If they maintain their average speeds, how far apart will they be in 4 hours?

   a. Use arrows and total distances.

   b. Find how far apart they are at the end of 1 hour. Use that amount to set up a proportion.

5. A 30-acre farm can produce 1,050 bushels of soybeans. At the same rate, how much can you expect from 100 acres?

   a. Unit rate:

   b. Proportion:

6. The area of the rectangle is the same as the area of the square. What is the measurement of each side of the square?

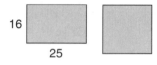

   a. Start by finding the area of the rectangle.

   b. Start by setting the two formulas equal to each other: $lw = s^2$. Then solve for the unknown.

7. If two towns are 150 miles apart and a map shows them to be 2.5 inches apart, what is the scale on the map?

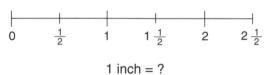

1 inch = ?

   a. Proportion:

   b. After finding what 1 inch represents on the map, find what $\frac{1}{2}$ inch represents. What does $1\frac{1}{2}$ inches represent?

8. Two people divide up 50 pounds of apples in a ratio of 4:1. How much should each person receive?

   a. Equation:

   b. Proportion:

9. Max makes $120 for an 8-hour day. How much should he make in 20 hours at the same rate?

   a. Unit price:

   b. Proportion:

10. The owner of a house with an assessed value of $120,000 pays $3,000 in property taxes each year. At the same assessment rate, what does the owner of a house worth $85,000 pay in property taxes?

   a. Unit price (tax rate):

   b. Proportion:

Unit 2 Review

A. Solve each of the following.

1. $\frac{2}{3}c = 24$

2. $30.2 = m + 4.9$

3. $\frac{x}{4} = -12$

4. $a - 9.6 = -5$

5. $7n + 12 = 5$

6. $3 = \frac{1}{2}w - 9$

7. $4(p + 3) = 20$

8. $9y + 5 = 3y - 19$

9. $8p - p = 17 + 18$

10. $3d - 2 \leq 19$

11. $2(b - 6) > 4$

12. $3 < r + 5$

B. Write and solve an equation that describes the relationship between the lines in each pair.

13.

14.

C. Solve each problem.

15. If $3a + 2c = 41$ and $c = 5a + 1$, what are the values of a and c?

16. The formula for finding the average of 4 items is $m = \frac{a + b + c + d}{4}$. The attendance at performances of a children's play at the Greenview Theater was 163 on Wednesday, 191 on Thursday, and 212 on Friday. Solve the formula for d. Then find the number of people who must attend the Saturday performance so that the average attendance for the 4 performances will be 200.

17. Kate is 60 years old, and her daughter Sophie is 40. Which of the following expresses the ratio of Kate's age to Sophie's age?

    (1) 20:1   **(2)** 1:20   **(3)** 3:2   **(4)** 2:3

18. Tomás and Andrea started driving in their cars at the same time, and they headed in the same direction. Tomás drove at an average speed of 40 miles per hour, and Andrea drove at 60 miles per hour. How far apart were they in 90 minutes?

19. The illustration at right shows the deck on Mel and Fabia's house. They want to increase the area of the deck by 40%. The side that now measures 18 feet cannot change. What will be the total measurement of the other side after they build the new section?

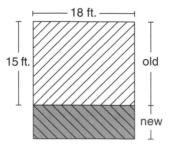

20. The ratio of renters to owners in the Greenview development is 2:3. Currently 420 families live in Greenview. How many of those families own their houses?

21. Hideo has 7 coins in his pocket. He has quarters and nickels only. If q represents the number of quarters, which expression represents the number of nickels?

(1) $5q$ **(2)** $7q$ **(3)** $5 - q$ **(4)** $7 - q$

Working Together

Do the following with a partner or with a group of other students.

1. Write the ratio of your age now to the age of someone you know who is not your age. Then write the ratio of your age 5 years from now to that person's age 5 years from now. Write the ratios again for your ages 10 years from now. Discuss what happens to the ratios. Do they stay the same as the ages change?

2. Make a floor plan of a room that you are familiar with. Find the area of the room. Then draw a plan for an extension to the room and have another group find the area of the new floor plan.

3. Write a set of distance and travel relationships based on your habits. If you walk regularly—to a grocery store or the post office—estimate how fast you walk. Try to find typical speeds for driving in town, on an expressway, and in the country. Compare your estimates with those of others in the class.

4. Select word problems from earlier in the book and see if you can find other ways to solve them. Compare your methods, and discuss different approaches with other groups.

5. Use an almanac or other resource to look up the population and area of different places in your state. Make a population density chart for your town, county, and state similar to the one on page 81. Discuss any general patterns that you find.

6. Bring in your favorite recipe. Swap recipes with a partner or group. Using proportion, create two new versions of the recipe: one that will make a larger number of servings and one that will make a smaller number of servings.

The Basics of Geometry

Skills

Properties of points, lines, and angles

Properties of quadrilaterals, triangles, and circles

Pairs of angles

Pythagorean theorem

Tools

Protractors

Rulers, yardsticks, and tape measures

Problem Solver

Changing units of measure

Application

Understanding maps

The word *geometry* comes from Greek words that mean "to measure the Earth." **Geometry** is the study of lines and angles, of flat and solid figures.

Everything built by people—the house or apartment you live in, the car you drive, and the bridge you walk across—depends upon geometric principles.

In this unit you will learn basic properties and terms used in geometry. You will use them throughout your work in the rest of this book.

How Do I Recognize Geometry?

You have already worked with triangles, squares, and rectangles that you can recognize in objects you see every day. Words are also important clues to recognizing geometric relationships.

Many words have exact meanings both in geometry and in nonmathematical settings. Think about the following words.

complement	adjacent	acute
supplement	vertical	parallel
opposite	horizontal	perpendicular
segment	intersect	symmetrical

The sentences below use some of the words in this list. Check each sentence for which you can explain the use of the word in *italics*.

☐ Sam takes a vitamin *supplement* every morning at breakfast.

☐ The parking lot is *adjacent* to the restaurant.

☐ Manny has to adjust the *vertical* control on his television.

☐ When Marylou was reunited with her twin sister, she realized that there were close *parallels* in their lives.

☐ Carmen felt an *acute* sense of relief when she paid off her credit card bill.

☐ The road we are looking for *intersects* the highway about three miles out of town.

☐ There is always a *segment* of the population that resists change.

☐ They say that *opposites* attract.

The word *complement* is often used in a nonmathematical sense, but it is tricky. The painting John selected may *complement* the color scheme in his office, but if you tell him that, you are giving him a *compliment*.

Throughout this unit, you may use a calculator wherever that would be useful. Information about using a calculator appears on page 224.

Talk About It

Which words from the list above can you use in their mathematical sense? Compare your answers to those of others in your class.

Points, Lines, and Angles

The characteristics of a geometric figure are called its **properties.**
Certain geometric properties are discussed below.

A **point** can be described by its position in space.

A
• Point

A **ray** is a straight path of points that starts at one
point and continues infinitely in one direction.

Ray

A **line segment** has definite length. In the illustration at right, the line
segment lies between its **endpoints** C and D.

C   D
Line Segment

A **line** is a straight path of points that continues in two directions. A line
has *infinite* length. In other words, it goes on and on. Arrows are used to
show that the line continues in both directions. (The word *line* is also
often used when talking about a ray or a line segment.)

Line

Some lines belong in special categories. **Vertical** lines run straight up and
down. **Horizontal** lines run left to right.

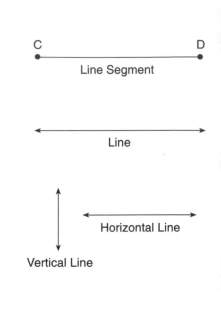

Horizontal Line

Vertical Line

Two or more lines that run in the same
direction are called **parallel** lines. No
matter how far parallel lines are extended,
they never cross, or **intersect.**

Parallel Lines

Lines that intersect to form square corners
(also called **right angles**) are called
perpendicular lines.

point of
intersection

Perpendicular Lines

A. Choose the correct illustration for each problem.

1. Choose the shirt with vertical stripes.

(1)   (2)

2. Choose the intersection where the streets are perpendicular.

(1)   (2)

3. Choose the pair of streets that are parallel.

(1)   (2)

Angles

A **vertex** is a point where two rays or two line segments intersect. An **angle** is formed by two rays. The rays that form an angle are called the **sides** of the angle.

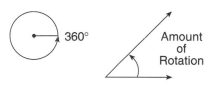

The size of an angle depends on the amount of **rotation** of the sides. Angles are measured in **degrees** (°). One full rotation is 360°.

360°

Amount of Rotation

Below are properties of four angles that you will need to know.

Name	Properties	Examples
right angle	exactly 90°	90° 90° 90° This symbol shows the angle is a right angle.
acute angle	less than 90°	32° 45° 68°
straight angle	exactly 180°	180° 180° 180°
obtuse angle	between 90° and 180°	127° 94° 135°

B. Solve each problem.

4. Match the illustrations with the descriptions.

_____ an acute angle   a.   b.   c.

_____ a right angle

_____ an obtuse angle

5. Which of the three angles, **a**, **b**, or **c**, is smallest? Why? *Hint:* The lengths of the sides do not affect the size of the angle.

a.   b.   c.

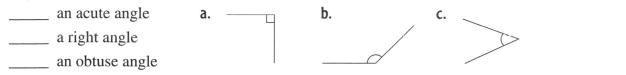

6. Tell the name of each of the following angles.

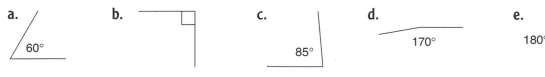

a. 60°   b.   c. 85°   d. 170°   e. 180°

Protractors

A **protractor** is a tool for measuring angles in degrees. A protractor looks like a half circle with a fanlike scale of numbers. One scale runs from left to right; the other from right to left.

To measure with a protractor, place one side of the angle you want to measure under one of the baselines of the protractor. The vertex of the angle should be under the crosshairs.

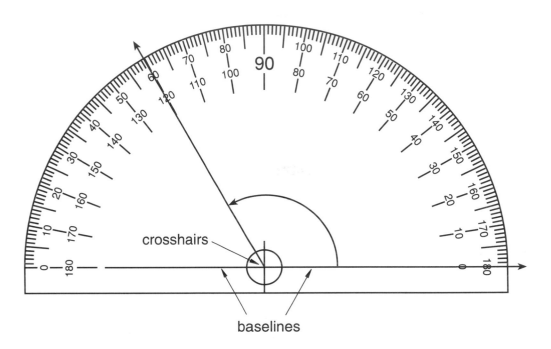

The illustration shows a protractor and an angle of 120°.

The symbol ∠ means angle. The angle in the illustration at right can be called ∠C or ∠ACU or ∠UCA.

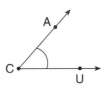

When three letters are used to name an angle, the vertex is always the middle letter.

Sometimes a small letter appears in the opening of the angle. In the illustration at right, ∠BDV is divided into two smaller angles, ∠x and ∠y.

A. Use matching to solve the problem.

1. Match the angle with the correct number of degrees. Use your judgment or a
   protractor if you have one.

   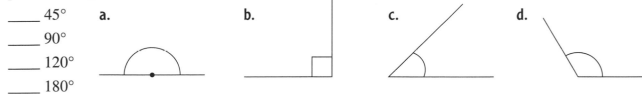

   _____ 45°   **a.**   **b.**   **c.**   **d.**

   _____ 90°

   _____ 120°

   _____ 180°

If an angle is made up of smaller angles, you can sometimes use information about
a known angle to find the size of an unknown angle.

Example: If ∠RST = 148°, find ∠PSR using the drawing at right.

∠RST − ∠PST = ∠PSR

148° − 100° = 48°

∠PSR = **48°**

B. Solve the following problems without using a protractor.
The first one is started for you.

2. ∠XYZ = 135°. Find ∠WYZ.

   ∠XYZ − ∠XYW = ∠WYZ

   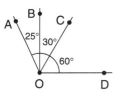

3. State the type of angle and number of degrees in ∠AOD,
   in ∠BOD, and in ∠AOC.

   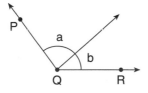

4. ∠PQR = 126° and ∠a is twice as big as ∠b. Find the measurements
   of both ∠a and ∠b. (*Hint:* If ∠b = x, how would you write ∠a?)

5. How many degrees are in the angles formed by the hands of a
   clock at

   a. 2:00   **b.** 3:00   **c.** 5:00   **d.** 6:00

6. **Compare** Determine the number of degrees formed by the hands of a
   clock at 12:30. Compare your answer to those of others in the class.

Pairs of Angles

The right angle pictured here is divided into two angles, ∠a and ∠b. If we know the measure of one of the angles, we can find the other by subtracting from 90°.

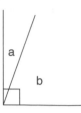

Two angles that add up to 90° are called **complementary angles.**

Finding Complementary Angles

Example: If ∠a in the illustration above measures 19°, what is the measure of ∠b?

Subtract the measure of ∠a from 90°.   90° − 19° = ∠b = **71°**
∠b is the **complement** to ∠a.

The angle pictured here is divided into two angles ∠d and ∠e. If we know the measure of one of the angles, we can find the other by subtracting from 180°.

Two angles that add up to 180° are called **supplementary angles.**

Finding Supplementary Angles

Example: If ∠d above measures 45°, what is the measure of ∠e?

Subtract the measure of ∠d from 180°.   180° − 45° = ∠e = **135°**
∠e is the **supplement** to ∠d.

A. Solve each problem. Use the drawings to visualize the problems.

1. Find the complement to each of the following angles.

    a. 21°   **b.** 89°   **c.** 45°   **d.** 8°   **e.** 4.5°

2. Find the supplement to each of the following angles.

    a. 21°   **b.** 150°   **c.** 45°   **d.** 91°   **e.** 115.5°

Two straight lines that intersect form two pairs of supplementary angles. The angles that share a side are called **adjacent angles;** they are also supplementary. ∠w and ∠x are both adjacent and supplementary angles.

The angles that do not share a side but are opposite each other are called **vertical angles;** they are also equal. ∠w and ∠y are vertical angles.

Example: If ∠w = 49° in the figure above, what is the measurement of each of the other angles?

Since ∠w and ∠x are supplementary, ∠x is 180° − 49° = **131°.**

Since ∠w and ∠z are also supplementary, ∠z is 180° − 49° = **131°.**

Since ∠y and ∠w are vertical angles, ∠y = ∠w = **49°.**

B. Solve each problem. Use the illustrations when needed.

3. Use the figure at the right to answer the following.
   a. Which angle is vertical to ∠m?
   b. Which angles are supplementary to ∠m?
   c. If ∠m = 112°, what is the measurement of each of these angles: ∠n, ∠s, and ∠r?

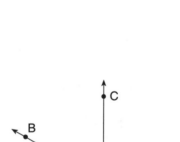

4. Are the adjacent angles formed when two lines intersect complementary, supplementary, or equal?

5. Are the vertical angles formed when two lines intersect complementary, supplementary, or equal?

6. Use the figure at the right to name
   a. a complementary angle to ∠BOC
   b. a supplementary angle to ∠COD

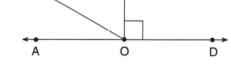

Making Connections: Understanding Street Patterns

The map shows a section of New York City. The intersecting streets form angles that are labeled with letters.

1. If ∠a and ∠e are equal, list any other angles equal to ∠a.

2. List the four angles that are supplementary to ∠a.

3. List the angles that are equal to ∠h.

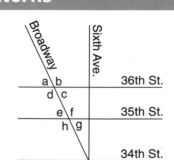

Rulers, Yardsticks, and Tape Measures

For most of the geometric figures you have seen so far in this book, you have calculated perimeter and area without specific units attached to the numbers. Most practical applications require that dimensions such as length and width be measured in units such as inches or feet. Measurement of length or distance is called **linear** measurement. The world uses two systems of linear measurement—the English system (still common in the United States) and the metric system.

Linear Units
English system
1 inch (in.) ⊢———————⊣
1 foot (ft.) = 12 inches
1 yard (yd.) = 3 feet
1 mile (mi.) = 5,280 feet
Metric system
1 millimeter (ml) = 0.1 centimeter
1 centimeter (cm) ⊢——⊣
1 meter (m) = 100 centimeters
1 kilometer (km) = 1,000 meters
Note: No periods are used with metric abbreviations.

You are probably familiar with some of the tools for measuring in the English system. Inch rulers, yardsticks, and tape measures are divided into inches and fractions of inches.

For the metric system, meter sticks and centimeter rulers are divided into centimeters and tenths of centimeters (or millimeters).

Look at the two rectangles below.

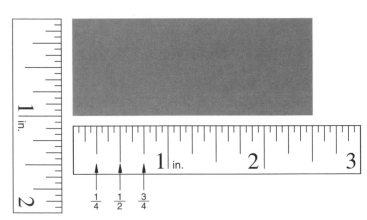

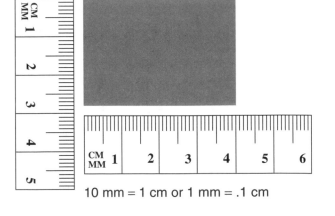

10 mm = 1 cm or 1 mm = .1 cm

Inch rulers are lined up beside the length and width of this rectangle.

Centimeter rulers are lined up beside the length and width of this rectangle.

Using Units of Measure

Example: Find the length, width, and perimeter of each rectangle on page 96.

Inches

length $= 2\frac{1}{2}$ inches
width $= 1$ inch
perimeter $= 2\left(2\frac{1}{2}\right) + 2(1)$
$\qquad = 5 + 2$
$\qquad = \mathbf{7\ inches}$

Centimeters

length $= 4$ centimeters
width $= 2.8$ centimeters
perimeter $= 2(4) + 2(2.8)$
$\qquad = 8 + 5.6$
$\qquad = \mathbf{13.6\ centimeters}$

Answer each question. Be sure to label your answers with the correct units.

1. Measure the length of each line segment. Label your answers in inches or centimeters.

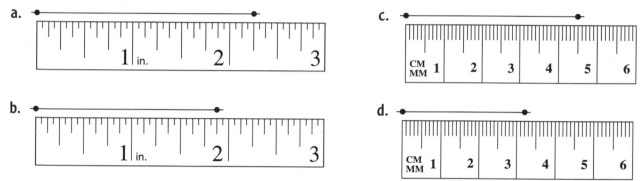

2. A pole 56 feet long is driven into the ground so that the ratio of the part above ground to the part underground is 6:1. What length of the pole is underground?

3. What is the length in inches of the curved line? Estimate or use a tape measure.

4. The perimeter of the triangle is 96 centimeters. Find the measurement of each side.

5. The length of a vegetable garden is 4 times the width, and the perimeter of the garden is 120 feet. What is the length?

6. **List** From the table of linear units on page 96, choose which English and which metric units of measure you would use to measure each of the following:

   a. the width of a book
   b. the length of a room
   c. the height of a door
   d. the distance between two towns

Changing Units of Measure

In the English system, inch (in.), foot (ft.), yard (yd.), and mile (mi.) are the basic units
of linear measurement.

Larger units changed to smaller units are
shown below.

Smaller units changed to larger units are
shown below.

Larger to Smaller
1 ft. = 12 in.
1 yd. = 3 ft.
1 mi. = 5,280 ft.

Smaller to Larger
1 in. = $\frac{1}{12}$ ft.
1 ft. = $\frac{1}{3}$ yd.
1 ft. = $\frac{1}{5,280}$ mi.

Changing English Units

Use substitution to change units.

Example 1: Change 25 feet to inches. Since you're changing from feet to inches,
multiply by 12 *(larger to smaller)*.
Substitute 12 inches for 1 foot and multiply.

1 ft. = 12 in.
25 ft. = 25(12 in.) = **300 inches**

Example 2: Change 24 inches to feet. Since you're changing from inches to feet,
multiply by $\frac{1}{12}$—the same as dividing by 12 (smaller to larger).
Substitute $\frac{1}{12}$ foot for 1 inch and multiply.

1 in. = $\frac{1}{12}$ ft.
24 in. = $24\left(\frac{1}{12}\text{ ft.}\right)$ = **2 feet**

**A. To change the following measurements to feet, first decide if the units
will go from smaller to larger or larger to smaller.**

  1. a. 48 inches **b.** 2 miles **c.** 20 yards **d.** 9 inches **e.** $1\frac{1}{2}$ yards

1 mm	= 0.001 m
1 cm	= 0.01 m
1 m	= 1,000 mm
	= 100 cm
1 km	= 1,000 m

In the metric system, the meter (m) is the basic unit. Other common units are
millimeter (mm), centimeter (cm), and kilometer (km).

The values of these metric units are shown in the table at the right.
The units are all based on the meter.

Changing Metric Units

Example: Change 6.2 meters to centimeters.

Substitute 100 centimeters for 1 meter.

1 m = 100 cm
6.2 m = 6.2(100 cm) = **620 centimeters**

B. Change each of the following measurements to meters.

2. a. 75 centimeters   **b.** 2 kilometers   **c.** 875 millimeters   **d.** 105 centimeters   **e.** 20 centimeters

To convert English to metric measurements use the table at the right. (The symbol ≈ means "is approximately equal to.")

1 in. = 2.54 cm
1 ft. = 30.48 cm
1 yd. ≈ 0.914 m
1 mi. ≈ 1.61 km

C. Solve each problem.

3. Find the perimeter of the rectangle

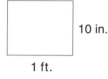

10 in.

1 ft.

   a. in inches

   b. in feet (*Hint:* Use your answer to **a.**)

   c. in centimeters

4. A football field is 100 yards long. What is the length in meters?

5. Max is 70 inches tall.

   a. Find his height in centimeters.

   b. Find his height in meters.

   c. Find his height in feet and inches.

6. Discuss A 5K run is 5 kilometers long. Which is a greater distance: a 5K run or a 5-mile run? Explain your reasoning.

Making Connections: Converting Metric to English

The English to metric chart at the top of this page shows the number of metric units for each English unit. Find the approximate number of inches in a centimeter by using the following proportion.

First, round the number of centimeters in an inch.
1 in. = 2.54 cm ≈ 3 cm

$$\frac{1 \text{ in.}}{3 \text{ cm}} = \frac{x \text{ in.}}{1 \text{ cm}} \qquad 1 = 3x$$
$$\frac{1}{3} = x$$

Use this proportion as a model to fill in the chart below. Round the metric equivalents before you solve the proportions.

Chicago
100 km

1 cm ≈ $\frac{1}{3}$ in.
1 cm ≈ _____ ft.
1 m ≈ _____ yd.
1 km ≈ _____ mi.

1. The air distance between Chicago and Rome is 7,420 kilometers. Use the number from your chart to find the approximate distance in miles.

2. The width of Maria's desk is 90 centimeters. Find the approximate width in inches.

Mixed Review

A. Choose the correct answer to each problem.

1.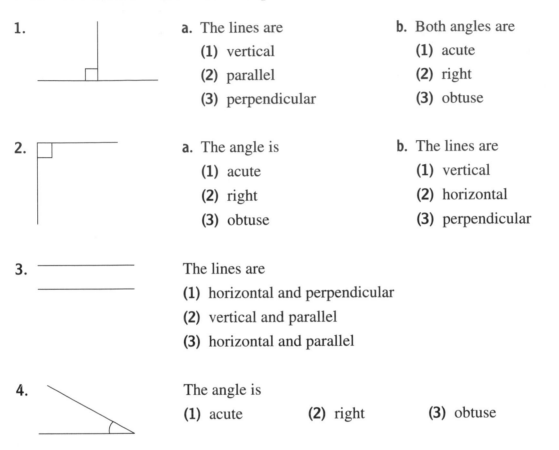
   a. The lines are
      - (1) vertical
      - (2) parallel
      - (3) perpendicular
   b. Both angles are
      - (1) acute
      - (2) right
      - (3) obtuse

2.
   a. The angle is
      - (1) acute
      - (2) right
      - (3) obtuse
   b. The lines are
      - (1) vertical
      - (2) horizontal
      - (3) perpendicular

3. The lines are
   - (1) horizontal and perpendicular
   - (2) vertical and parallel
   - (3) horizontal and parallel

4. The angle is
   - (1) acute
   - (2) right
   - (3) obtuse

B. Measure the number of degrees in each angle and tell whether the angle is right, acute, obtuse, or straight.

5.

6.

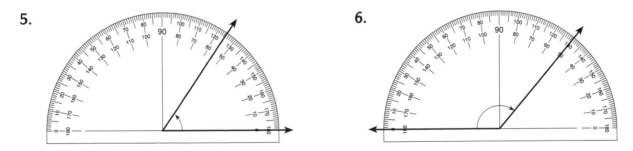

C. Use the figure at the right to solve problems 7–9.

7. Find the number of degrees in ∠LON. What type of angle is it?

8. What kind of angle is ∠KOM?

9. Find the number of degrees in ∠KON. What type of angle is it?

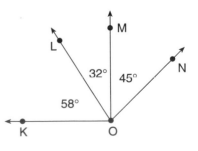

D. Solve each problem.

10. The sum of two complementary angles is _____.

11. If ∠b = 26.5°, what is the measurement of ∠a?

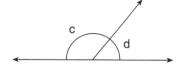

12. If ∠c = 129°, what is the measurement of ∠d?

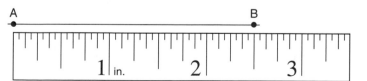

E. Use the illustration to solve problems 13–15.

13. Which angle is vertical to ∠e?

14. Name the two angles that are adjacent to ∠h.

15. If ∠f = 136°
    a. how many degrees are in ∠g?
    b. how many degrees are in ∠h?

F. Use the illustration to solve problems 16–18.

16. What is the length of the rectangle?

17. What is the width of the rectangle?

18. What is the perimeter of the rectangle?

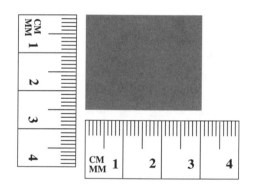

G. Solve each problem.

19. What is the length of the line segment in centimeters? (1 in. = 2.54 cm)

20. The distance between Seattle and New York is 2,900 miles. What is the approximate distance between the cities in kilometers? (1 mi. ≈ 1.6 km)

Properties of Quadrilaterals

A **polygon** is a closed, plane figure made up of line segments. *Closed* means that the sides meet. *Plane* means flat.

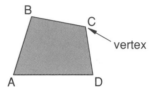

closed   not closed

A **quadrilateral** is a polygon with four sides. Squares and rectangles are the two most common quadrilaterals.

In the quadrilateral ABCD, each point where the sides meet is called a **vertex.** The four points are the **vertices** of the figure.

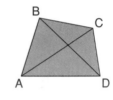

vertex

Sides AB and CD are **opposite** (across from) each other. Sides BC and AD are also opposite each other. Sides AB and AD are **adjacent.** This means that they share an endpoint.

A straight line running from A to C is called a **diagonal.** Line BD is also a diagonal.

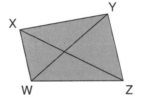

A. Use figure WXYZ to solve problems 1–4.

1. Which side is opposite WX?

2. Name two sides that are adjacent to YZ.

3. Name the two diagonals.

4. Which vertex is opposite W?

Below are five common quadrilaterals and their properties.

  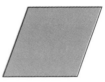  

square	**rectangle**	**rhombus**	**parallelogram**	**trapezoid**
four equal sides, four right angles	opposite sides equal, four right angles	four equal sides, opposite sides parallel	opposite sides equal, two pairs of parallel sides	one pair of parallel sides

B. Identify each figure.

5. a.   b.   c.   d.

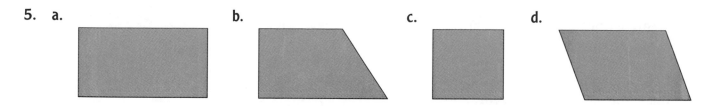

C. Solve the problems about quadrilaterals.

6. What is the sum of the angles in a rectangle?

7. Which figures from the list—square, rectangle, rhombus, parallelogram, trapezoid—must have the following properties?
   a. opposite sides parallel
   b. adjacent sides perpendicular
   c. opposite sides equal
   d. four equal sides

8. The perimeter of the trapezoid is 72. Find the measurement of side AD.

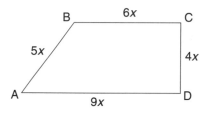

9. a. What kind of quadrilateral is figure PDQB?
   b. What is the perimeter of the figure?
   c. If angle P gets smaller, what happens to the perimeter of the figure?

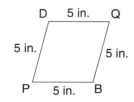

10. Use the list of properties to decide whether
    a. a rectangle can be a parallelogram. Tell why or why not.
    b. a square can be a rhombus. Tell why or why not.

11. **List** Many things are shaped like rectangles. Most doors, windows, and tabletops are examples of rectangles. Name some common examples of a square, a parallelogram, and a rhombus. Compare your examples to those of others in your class.

Properties of Circles

A **circle** is a closed set of points in a plane. Every point on a circle is the same distance from the center.

Picture a sprinkler spinning and watering a circular area. The edge of that circle is called the **circumference (C).** A line segment through the center of the circle with its endpoints on the circle's edge is the **diameter (d).** Half of the diameter is the **radius (r).** The length of the radius tells the distance from the center to any point on the circle.

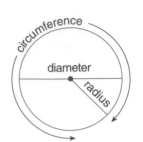

Greek mathematicians discovered a relationship between the circumference of a circle and its diameter. Whatever the size of the circle, the circumference is always a little more than three times the diameter. They called this number π (the Greek letter pi). They found the value of π is close to 3.14 or $\frac{22}{7}$.

To find the circumference (C) of a circle, use the formula $C = \pi d$ where $\pi \approx 3.14$ and $d =$ the diameter.

A. Use the circle below to solve problems 1–4.

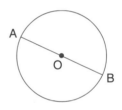

1. Line segment AB is the _____ of the circle.

2. Line segment AO is the _____ of the circle.

3. If AB is 20 inches, what is the measurement of AO?

4. If AO is 6.5 centimeters, what is the measurement of AB?

B. Using the definitions of circumference, diameter, and radius, solve using the terms indicated. Problem 5 is done as an example.

> **Tip**
> $C = \pi d$

5. d in terms of r
   $d = 2r$

6. r in terms of d
   (*Hint:* What should you do to get r alone on one side of the equation?)

7. π in terms of C and d

8. C in terms of π and r
   (*Hint:* $d = ?r$)

C. **The formula for finding the circumference of a circle is $C = \pi d$. Use it to solve these problems. You may use a calculator.**

9. Find the circumference of a plate with a diameter of 10 inches. Use 3.14 as the value of π.

10. The circumference of a round lid represents the distance a can opener moves as it cuts open a can. Find the circumference of a coffee can that has a diameter of 4 inches. (Use 3.14 for π.)

11. A factory manufactures pans for making pizzas. What would be the circumference of a pan that holds a 16-inch pizza? (*Hint:* 16 inches is the diameter.)

12. A manufacturer makes plastic lids to fit cups. How would you find the center of the lid to insert a hole for a straw?

Making Connections: Lines of Symmetry

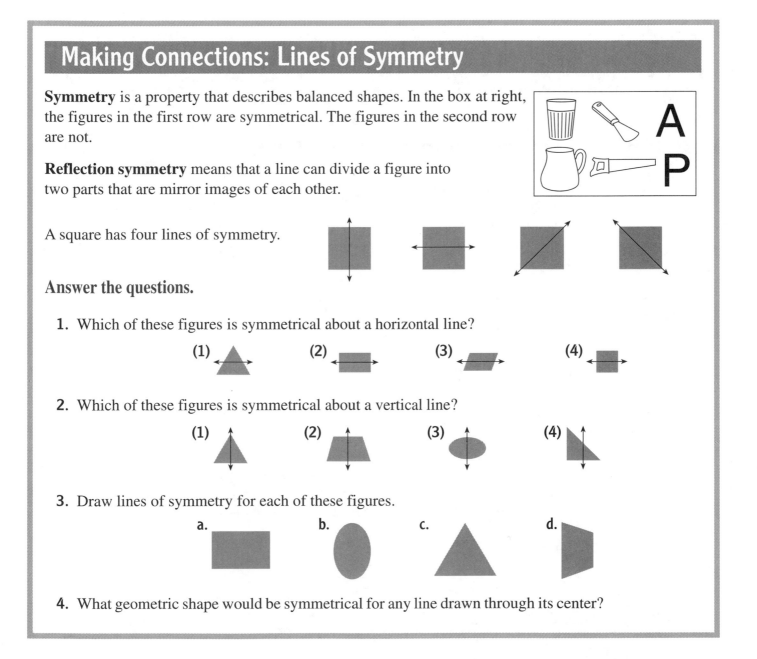

Symmetry is a property that describes balanced shapes. In the box at right, the figures in the first row are symmetrical. The figures in the second row are not.

Reflection symmetry means that a line can divide a figure into two parts that are mirror images of each other.

A square has four lines of symmetry.

Answer the questions.

1. Which of these figures is symmetrical about a horizontal line?

   (1)   (2)   (3)   (4)

2. Which of these figures is symmetrical about a vertical line?

   (1)   (2)   (3)   (4)

3. Draw lines of symmetry for each of these figures.

   a.   b.   c.   d.

4. What geometric shape would be symmetrical for any line drawn through its center?

Properties of Triangles

A **triangle** is a polygon with three sides.

► The sum of the angles in a triangle is 180°.

To see this, draw a diagonal through a square. Remember, a
square has four right angles that total 360° (4 · 90°). The square
is divided into two equal triangles. The sum of the three angles
in one of the triangles is 45° + 45° + 90° = 180°.

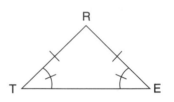

► Equal sides are opposite equal angles.

In triangle TRE, ∠T and ∠E are equal. The sides across from
them, RE and TR, are also equal.

► The longest side is opposite the largest angle.

In triangle TRE, ∠R is the largest angle. The side across from it,
TE, is the longest side.

Names of triangles come from the relationships among the angles and the sides.

Name	Properties	Examples
equilateral	3 equal sides, 3 equal angles	2 cm 60° 2 cm 60° 60° 2 cm
isosceles	2 equal sides, 2 equal angles	
right	1 right angle	

> **Tip**
> If the sides of a triangle
> are equal, so are the
> angles. If the angles are
> equal, so are the sides.

A. Identify each triangle.

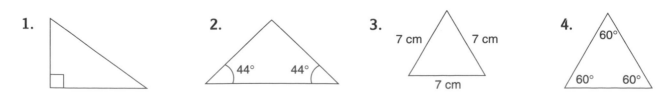

1.

2. 44° 44°

3. 7 cm 7 cm 7 cm

4. 60° 60° 60°

106

B. Solve each problem.

5. Which of the following combinations of angles *cannot* form a triangle? Tell why.

   a. 30°, 60°, 80°   **b.** 50°, 65°, 65°   **c.** 40°, 50°, 100°   **d.** 30°, 30°, 120°

6. Find the missing angle(s) in each triangle. Remember that there are 180° in all triangles.

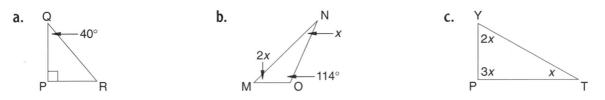

   a.   **b.**   **c.**

7. What is the sum of the two acute angles in a right triangle?

8. Can a triangle have two right angles? (If yes, ask yourself, "What would be the size of the third angle?")

9. What is the longest side in triangle ABC? Why?

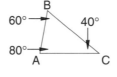

10. What is the largest angle in triangle GHI? Why?

11. In an isosceles triangle, the two equal angles are called **base angles,** and the other angle is called the **vertex angle.** In isosceles triangle KHL, each base angle measures 65°. How many degrees are in the vertex angle?

12. In triangle STU, ∠S = ∠U and ∠T = 42°. How many degrees are in each base angle?

13. **Discover** Can every combination of three sides form a triangle? Use a ruler and strips of paper or cardboard. Try to construct triangles by matching endpoints of each strip in the following combinations.

   a. 5 inches, 9 inches, 12 inches

   b. 7 inches, 8 inches, 16 inches

   c. 4 inches, 5 inches, 9 inches

   d. 3 inches, 4 inches, 5 inches

   Which of the combinations *cannot* be a triangle? Write a property (or description) that describes the relationship among the sides of a triangle.

The Pythagorean Theorem

You learned that a right triangle has a right angle, which equals 90°. The two sides that form the right angle are called **legs.** The side opposite the right angle is called the **hypotenuse.** Since the right angle is the largest angle, the hypotenuse is the longest side.

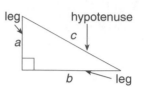

About 2,500 years ago, a Greek philosopher named Pythagoras discovered many properties about numbers, including the relationship among the sides of right triangles called the **Pythagorean theorem.**

The Pythagorean theorem states that, in a right triangle, the sum of the squares of the legs equals the square of the hypotenuse.

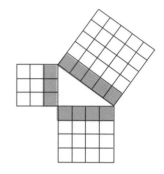

► The formula for the Pythagorean theorem is $a^2 + b^2 = c^2$ where a and b are the legs of a right triangle and c is the hypotenuse.

The illustration shows a right triangle with legs of 3 and 4 and a hypotenuse of 5. The sum of the squares of the legs is $3^2 + 4^2 = 9 + 16 = 25$. The square of the hypotenuse is $5^2 = 25$.

Finding the Hypotenuse

Example: The lengths of the legs of a right triangle are 6 and 8. Find the length of the hypotenuse.

Step 1. Substitute 6 for a and 8 for b in the Pythagorean theorem formula.

$$a^2 + b^2 = c^2$$
$$6^2 + 8^2 = c^2$$

Step 2. Evaluate the left side of the equation.

$$36 + 64 = c^2$$
$$100 = c^2$$

Step 3. Find $\sqrt{100}$. The hypotenuse is 10 units long.

$$\sqrt{100} = c$$
$$\mathbf{10 = c}$$

A. Find the missing hypotenuse for each figure.

1. Find the measurement of side MN.

2. In the rectangle shown here, side RE is 7 and side RT is 24. Find diagonal RC.

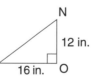

3. The diagram shows the shape of a park. The grounds crew is installing a sidewalk from the southwest to the northeast corner. How many yards will it save to walk on the new sidewalk instead of walking along the edge of the park?

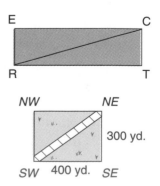

Finding a Leg of a Right Triangle

Example: The hypotenuse of a right triangle has a length of 15, and one of the legs is 12 units long. Find the other leg.

Step 1. Substitute 12 for a and 15 for c in the Pythagorean theorem formula.

Step 2. Simplify the equation.

Step 3. Find $\sqrt{81}$. The leg is 9 units long.

$$a^2 + b^2 = c^2$$
$$12^2 + b^2 = 15^2$$
$$144 + b^2 = 225$$
$$b^2 = 81$$
$$b = \sqrt{81}$$
$$\boldsymbol{b = 9}$$

B. Solve each problem.

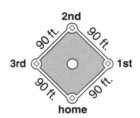

4. What is the measurement of side PR?

5. A box manufacturer needs to make a box with a diagonal length of 10 inches across the lid and a length of 8 inches. What width should the box have?

6. The diagram shows a baseball diamond. To the nearest tenth, what is the direct distance from home plate to second base? (Use a calculator.)

Making Connections: Pythagorean Triples

a	b	c
3	4	5
6	8	10
9	12	15

You may have noticed that most of the numbers you worked with in the examples and problems were whole numbers. A set of whole numbers that works in the Pythagorean theorem is called a **Pythagorean Triple.**

The table shows sets of numbers that are Pythagorean Triples.

1. Find the pattern in the table. Then use the pattern to fill in the next two rows of the table. Check your numbers using the theorem.

2. Use the pattern you found in the table to fill in a new table of Pythagorean Triples starting with 5, 12, and 13. Fill in at least two rows. Then check your answers.

Understanding Maps

Map reading involves solving proportions and sometimes using the Pythagorean theorem. When reading any map, look for the **key** or **legend.** This usually appears in one corner, and it tells you the scale at which the map is drawn. (Look back at problem 16 on page 83.)

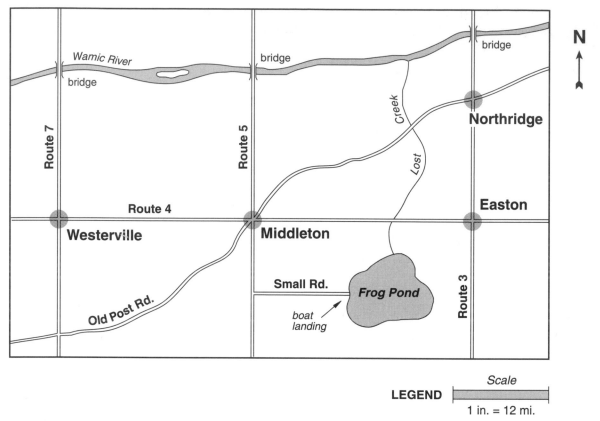

LEGEND

Scale

1 in. = 12 mi.

A. On the map, every inch represents 12 miles. Use the map and a ruler to solve problems 1–3. (If you don't have a ruler, trace the scale on the edge of a piece of paper.)

1. Find the distance in miles
   a. from Middleton to Easton by Route 4
   b. from Middleton to Westerville by Route 4
   c. from Middleton to the nearest Wamic River bridge
   d. from Easton to Northridge by Route 3
   e. from Middleton to Frog Pond by Route 5 and Small Road

2. Calculate the shortest distance ("as the crow flies") from Middleton to the boat landing at Frog Pond.

3. The distance from Middleton to Northridge by Old Post Road can be shown by which expression?
   (1) $x < 27$ mi.   **(2)** $x > 27$ mi.

City maps often show sections of a city in greater detail.

B. In the map below, every inch represents 200 feet. Use the map to solve problems 4–7.

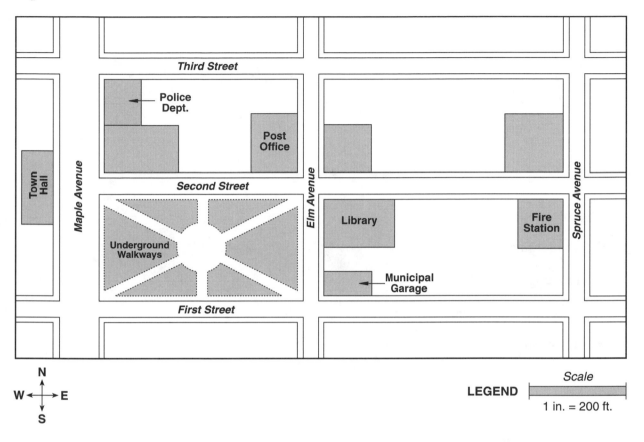

4. What is the approximate length of the water main running along Third Street from the east side of Elm Avenue to the west side of Spruce Avenue?

   (1) 200 feet   **(2)** 350 feet   **(3)** 500 feet   **(4)** 650 feet

5. What is the approximate walking distance from the police department to the fire station? Do not cut diagonally through a block.

   (1) 2,000 feet   **(2)** 1,200 feet   **(3)** 800 feet   **(4)** 500 feet

6. To the nearest 10 feet, calculate the length of the underground walkway that would take people from Town Hall to the municipal garage.

7. **Explain** What is the shortest way to get from the corner of Maple and First to the fire station?

Unit 3 Review

A. Find the number of degrees in each ∠x.

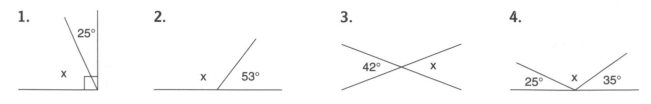

1. 25° x
2. x 53°
3. 42° x
4. 25° x 35°

B. Match each description with the correct illustration.

_____ 5. acute angle

_____ 6. parallel lines

_____ 7. right angle

_____ 8. supplementary angles

_____ 9. obtuse angle

_____ 10. complementary angles

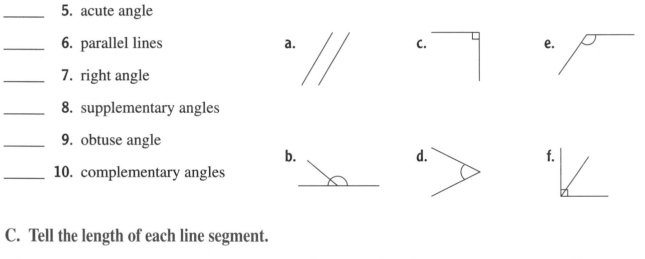

a.

b.

c.

d.

e.

f.

C. Tell the length of each line segment.

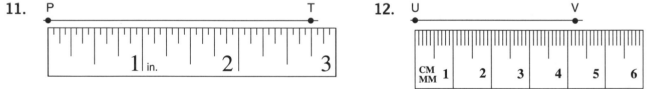

11. P   T

12. U   V

D. Use the diagram of the house and garden to solve problems 13 and 14.

13. Which of the following is *not* adjacent to the wooden fence?

    (1) north wall of the house   **(2)** stone wall   **(3)** street

14. What is the diagonal distance across the garden?

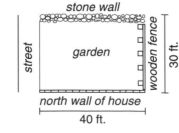

stone wall

street

garden

wooden fence

30 ft.

north wall of house

40 ft.

E. Use the illustration of the circular fountain to solve problems 15 and 16.

15. What is the diameter of the circular fountain at right?

16. The circumference of a circle is given by the formula $C = \pi d$. To the nearest foot, what is the circumference of the fountain? Use $\pi = 3.14$.

F. Solve each problem.

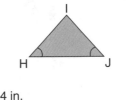

17. If one of the base angles in isosceles triangle HIJ measures 48°, what is the measurement of the vertex angle?

18. A typical business envelope is $9\frac{1}{2}$ inches long and 4 inches wide. What are the length and width to the nearest centimeter? (1 in. = 2.54 cm)

19. According to the map, what is the approximate distance from Centerville to the bridge over Muddy River?

    (1) 15 miles   (3) 45 miles

    (2) 25 miles   (4) 60 miles

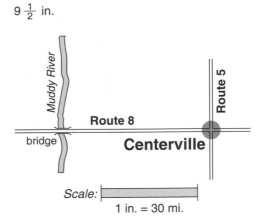

Working Together

Do the following with a partner or with a group.

1. Conduct an experiment to discover whether the relationship between a circle's circumference and its diameter is the same no matter what the size of the circle. Collect samples of different size circles, such as a dinner plate, the rim of a coffee cup, and a plastic lid. Use a string to measure the circumference of each circle. Then measure the string with a yardstick or ruler. Divide each circumference by the diameter of the circle to find your estimate of π. Find the average of your values for π. Compare your group's answers to those of others in the class.

2. Convert familiar linear measurements in English units—such as your height, the length and width of your bedroom, the distance you travel to school—into their metric equivalents. Discuss advantages the metric system has over the English system.

3. Construct a series of isosceles triangles, each with a base of 2 inches. Make the base angles of the first triangle 45°. Give each successive triangle smaller and smaller base angles. Measure the perimeter of each triangle. Discuss what happens to the perimeter as the base angles get smaller. What whole number does the perimeter get closer to?

Unit 4

Using Geometry

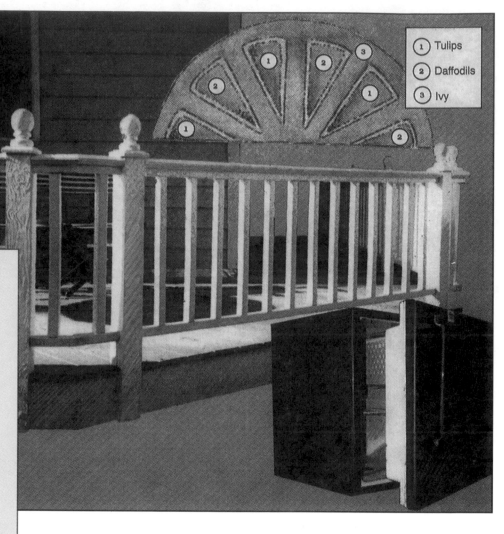

①	Tulips
②	Daffodils
③	Ivy

Skills

Solving complex perimeter problems

Solving complex area problems

Solid figures

Surface area

Tools

Perimeter and circumference formulas

Area formulas

Volume formulas

Problem Solvers

Choosing perimeter, area, or volume

Drawing a picture

Applications

Seeing geometric figures

Renovating a room

Using the cost formula

Geometry may be the most practical branch of mathematics. A farmer uses perimeter to build a fence. A mother uses area when carpeting her child's bedroom floor. A builder uses volume when digging a hole to build a foundation.

Geometry is so much a part of our lives that we often use it without thinking about its precise terms and formulas.

In this unit you will learn to choose and apply the correct geometric formula to a given situation.

How Do I Use Geometry?

Geometry applications can be found in every example of construction—from birdhouses to skyscrapers.

Check each situation that you have worked with or that you think you could solve.

☐ **1.** the number of square yards of carpet needed to cover a floor

☐ **2.** the number of feet of fencing required to enclose a garden

☐ **3.** the amount of earth you would need to remove in order to pour a foundation

☐ **4.** the amount of paint required to cover the interior walls of a house

☐ **5.** the amount of water needed to fill a swimming pool

☐ **6.** the length of wood you need to buy to make a picture frame

☐ **7.** the amount of grass seed needed to seed a lawn

☐ **8.** the amount of concrete mix needed in order to build a patio

These situations illustrate the three basic applications of geometry—perimeter, area, and volume. So far in this book, you have learned to calculate perimeter and area.

Situations 2 and 6 above are examples of perimeter applications. Situations 1, 4, and 7 are area applications. Situations 3, 5, and 8 are applications of calculating volume—a topic that you will study in this unit.

Throughout this unit, you may use a calculator wherever that would be useful. Information about using a calculator appears on page 224.

Talk About It

Discuss the difference between finding perimeter and finding area. You can use the situations above to guide your discussion. Tell what you know about finding volume. What do you know about the units used to measure perimeter, area, and volume? Compare your answers to those of others in your class.

Perimeter and Circumference Formulas

Whether you're buying fencing for your garden or putting trim around a lampshade, you're basing your purchases on geometric principles.

Perimeter is the distance around flat figures with straight sides, while **circumference** is the distance around a circle.

The perimeter of this five-sided figure is $5 + 5 + 6 + 6 + 7 =$ **29 feet.**

Typical units of measure for perimeter and circumference are inches, feet, yards, miles, centimeters, meters, and kilometers.

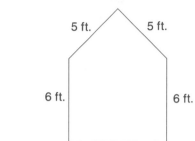

Formulas for Perimeter (*P*) and Circumference (*C*)

Rectangle
$P = 2l + 2w$
where $l =$ length
$w =$ width

Square
$P = 4s$
where $s =$ side

Polygon with n sides
$P = s_1 + s_2 + \ldots + s_n$
where s_1, etc. $=$ each side

Circle
$C = \pi d$ or $C = 2\pi r$
where $\pi \approx 3.14$
$d =$ diameter
$r =$ radius

A. Find the perimeter of each figure.

1.
$l = 12$ ft.
$w = 5$ ft.

2.
$s = 16$ cm

3.
8 in. 8 in.
10 in.

4.
4 in.
5 in. 5 in.
5 in. 5 in.
4 in.

B. Find the circumference of each circle. Use $\pi = 3.14$.

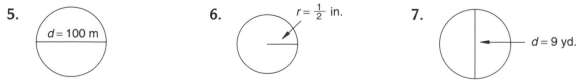

5.
$d = 100$ m

6.
$r = \frac{1}{2}$ in.

7.
$d = 9$ yd.

C. Solve each problem.

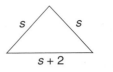

8. Write and simplify an expression for the perimeter of the triangle.

9. What is the perimeter of the triangle in problem 8 if $s = 8$ cm?

10. For the picture shown here, the length is twice the width ($l = 2w$). Write and simplify an expression for the perimeter.

11. The width of the picture in problem 10 is 10 inches. Find the perimeter of the picture in order to frame it.

12. The illustration shows a circle inscribed in (drawn inside) a square.

    a. What is the circumference of the circle?

    b. What is the perimeter of the square?

13. This illustration shows a square inscribed in a circle.

    a. Use the Pythagorean theorem to choose the closest estimate for the length in centimeters of the diagonal labeled s.

    (1) $s \approx 5$ cm   (2) $s \approx 6$ cm   (3) $s \approx 7$ cm   (4) $s \approx 8$ cm

    b. What is the approximate perimeter of the square?

> **For another look**
> at the Pythagorean theorem, turn to page 224.

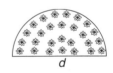

14. The illustration shows the plan of a flower bed in a public park. The shape is a half circle or semicircle.

    a. Which expression tells the distance around the semicircle?

    (1) πd (2) $d + \frac{1}{2}\pi d$ (3) $\frac{1}{2}\pi d$

    b. Find the amount of edging needed to surround the flower bed if $d = 49$ ft. and $\pi = \frac{22}{7}$.
    (*Remember:* Both 3.14 and $\frac{22}{7}$ are estimates of π.)

15. **Investigate** Bill wants to fence in a rectangular space in his yard to make a safe place for his children to play. He has a total of 120 feet of fencing. Assume that he uses all of the fencing. Calculate the length of the play space if the width is

    a. 25 feet   b. 20 feet   c. 15 feet   d. 10 feet

Solving Complex Perimeter Problems

To calculate the perimeter of the L-shaped room shown here, you need the measurement of the left side, labeled *x*, and the short horizontal side labeled *y*. The length of *x* is the *sum* of the two vertical sides, 3 meters and 4 meters. The length of *y* is the *difference* between the two horizontal sides, 11 meters and 5 meters.

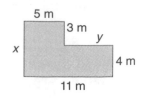

Finding Unknown Sides

Example: What is the perimeter of the room shown above? Since there are 6 walls in the room, find the measure of walls *x* and *y* before adding.

Step 1. Add the two vertical sides. $x = 3 + 4 = 7$

Step 2. Subtract the two horizontal sides. $y = 11 - 5 = 6$

Step 3. Add all the sides to find the perimeter in meters. $5 + 3 + 6 + 4 + 11 + 7 = P$

36 meters = *P*

A. First find each missing side. Then find the perimeter.

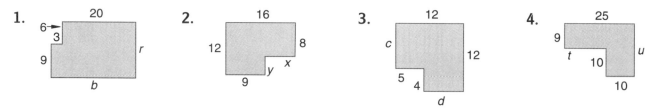

1.
2.
3.
4.

B. Solve the problems.

5. This drawing shows the plan of an L-shaped living room and dining room. What is the perimeter of the combined rooms?

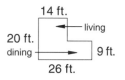

6. The illustration shows the plan of a swimming pool with an 8-foot-by-12-foot diving area on one side. Find the perimeter of the swimming pool.

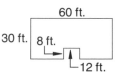

7. The drawing shows a room in which a diagonal wall, labeled *C*, hides a chimney.

   a. Find the length of *C*.
      (*Hint:* Use the Pythagorean theorem.)

   b. Find the perimeter of the room.

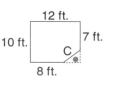

For another look
at the Pythagorean theorem, turn to page 224.

118

For some figures, perimeter is made up of the parts of different shapes.

Adding Partial Perimeters

Example: What is the perimeter of this figure?

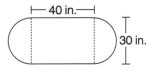

The figure is made up of a rectangle and a half circle. The perimeter is the sum of three sides of the rectangle and half the circumference of the circle.

Step 1. Add three sides of the rectangle.

$$10 + 8 + 10 = 28$$

Step 2. Find half the circumference of a circle with a diameter of 8.

$$\tfrac{1}{2}\pi d = \tfrac{1}{2} \cdot 3.14 \cdot 8 = 12.56$$

Step 3. Add the two partial perimeters.

$$P = 28 + 12.56 = \mathbf{40.56}$$

C. Match each drawing with one of the descriptions that follows.

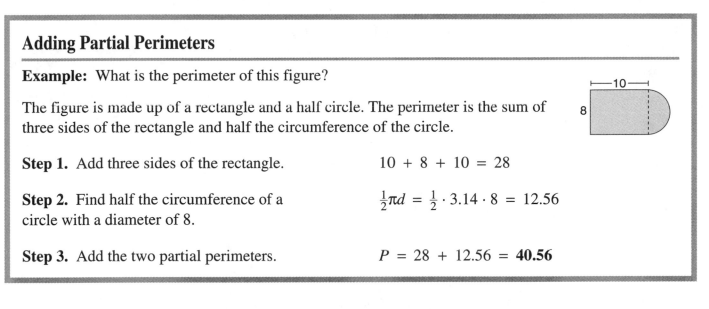

8.   9.   10.   11.

    a. a rectangle and three fourths of a circle

    b. a rectangle and a triangle

    c. a partial rectangle and one fourth of a circle

    d. a trapezoid and a rectangle

D. Solve each problem.

12. The drawing shows the top of a desk with half circles at each end. What is the distance around the desk? (*Hint:* The 2 half circles equal 1 circle.)

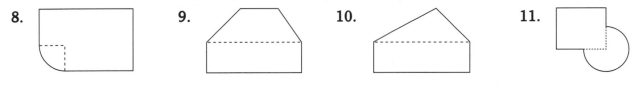

13. The illustration shows an arrangement of dining tables that measure 3 feet by 6 feet set up for a banquet. The planners decided that each diner needs 2 feet of space along the sides indicated with the bold lines. How many people can sit in this arrangement?

14. **Compare** If the side measuring 3 units increases to 4 and the side measuring 2 units increases to 3 while the remaining labeled sides stay the same, what happens to the perimeter? Draw a picture showing the new measurements before solving.

Area Formulas

What does installing carpeting have in common with sealing blacktop parking lots? You need to know the area of the surface you're working with. **Area** is a measure of the amount of surface.

Typical units of measure for area are square inches (in.²), square feet (ft.²), square yards (yd.²), square miles (mi.²), square centimeters (cm²), square meters (m²), and square kilometers (km²). The English units are sometimes represented with abbreviations such as sq. in. (for square inches), sq. ft., or sq. yd.

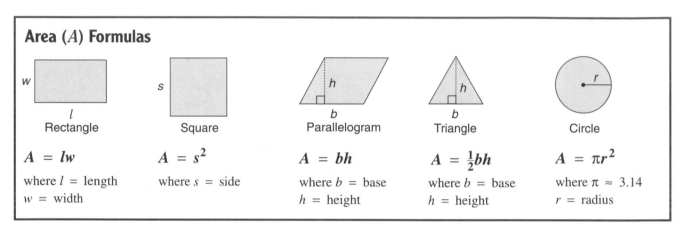

Area (A) Formulas

Rectangle	Square	Parallelogram	Triangle	Circle
$A = lw$	$A = s^2$	$A = bh$	$A = \frac{1}{2}bh$	$A = \pi r^2$
where l = length w = width	where s = side	where b = base h = height	where b = base h = height	where $\pi \approx 3.14$ r = radius

Note: Perimeter is a *sum* of numbers (addition), and area is a *product* of numbers (multiplication).

Look at the examples of a parallelogram and a triangle in the table above. The numbers that are multiplied together (the base and the height) must be *perpendicular* (at right angles) to each other.

A. Find the area of each figure. Remember to label your answers in square units.

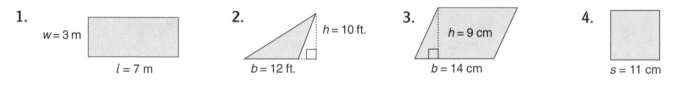

1. $w = 3\,m$ $l = 7\,m$

2. $h = 10$ ft. $b = 12$ ft.

3. $h = 9$ cm $b = 14$ cm

4. $s = 11$ cm

B. Find the length of each missing side. The first one is started for you.

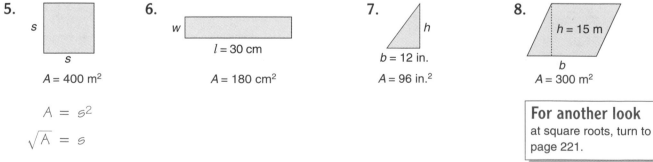

5. s s $A = 400\,m^2$

$A = s^2$

$\sqrt{A} = s$

6. w $l = 30$ cm $A = 180\,cm^2$

7. h $b = 12$ in. $A = 96$ in.²

8. $h = 15\,m$ b $A = 300\,m^2$

For another look
at square roots, turn to page 221.

120

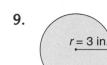

C. Find the area of each circle. Use π = 3.14. You may use a calculator.

9.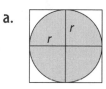
r = 3 in.

10.
r = 100 m

11.
d = 2 in.

D. The illustrations below show a circle inscribed in a square. Use the illustrations to solve problems 12–14.

a.   b.   c.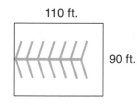

12. Which expression tells the area of the circle (the shaded part of **a**)?

    (1) πr^2 (2) $2\pi r$ (3) $4r$

13. Which expression tells the area of the small square (the shaded part of **b**)?

    (1) $4r$ (2) r^2 (3) πr

14. Which expression tells the area of the large square (the shaded part of **c**)?

    (1) $4\pi r^2$ (2) $4r$ (3) $4r^2$

E. Solve each problem. You may use a calculator.

15. What is the area of the rectangular parking lot shown here?

    110 ft.
    90 ft.

16. The illustration shows a semicircular window.

    a. Which expression tells the area of the window?

       (1) πr^2 (2) πd (3) $\frac{1}{2}\pi r^2$

    b. What is the area of the glass in the window if $r = 2$ ft. and $\pi = 3.14$?

17. **Investigate** Find the area of each rectangle. Continue the pattern for a width of $\frac{1}{8}$ inch and a width of $\frac{1}{16}$ inch. What happens to each area?

    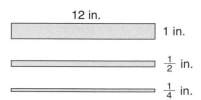
    12 in.
    1 in.
    $\frac{1}{2}$ in.
    $\frac{1}{4}$ in.

Solving Complex Area Problems

For some figures, the area is the *sum* of the areas of simple figures. For example, to find the amount of flooring needed for a combination kitchen and eating area, you need to find the floor area of both spaces, then add them.

Adding Areas

Example: What is the area of the figure in the illustration?

Step 1. Find the area of rectangle A. $A = lw = 8 \cdot 7 = 56$

Step 2. Find the area of square B. $A = s^2 = 3^2 = 9$

Step 3. Add the areas. $A = 56 + 9 = $ **65 square feet**

A. Find the area of each figure.

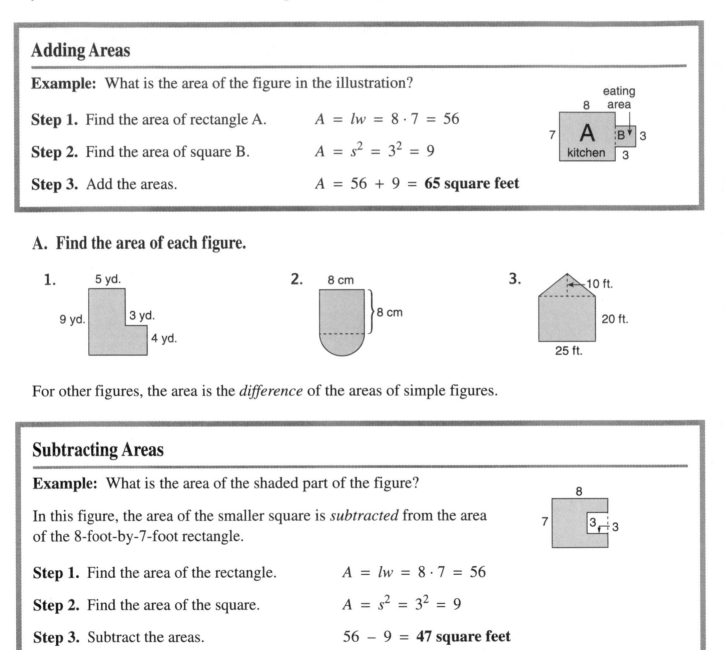

For other figures, the area is the *difference* of the areas of simple figures.

Subtracting Areas

Example: What is the area of the shaded part of the figure?

In this figure, the area of the smaller square is *subtracted* from the area of the 8-foot-by-7-foot rectangle.

Step 1. Find the area of the rectangle. $A = lw = 8 \cdot 7 = 56$

Step 2. Find the area of the square. $A = s^2 = 3^2 = 9$

Step 3. Subtract the areas. $56 - 9 = $ **47 square feet**

B. Find each area. Draw lines to see the simple figures in the more complex figures.

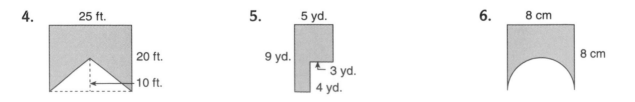

C. Explore the following areas. The figures in problems 7–10 are all the same size. Do all the figures have the same area? Explain why or why not.

7.
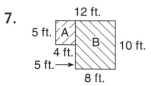

the sum of A and B

9.

the sum of E, F, and G

8.
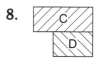

the sum of C and D

10.
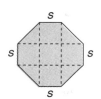

the difference between H and I

D. Solve each problem.

11. The shaded area represents the walkway around a swimming pool. What is the area of the walkway?

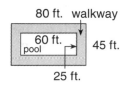

12. Which of the following expresses the area of the octagon (an 8-sided figure)? *Hint:* How many full squares and how many half squares are there?

  (1) $5s^2$ **(2)** $6s^2$ **(3)** $7s^2$ **(4)** $8s^2$

13. What is the area of the octagon in problem 12 if s equals 10 centimeters? *Hint:* After substituting the value for s, solve the power first.

14. Which of the following expresses the area of the figure in the illustration? *Hint:* $s^2 + s^2 = 2s^2$

  (1) $10s^2$ **(2)** $9s^2$ **(3)** $8s^2$ **(4)** $7s^2$

15. What is the area of the figure in problem 14 if s measures 3 inches?

16. Compare The drawings below show the floor plans of three different rooms. Which plan do you think has the greatest perimeter? The greatest area? Find the perimeter and area of each plan to see if you are right.

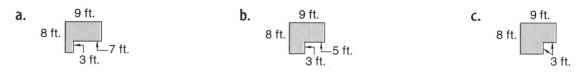

Solid Figures

In previous lessons, you have studied one-dimensional figures, such as lines, and two-dimensional figures, such as polygons and circles.

The box in the illustration is an example of a solid figure. The shape is called a **rectangular solid.** A rectangular solid is a three-dimensional figure.

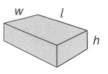

A rectangular solid has **length, width,** and **height** (or depth).

A rectangular solid has six **faces.** These are the rectangles or squares that are the sides of the figure.

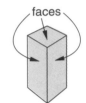

The space inside a rectangular solid is the **volume.** Volume is a measure of how much a solid can hold. For example, volume tells how much water a pool holds or how much air is in a room.

(3 faces don't show.)

Volume is measured in cubic inches (in.^{3}), cubic feet (ft.^{3}), cubic yards (yd.^{3}), cubic centimeters (cm^3), and cubic meters (m^3). A cubic foot, for example, is one foot long, one foot wide, and one foot high. The English units can also be abbreviated as cu. in., cu. ft., etc.

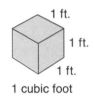

1 cubic foot

▶ For a rectangular solid **volume = length × width × height.**
The formula for the volume (V) of a rectangular solid is $V = lwh$, where l = length, w = width, and h = height.

Finding the Volume of a Rectangular Solid

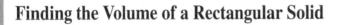

Example: What is the volume of this cardboard box?

Multiply length by width by height.

$V = lwh$
$V = 10 \cdot 8 \cdot 3$

The volume is 240 cubic inches.

$V = \textbf{240 cubic inches}$

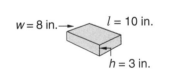

A. Find the volume of each figure.

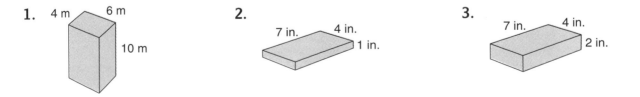

1. 4 m   6 m
    10 m

2. 7 in.   4 in.   1 in.

3. 7 in.   4 in.   2 in.

A cube is a solid whose faces are all squares.

► For a cube, **volume = side³**. The formula for the volume (V) of a cube is $V = s^3$ where s is the measure of one side and all sides are equal.

Finding the Volume of a Cube

Example: Given the inner measurements shown here, what is the volume of this small refrigerator?

Find 2 to the third power.

$$V = s^3$$
$$V = 2^3$$
$$V = 2 \cdot 2 \cdot 2$$

The volume of the cube is 8 cubic feet.

$$V = \textbf{8 cubic feet}$$

B. Find the volume of each figure.

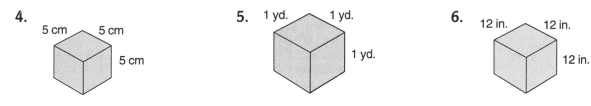

4.   5 cm   5 cm   5 cm

5.   1 yd.   1 yd.   1 yd.

6.   12 in.   12 in.   12 in.

C. Solve each problem.

7. What is the volume of the rectangular pond shown in the illustration?

40 yd.   20 yd.   2 yd.

8. A classroom is 30 feet long, 20 feet wide, and 10 feet high. How many cubic feet of air are in the classroom?

9. Which of the two packing crates can hold more (has a larger volume)?

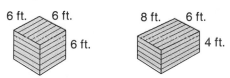

6 ft.   6 ft.   6 ft.   8 ft.   6 ft.   4 ft.

10. What is the volume of the concrete sidewalk pictured here?

16 ft.   4 ft. $\frac{1}{2}$ ft.

11. **Discover** What happens to the volume of a cube if you double the length of each side? Find the volume of a cube whose sides each measure 3 inches. Then double the sides, calculate the new volume, and compare the two volumes.

Volume Formulas

In the last lesson you learned to find the volume of rectangular solids and cubes. Another common three-dimensional figure is the **cylinder.** Like rectangular solids and cubes, cylinders have volume. A cylinder has equal, parallel bases. Each base is a circle. Most metal cans are cylinders.

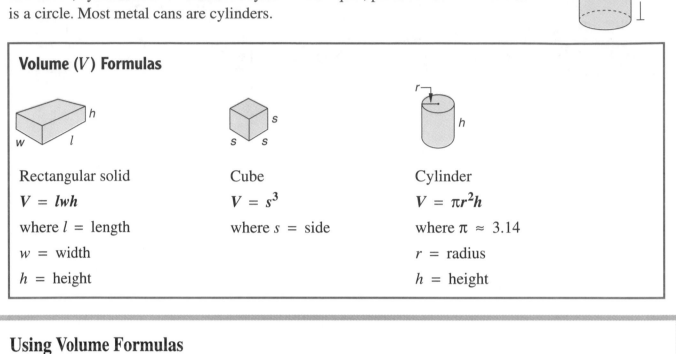

Volume (V) Formulas

Rectangular solid

$V = lwh$

where l = length

w = width

h = height

Cube

$V = s^3$

where s = side

Cylinder

$V = \pi r^2 h$

where $\pi \approx 3.14$

r = radius

h = height

Using Volume Formulas

Example: Find the volume of the cylindrical storage tank.

Replace π with 3.14, r with 3, and h with 10 in the formula for the volume of a cylinder.

$V = \pi r^2 h$
$V = 3.14 \cdot 3^2 \cdot 10$
$V = 3.14 \cdot 9 \cdot 10$
$V = \textbf{282.6 cubic feet}$

$r = 3$ ft.

10 ft.

Notice that the height in the figure in the example is not vertical. The height is *perpendicular* to the circular bases (meets them at a 90° angle).

A. **Find the volume of each figure. Remember to label your answers in the correct cubic units.**

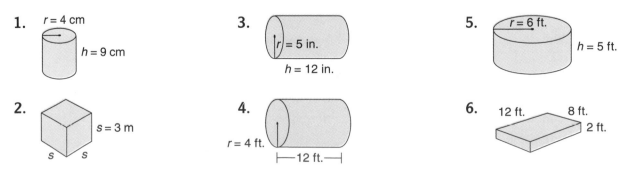

1. $r = 4$ cm, $h = 9$ cm

2. $s = 3$ m

3. $r = 5$ in., $h = 12$ in.

4. $r = 4$ ft., 12 ft.

5. $r = 6$ ft., $h = 5$ ft.

6. 12 ft., 8 ft., 2 ft.

B. Solve each problem.

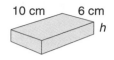

7. Use the rectangular solid in the illustration to answer **a** and **b**.
   Hint: $V = lwh$, so $\frac{V}{lw} = h$.

   a. What will the height of the figure be if the volume is 120 cubic centimeters?

   b. What will the height of the figure be if the volume is 300 cubic centimeters?

For another look at measurement units, turn to page 222.

8. The drawing shows the plan for a concrete patio. Find the volume of the patio in cubic feet. (*Hint:* Change the height to feet.)

9. The drawing shows a milk truck. The tank is a cylinder whose circular base has a diameter of 8 feet. The length of the tank is 20 feet.

   a. Find the volume of the tank.

   b. A cubic foot contains approximately 7.5 gallons. How many gallons of milk can the truck carry when it is full?

10. **Investigate** The illustration shows a cylindrical can and a rectangular metal box. If the can is full, is it possible to pour the contents into the box without the box overflowing?

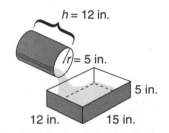

Making Connections: Finding Capacity

The amount of liquid a container can hold is the container's **capacity.**

Amounts of liquid are measured in units such as quarts, gallons, or liters. One gallon, for example, occupies approximately 230 cubic inches.

To make apple cider, the owner of an apple orchard uses rectangular metal containers like the one shown in the illustration. Estimate how many gallons of cider can be filled from the contents of the rectangular container. You may use a calculator.

(1) 20 gallons   **(2)** 30 gallons   **(3)** 40 gallons   **(4)** 50 gallons

Surface Area

When working with solid figures, you may need to measure the outer surface as well as the volume. The box pictured here has a volume of 216 cubic feet. ($V = 12 \cdot 9 \cdot 2$).

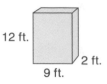

12 ft.

2 ft.

9 ft.

This illustration shows the box flattened out. **Surface area** is the sum of the areas of the faces of a solid.

To find the surface area of the box, find the area of each of the six faces and add them.

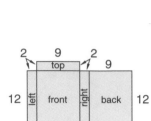

Finding Surface Area of a Rectangular Solid

Example: What is the surface area of the box pictured above?

Step 1. Find the area of each face.

Step 2. Add the areas.

Face	Area in ft.^{2}
front	$9 \cdot 12 = 108$
back	$9 \cdot 12 = 108$
left	$2 \cdot 12 = 24$
right	$2 \cdot 12 = 24$
top	$2 \cdot 9 = 18$
bottom	$2 \cdot 9 = 18$
Total	$= \textbf{300 square feet}$

The surface area of the figure is **300 square feet.**

Solve each problem.

1. If s represents the length of one side of a cube, which expression tells the surface area of the cube? (*Hint:* How many faces are on a cube?)

    (1) $4s$ (2) $6s$ (3) $4s^2$ (4) $6s^2$

2. If the measurement of s in problem 1 is 10 centimeters,

    a. what is the surface area of the cube?

    b. what is the volume of the cube?

3. Find the surface area of a rectangular solid 15 feet high, 10 feet long, and 5 feet wide. Draw a figure to help you picture the problem. (*Hint:* Remember that the figure has a front and a back, a left side and a right side, and a top and a bottom.)

4. What is the volume of the figure in problem 3?

5. Find the surface area in square feet of the trunk pictured here.

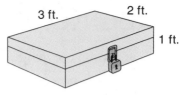

6. What is the volume of the trunk in problem 5?

7. Which of the following shows a correct pattern for making a closed cardboard carton from a flat piece of cardboard? The dotted lines represent folds.

(1)

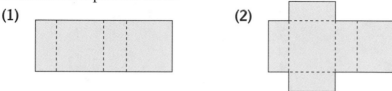

(2)

(3)

8. The illustration shows a truck bed with no top. What is the surface area of the inside of the truck bed?

9. What is the surface area of a cube that measures 1 inch on each side?

10. A 7-ounce cereal box is 16 centimeters long, 6 centimeters wide, and 24 centimeters high.

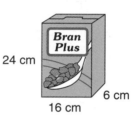

a. Find the surface area of the cereal box.

b. Find the volume of the cereal box.

Making Connections: Finding the Surface Area of a Cylinder

The illustration shows three stages in taking apart the surfaces of a cylinder. The surface area of the cylinder is the sum of the area of the circle on the top, the area of the circle on the bottom, and the area of the rectangle formed by flattening the vertical surface of the cylinder.

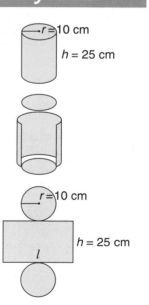

1. Which of the following tells the correct expression for the length l of the flattened vertical surface of the cylinder?

(1) r^2 **(2)** $2r$ **(3)** πr^2 **(4)** πd

2. Using your answer from problem 1, write an equation that shows how to find the area of the rectangle with sides h and l.

3. Write an equation that shows how to find the area of each circular base.

4. Describe how you would find the total surface area of the cylinder.

Mixed Review

Use any formulas on pages 223–224 that you need.

A. Find the perimeter of each figure.

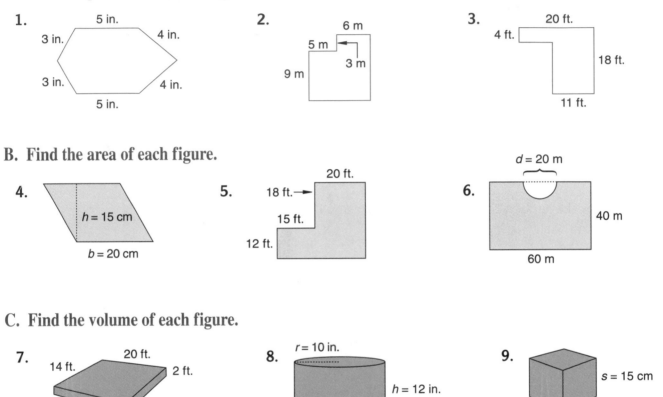

1. 5 in. 3 in. 4 in. 3 in. 4 in. 5 in.

2. 6 m 5 m 3 m 9 m

3. 20 ft. 4 ft. 18 ft. 11 ft.

B. Find the area of each figure.

4. $h = 15$ cm $b = 20$ cm

5. 20 ft. 18 ft. 15 ft. 12 ft.

6. $d = 20$ m 40 m 60 m

C. Find the volume of each figure.

7. 20 ft. 14 ft. 2 ft.

8. $r = 10$ in. $h = 12$ in.

9. $s = 15$ cm

D. Use this drawing of a box to solve problems 10–12.

2 in. 5 in. 8 in.

10. Which of the following drawings represents the entire surface area of the box?

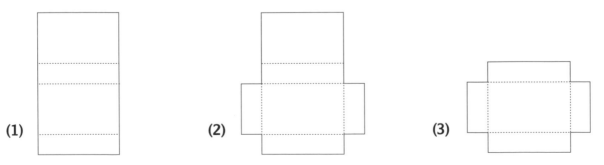

(1) (2) (3)

11. What is the surface area of the box?

12. What is the volume of the box?

E. Solve each problem.

13. The drawing shows the floor plan of a porch. The length of the porch is 3 times the width. The width is 7 feet.

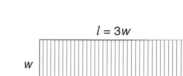

   a. What is the perimeter of the porch?

   b. What is the area of the porch?

   c. If a carpenter builds a top railing for one length and both widths, how long will the railing be?

   d. If a can of stain covers 50 square feet, how many cans of stain are required to cover the floor of the porch?

14. The illustration shows a house, a driveway, and the lot that the house sits on.

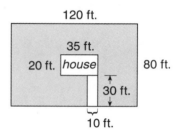

   a. What is the area of the yard (the shaded part of the drawing)?

   b. If a bag of grass seed is enough to seed 1,000 square feet, how many bags are needed to seed this yard?

15. The figure shows a patio with a curved corner. The curved section represents a part of a circle. Which of the following expresses the area of the patio?

   (1) $4r^2$ **(2)** $3r^2 + \frac{1}{4}\pi r^2$ **(3)** $4\pi r^2$

16. The drawing shows a concrete slab. What is the volume of the slab?

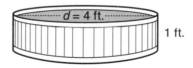

17. The illustration shows a small wading pool. What is the volume of the pool?

18. If 1 cubic foot equals approximately 7.5 gallons, how many gallons of water does the pool hold?

Seeing Geometric Figures

Geometric shapes are used in many things made by people. This lesson draws attention to a few of these shapes.

A. Use the drawing of the wall of a room to solve problems 1–5.

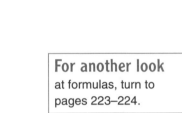

1. The wall, the window, and the door are each examples of what geometric shape?

2. What are the dimensions (the length and width) of the
   a. wall?
   b. door?
   c. window?

3. Find the area of the window.

4. Find the area of the door.

5. Find the area of the wall *not* including the door and window.

> **For another look**
> at formulas, turn to pages 223–224.

B. Use the drawing of a basketball court to solve problems 6–11.

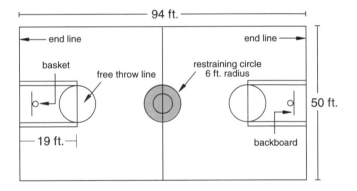

6. What is the distance from the free throw line to the nearest end line?

7. What is the radius of the restraining circle at center court?

8. What is the area of the restraining circle?

9. What is the area of the entire court?

10. What is the perimeter of the entire court?

11. This diagram shows the height of the basket and the horizontal distance from the free throw line to the basket. Use the Pythagorean theorem to calculate to the nearest foot the diagonal distance from the free throw line to the point where the basket is attached to the backboard. You may use a calculator.

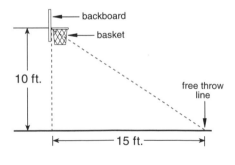

> **For another look**
> at the Pythagorean theorem, turn to page 224.

C. Use the drawing of the storage tank to solve problems 12–14.

12. What is the radius of the storage tank?

13. What is the area of the top of the storage tank?

14. Think of the storage tank as a cylinder. If the height (depth) of the storage tank is 5 feet, what is the volume of the tank?

D. The illustration shows a softcover book. Use the illustration to solve problems 15–17.

15. The basic shape of the book is a
    (1) cylinder
    (2) square
    (3) rectangle
    (4) rectangular solid

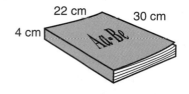

16. What is the volume of the book?

17. Think of the outside cover as faces that protect the front, the back, and one side. What is the surface area of the outside cover?

E. Use the picture of a coffee can to solve problems 18–21.

18. The basic shape of the coffee can is a
    (1) cylinder
    (2) square
    (3) rectangle
    (4) rectangular solid

19. Which expression shows the volume of the coffee can?
    (1) $3.14 \cdot 10 \cdot 14$
    (2) $3.14 \cdot 5 \cdot 14$
    (3) $3.14 \cdot 10^2 \cdot 14$
    (4) $3.14 \cdot 5^2 \cdot 14$

20. Which of the following expresses the surface area of the label?
    (1) πd (2) πr^2 (3) $\pi d h$ (4) πh

21. **Investigate** You found the expression that shows the surface area of the part of the can with the label. Write an expression that shows the surface area for the entire can: lid, bottom, and middle.

Answers start on page 206.   **133**

Choosing Perimeter, Area, or Volume

You have practiced finding perimeter, area, and volume in this book. Knowing when to use each of these takes practice. Keep the following in mind.

- Perimeter measures the distance around a figure.

- Area measures the surface of a two-dimensional figure.

- Volume measures the space inside a three-dimensional figure.

A. First choose whether you need to find perimeter, area, or volume. Then solve each problem.

1. Phil wants to install new 4-inch wide baseboards—molding that covers the joint between the floor and the walls—in his bedroom. The illustration shows the floor plan of Phil's bedroom. Allow 3 feet for the doorway. How much molding does he need?

   a. Perimeter, area, or volume?

   b. Answer:

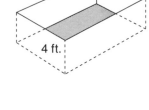

2. Carla wants to put carpet in the hallway of her house. The illustration shows the plan of Carla's hallway. How much carpet does she need?

   a. Perimeter, area, or volume?

   b. Answer:

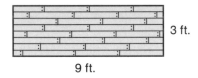

9 ft.

3. Sal plans to dig a hole to bury an oil tank beside his repair shop. The illustration shows the size of the hole required to hold the tank. How much earth does Sal have to remove?

   a. Perimeter, area, or volume?

   b. Answer:

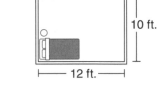

4. Marta wants to cover the work space of her kitchen counter with 2-inch by 2-inch tiles. The countertop is 30 inches wide and 50 inches long. How many tiles does Marta need to cover the countertop?

   a. Perimeter, area, or volume?

   b. Answer:

B. First choose the correct unit of measure. Then use the information in the illustration to solve each problem. Problem 5 is started as an example.

Remember that perimeter, area, and volume are measured in different units. Perimeter is measured in plain (or linear) units. Area is measured in square units. Volume is measured in cubic units.

5. Find how much concrete is needed to pour a pad for a front step.
   Hint: Think of 4 inches as $\frac{4}{12} = \frac{1}{3}$ ft.

   a. Unit: *cubic feet*

   b. Solution: $V = lwh \quad V = 6 \cdot 6 \cdot \frac{1}{3} =$

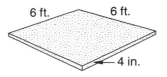

6 ft. 6 ft. 4 in.

6. Raúl plans to put new linoleum on his kitchen floor. How much linoleum does he need?

   a. Unit:

   b. Solution:

9 ft.

12 ft.

7. Boris has to load boxes on a truck. In order to put as many boxes on the truck as possible, he wants to know the size of the storage space in the truck bed.

   a. Unit:

   b. Solution:

   c. If each box measures 2 feet by 2 feet by 2 feet, how many boxes can be loaded on the truck?

10 ft. 8 ft. 4 ft.

Making Connections: Comparing Perimeter and Area

The drawing shows two boat landings (A and C) connected by a walkway (B).

1. Fill in the chart below at right.

2. Which shape (A, B, or C) has the *largest* perimeter?

3. Which shape has the *smallest* area?

4. Which shapes have the same perimeter?

5. Which shapes have the same area?

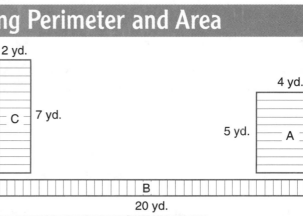

2 yd.

C   7 yd.

4 yd.

5 yd.   A

1 yd.   B

20 yd.

Shape	Perimeter	Area
A		
B		
C		

6. Which of the following shapes is likely to have a large perimeter and a small area?

   (1)   **(2)**   **(3)**

Drawing a Picture

Often drawings are more useful than words for explaining how things are made. Carpenters, tailors, engineers, and architects use drawings to show the way things are put together. You may choose to draw a picture to help you solve a problem.

Drawing a New Picture

Example: Anna wants to buy a rug for her living room. The rug will be 3 feet from each wall. How many square feet will the rug be?

Draw a rectangle that is 3 feet from each side. The new rectangle is 12 feet long and 9 feet wide. The rug will be $12 \cdot 9 =$ **108 square feet.**

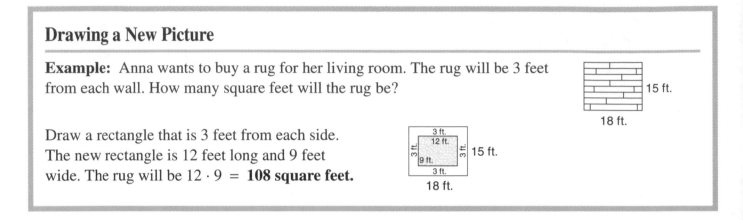

For each problem the drawing is started. First complete the drawing. Then solve each problem. Use any formulas on pages 223–224 that you need. You may use a calculator.

1. A circular walk around a garden has an outer radius of 30 feet. The inner radius, marking the inside of the walk, is 20 feet. The walk is paved with bricks. *Hint:* Draw a second circle inside the first circle.

    a. Find the area of the larger circle.

    b. Find the area of the inner circle.

    c. Find the total area of the paved walk.

    d. Which is larger, the area of the paved walk or the area of the inner circle?

    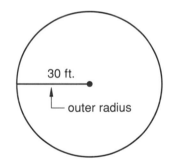

2. José was hired to build a deck 20 feet long and 15 feet wide behind a customer's house. The home owner wants to save a large tree in the backyard. In order to save the tree, José decided to make a diagonal cut off one corner of the deck. The cut will take 6 feet off the 20-foot length and 6 feet off the 15-foot width. Find the area of the deck.

    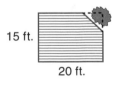

3. In Central Square, there is a circular flower bed with a diameter of 20 feet. Park planners want to divide the flower bed into four equal parts, each of which will be planted with a different kind of flower. Find the area of each section.

    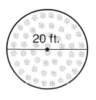

Making Connections: Using Scale Drawings

You can use **scale drawings** to calculate perimeter and area. First, measure each drawing and use proportion to find the dimensions of each shape. Then use these dimensions to make calculations.

1. The illustration shows the roof plan of a house. Find each of the following.

    a. Length:

    b. Width:

    c. Perimeter:

    d. Is all of the necessary information provided to find the area of the roof?

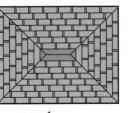

scale: $\frac{1}{4}$ in. = 5 ft.

2. The illustration shows the plan of a large vegetable garden. Find each of the following.

    a. Length:

    b. Width:

    c. Perimeter:

    d. Area:

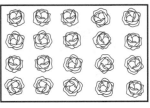

scale: $\frac{1}{4}$ in. = 15 ft.

3. The illustration shows the surface of a round swimming pool. Find each of the following.

    a. Diameter:

    b. Radius:

    c. Circumference:

    d. Area:

scale: $\frac{1}{2}$ in. = 12 ft.

4. The depth of the pool in problem 3 is 4 feet.

    a. What is the pool's volume (to the nearest cubic foot)?

    b. How many gallons of water will the pool hold if 1 cubic foot contains 7.5 gallons?

Renovating a Room

Building construction requires countless applications of geometry. This lesson gives you a chance to apply your geometry skills to the practical problems of house renovation.

In the next lesson you can use the information you find here to calculate the cost of the renovation.

The job described in these two lessons involves replacing windows, doors, walls, floor, and ceiling in one room of a house and building a pass-through from the kitchen.

A. Use the floor plan to find each of the following measurements.

1. perimeter of the floor

2. total width of openings for doors

3. perimeter of the floor minus door openings

4. area of the floor

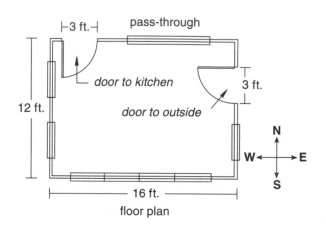

floor plan

B. Use the drawing of the north wall of the room to find each of the following measurements.

5. area of the door to the kitchen

6. area of the pass-through

7. area of the wall

8. area of the wall not including the door and the pass-through

9. perimeter of the pass-through

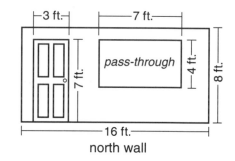

north wall

C. Use the drawing of the south wall of the room to find each of the following amounts.

10. the number of windows

11. area occupied by all of the windows

12. area of the wall

13. area of the wall not including windows

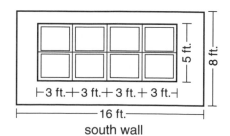

south wall

138

D. Use the drawing of the east wall of the room to find each of the following amounts.

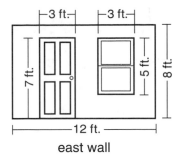

east wall

14. area of the exterior door

15. the number of windows

16. area of the window

17. area of the wall

18. area of the wall not including the door and window

E. Use the drawing of the west wall of the room to find each of the following amounts.

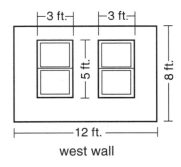

west wall

19. the number of windows

20. area of the windows

21. area of the wall

22. area of the wall not including windows

F. This illustration shows a plan of the ceiling. Use the illustration to find each of the following measurements.

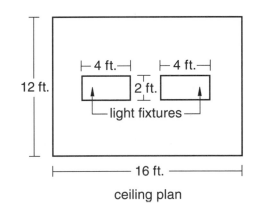

ceiling plan

23. area of the ceiling

24. area of the light fixtures

25. area of the ceiling not including light fixtures

G. Use your answers from Parts B–E to make the following partial summary.

26. Number of windows (See problems 10, 15, and 19.)

27. Total wall area (See problems 7, 12, 17, and 21.)

28. Total wall area minus openings (See problems 8, 13, 18, and 22.)

29. Draw Measure the length, width, and ceiling height of your classroom or a room in your home. Make scale drawings (at $\frac{1}{4}$ inch = 1 foot) of each wall, the floor, and the ceiling. Show the exact placement of windows, doors, and light fixtures.

Using the Cost Formula

Builders use calculations like the ones you did in the last lesson to estimate the cost of construction projects.

The table below is based on the renovation job described in the last lesson. The *Quantity* column corresponds to *n* in the cost formula $c = nr$, where *c* is the total cost, *n* is the number of items, and *r* is the price (rate) for one item. The *Unit Price* column corresponds to *r* in the formula.

Look at the abbreviations in the column labeled *Unit.*

- EA means **each.** This is used for individual items, such as doors and windows. (The prices listed here include cost and installation.)

- LF means **linear feet.** This is used for items that are measured in length or perimeter, such as baseboard molding.

- SF means **square feet.** This is used for area items, such as floors.

- LS means **lump sum.** This is used for items that are not measured. In this case the plumbing cost is a lump sum.

A. **Fill in the table. The first line is completed as an example. The numbers in parentheses refer to the problems on pages 138–139. Use the illustrations and your answers to those problems to find the right quantities. You may use a calculator.**

Type of Work	Quantity (*n*)	Unit	Unit Price (*r*)	Total
1. new interior door	1	EA	$300	$300
2. new exterior door	1	EA	350	
3. new window (26)		EA	375	
4. framing around pass-through (9)		LF	7	
5. new gypsum board walls (28)		SF	3	
6. new gypsum board ceiling (23)		SF	4	
7. light fixtures (24)		EA	80	
8. new hardwood floor (4)		SF	6	
9. baseboard molding (3)		LF	3	
10. painting walls (27)		SF	.80	
11. painting ceiling (23)		SF	1	
12. electrical work (4)		SF	4	
13. plumbing for radiators	—	LS	400	
14. **Total (before tax)**				$

- Notice that line 10 is based on the entire area of the walls. Painters use the area of the entire wall to estimate expenses even if the walls have several windows or doors. They reason that painting the trim of the windows and doors will take extra time, so the cost evens out if they charge for the whole wall.

- Notice also that line 12 is based on the area of the floor even though the floor has little to do with electricity. Electricians often make their estimates based on the square feet of floor space.

- The total you found for line 14 is, in fact, not the total price most builders would charge. Line 14 represents a subtotal. Builders often add 10% to the subtotal for *contingencies* (the problems nobody anticipated) and 20% for *overhead and profit* (the builder's expenses and income).

B. Calculate each of the following. You may use a calculator.

Subtotal from line 14	
15. Contingencies (10%)	
16. Overhead and profit (20%)	
17. Total (not including tax)	

Making Connections: Multiplying Units

In the cost formula $c = nr$, you multiply a number of items by a rate and get an amount of money as a result. In fact, the units divide (cancel) to leave dollars in the end.

Example: Think about finding the cost of 80 square feet of flooring at a cost of $6 per square foot. Notice how the square feet cancel to leave dollars as the only unit.

$$\frac{80 \ \cancel{ft^2}}{1} \cdot \frac{\$6}{1 \ \cancel{ft^2}} = \frac{\$480}{1} = \mathbf{\$480}$$

1. Divide (cancel) units and find the cost of 30 linear feet of framing at the cost of $7 per linear foot.

2. Divide (cancel) units and find the cost of 120 square feet of hardwood flooring at the cost of $6 per square foot.

Unit 4 Review

A. Choose the correct answer.

1. Cubic feet is a unit of measurement for

    (1) perimeter   **(2)** area   **(3)** volume   **(4)** surface area

2. Area is a measure of the space inside a

    (1) flat figure   **(2)** cylinder   **(3)** three-dimensional figure

3. The sum of the areas of the faces of a three-dimensional figure is called the

    (1) volume   **(2)** perimeter   **(3)** diameter   **(4)** surface area

B. Find the perimeter of each figure.

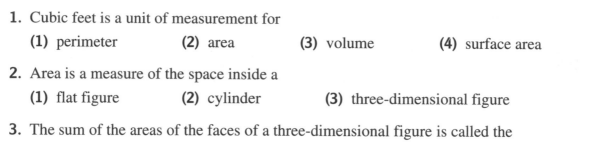

4. 13 m, 5 m, 7 m, 10 m

5. 7 in., 7 in., 5 in., 5 in., 8 in.

6. $r = 12$ cm

C. Find the area of each figure.

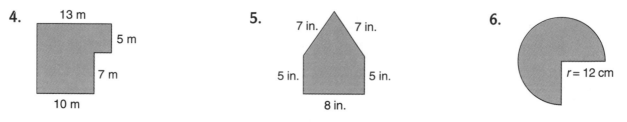

7. 18 in., 8 in., 11 in., 8 in.

8. 15 ft., 20 ft., 6 ft., 6 ft.

9. $r = 8$ cm

D. Find the volume of each figure.

10. 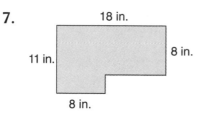 3 cm, 9 cm, 20 cm

11. 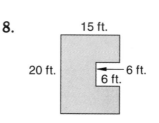 $r = 1$ m, $h = 3$ m

12. 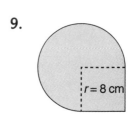 8 ft., 8 ft., 8 ft.

E. Solve each problem.

13. The child's block shown in the illustration is a cube measuring 3 inches on a side. Find the surface area of the cube.

14. Paulo works at a public swimming pool. While the pool is being cleaned, Paulo puts a rope fence around the edge of the walk around the pool. How many feet of rope does Paulo need?

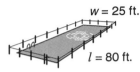

15. At the cost of $7 a square foot, which of the following represents the cost of putting a new oak floor in the room shown in the drawing?

    (1) $18 \cdot 14 \cdot \$7$ **(2)** $\frac{18 \cdot 14}{\$7}$ **(3)** $\frac{\$7}{18 \cdot 14}$

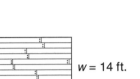

Working Together

Do the following with a partner or a group of other students.

1. Calculate the perimeter (or circumference) and the area for three different shapes—a circle, such as a round clock face; a rectangular shape, such as the lid of a cardboard box; and a long, thin shape, such as the face of a ruler. What conclusions can you make from the shape of the object and the size of the perimeter and area?

2. Make a list of at least 10 improvements you would like to make to your home. Think of at least two improvements that involve calculating perimeter and two that involve calculating area.

3. Collect advertisements for hardware stores or building supply stores. Find the unit prices for items such as sheetrock, floorboards, ceramic tiles, bricks, and roofing shingles. Calculate the cost of using some of these materials to renovate your home or school.

4. Read the labels on paint cans. Find out how many square feet a gallon of paint will cover. Calculate the number of gallons of paint you would need to give a room in your school one coat of paint.

5. Try to cut and fold a piece of cardboard so that it forms the shape of a rectangular solid.

Combining Algebra and Geometry

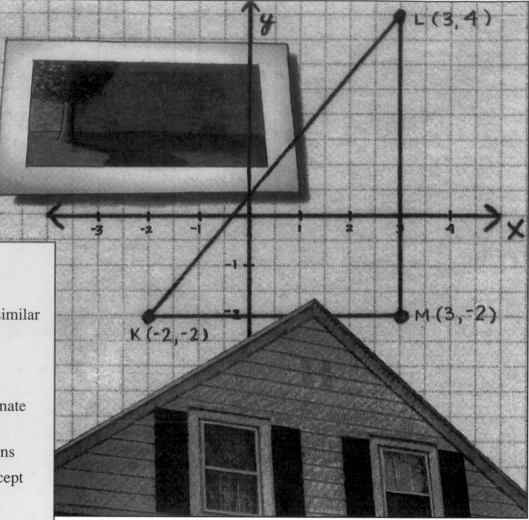

Skills

Similar figures

Using proportion with similar figures

Using equations with geometric figures

Distances on the coordinate system

Graphing linear equations

Finding slope and intercept

Tools

The coordinate system

Tables and patterns

Problem Solver

Setting up solutions

Applications

Using algebra to find missing dimensions

Working with linear equations and graphs

The different branches of mathematics depend on each other. You have seen how the rules of arithmetic apply to both algebra and geometry.

You have also seen ways in which algebra and geometry work together. For example, you know that geometric formulas are written in the language of algebra.

In this unit you will see that many problems can be solved by combining the rules and principles of algebra and geometry.

How Can Algebra and Geometry Work Together?

This unit is divided into two parts. In the first part, you will see how closely algebra and geometry are connected.

Check each of the following problems that you think you can solve now.

☐ You know the width of a rectangular garden and its perimeter. You can find the length.

☐ You can estimate a 15% tip on any meal.

☐ You can determine the number of 1-foot-square floor tiles you need for the kitchen *before* you buy the tiles.

☐ You can find the amount of sand needed to fill a sandbox.

The second part of the unit explores the rectangular coordinate system. This is a way of expressing number relationships using two number lines. One number line is horizontal, and the other is vertical. The coordinate system makes it easier to see the connection between algebraic expressions and geometric figures.

Besides the rectangular coordinate system, many things use scales that are perpendicular to each other. Check the items you have used in the past.

☐ bar graphs

☐ line graphs

☐ a monthly calendar

☐ a stadium with seating labeled 2D or 5E

☐ the multiplication table

☐ the TV program guide that lists programs, times, and channels

Talk About It

Is there a difference between formulas and equations? If so, what is it? Compare and discuss your answer with those of others in your class.

or

Discuss how to use each of the items in the second checklist above. Describe or look up examples of each.

Throughout this unit, you may use a calculator wherever that would be useful. Information about using a calculator appears on page 224.

Similar Figures

In geometry, figures are **similar** if they have the same shape and the same proportions. This means, for similar figures, the ratios of the measures of corresponding sides (such as lengths and widths) are equal. The triangles in Box A are similar. The rectangles in Box B are not similar.

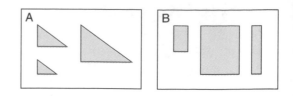

Checking for Similarity

Example 1: Are these two rectangles similar?

Step 1. Check to see if the figures appear to have the same shape.

Yes, the rectangles seem to have the same shape.

Step 2. Find the ratio of the lengths.

$$\frac{10}{5} = \frac{2}{1}$$

Step 3. Find the ratio of the widths.

$$\frac{6}{3} = \frac{2}{1}$$

Since the ratios are equal, **the rectangles are similar.**

$$\frac{2}{1} = \frac{2}{1}$$

Example 2: Are these two triangles similar?

Step 1. Check to see if the figures appear to have the same shape.

Yes, the triangles seem to have the same shape.

Step 2. Find the ratio of the hypotenuses.

$$\frac{13}{5}$$

Step 3. Find the ratio of the shorter legs.

$$\frac{5}{3}$$

Step 4. Find the ratio of the longer legs.

$$\frac{12}{4} = \frac{3}{1}$$

Since the ratios are not equal, **the triangles are not similar.**

$$\frac{13}{5} \neq \frac{5}{3} \neq \frac{3}{1}$$

> **Tip**
> $\neq$ means "is not equal to."

Comparing Length to Width

Two rectangles are similar if the ratio of the length to the width of one rectangle equals the ratio of the length to the width of the other rectangle.

Example: Are these two rectangles similar?

Step 1. Check to see if the figures appear to have the same shape.

Yes, the rectangles seem to have the same shape.

Step 2. Find the ratio of the length to the width for one rectangle.

$$\frac{8}{5}$$

Step 3. Find the ratio of the length to the width for the other rectangle.

$$\frac{16}{10}$$

Since both the ratios are equal, **the rectangles are similar.**

$$\frac{8}{5} = \frac{16}{10}$$

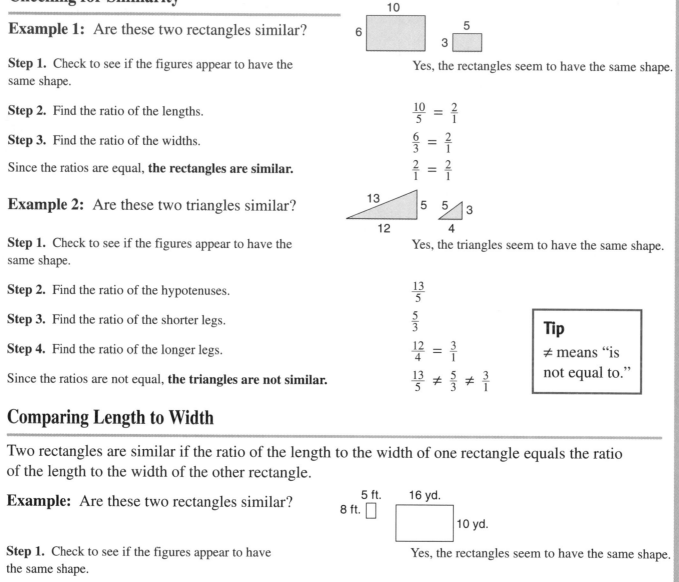

A. Decide whether the figures in each pair are similar.

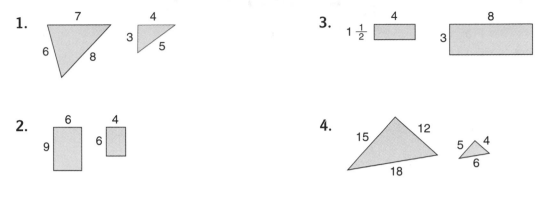

1.

2.

3.

4.

B. Solve each problem.

5. The illustration shows a 10-inch-by-12-inch picture with a 3-inch-wide mat surrounding it. Are the outside edge of the picture and the outside edge of the mat similar figures? Do they need to be similar figures for the picture to fit the mat?

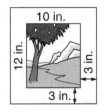

6. Which of the figures in the illustration are similar? Explain.

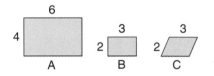

7. The diagram shows a regulation high school basketball court. A college basketball court also is 50 feet wide, but it is 94 feet long. Are the two courts similar? Can you tell without making a calculation?

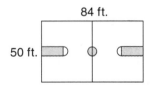

8. Use the two triangles to answer the following questions.
   a. What is the ratio of side AB to side DE?
   b. What is the ratio of side BC to side EF?
   c. What is the ratio of side AC to side DF?
   d. Are the two triangles similar?

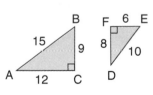

9. Barbara had a $3\frac{1}{2}$-inch-by-5-inch photograph enlarged to 8 inches by 10 inches. Is the enlargement similar to the original? Explain.

10. **Consider** Answer each question, and give your reasoning for each answer.
    a. Are all squares similar?
    b. Are all equilateral triangles similar?
    c. Are all right triangles similar?
    d. Are all isosceles triangles similar?

Using Proportion with Similar Figures

The illustration shows two tabletops. The two tables have the same shape, so the rectangular tabletops are similar. You can use proportion to calculate the measure of a missing side in similar figures. Review the proportion lesson starting on page 82 if you need to.

30 in. 20 in. 24 in. x

Finding a Missing Side

Example: What is the width of the smaller tabletop shown above?

Step 1. Set up a proportion with corresponding sides.

$$\frac{\text{length}}{\text{width}} = \frac{30}{20} = \frac{24}{x}$$

Step 2. Cross multiply and solve for x.

$$30x = 480$$

The width of the smaller table should be 16 inches.

$$x = \textbf{16 inches}$$

When the sun casts a shadow of a straight object, the height of the object represents one leg of a right triangle. The length of the shadow represents the other leg. The hypotenuse is formed by an imaginary line from the top of the object to the end of the shadow.

Finding the Height of a Tall Object

Example: In the illustration, an object 3 feet tall casts a 2-foot shadow. The triangle formed by that object and its shadow and the triangle formed by the tree and its shadow are similar. You can measure the shadow of the tree and calculate the height of the tree.

Step 1. Let x represent the height of the tree. Set up a proportion with corresponding sides.

$$\frac{\text{height}}{\text{shadow}} = \frac{3}{2} = \frac{x}{40}$$

Step 2. Cross multiply and solve for x.

$$2x = 120$$

The height of the tree is 60 feet.

$$x = \textbf{60 feet}$$

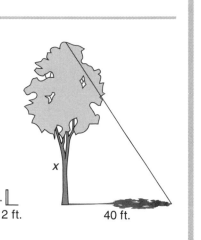

3 ft. 2 ft. x 40 ft.

A. In each of the following pairs, the figures are similar. Use proportion to find the length of each side labeled *y*.

1.

7
4
12
y

2.

12
20
18
y

3.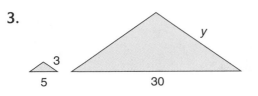

4.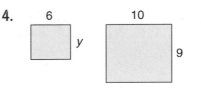

B. Solve each problem.

5. Quadrilateral ABCD is similar to EFGH. Use the ratio between sides AB and EF to find the length of

   a. side FG   **b.** side GH   **c.** side EH

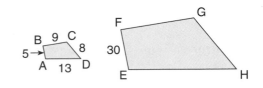

6. Ami designed the roof plan of a house and a barn. If the two shapes are similar, what is the width of the barn?

7. A 5-foot-high vertical pole casts a shadow 2 feet long. How long is the shadow of the 40-foot-high telephone pole?

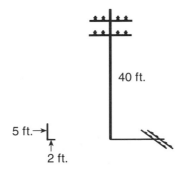

8. A 4-foot vertical pole casts a shadow 3 feet long. At the same time, a building casts a shadow 36 feet long. How tall is the building?

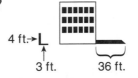

9. Bear County is a rectangle 32 miles long and 24 miles wide. On a map the width is 6 inches. What is the length of the county on the map?

Making Connections: Finding the Size of Reductions

A copy machine can reduce the length and width of a document to 75% of the original size. Sarah reduced a document measuring 8 inches by 12 inches. (*Hint:* 75% = .75)

1. Calculate each of the following:

   a. the new width   **b.** the new length

2. Is the original document size similar to the reduced document size? Are the ratios of the corresponding sides of the document equal?

3. **Discuss** How could you tell if the sizes were similar without making a calculation?

Finding Missing Dimensions

The area of this square terrace is 400 square feet. To build a railing around the terrace, you must first find the measure of one side and then the perimeter of the terrace.

Finding and Using a Missing Dimension

Example: Find the perimeter of the square pictured above.

Step 1. First solve $A = s^2$ for s.
Using a calculator, enter 4 0 0.
Press the square root key $\sqrt{}$.

$$A = s^2$$
$$400 = s^2$$
$$\sqrt{400} = s$$
$$20 \text{ ft.} = s$$

Step 2. You need to find the perimeter. Use the value for s you found in Step 1.
Substitute 20 for s in $P = 4s$.
The perimeter of the square is 80 feet.

$$P = 4s$$

$$P = 4(20)$$
$$\mathbf{P = 80 \text{ feet}}$$

A. Solve each problem. Use any formulas on pages 223–224 that you need. You may use a calculator.

1. The area of the rectangle pictured here is 300 square centimeters. What is the perimeter of the rectangle?
   Hint: Solve $A = lw$ for l (the unknown).
   $\frac{A}{w} = l$

   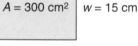

2. The cardboard box in the illustration is shaped like a cube and has a surface area of 726 square inches. Find the measure of each edge. (*Hint:* A box has 6 faces. First find the area of one face.)

3. The concrete slab pictured here is the base for a generator. The volume of the slab is 75 cubic feet. What is the depth? ($V = lwh$, where $h = $ depth)

4. The cylindrical water tank pictured here holds a total of 6,280 cubic feet of liquid. What is the height of the tank? ($V = \pi r^2 h$)

In the illustration, the area of the rectangle and the area of the square are equal. Use this information to find the width of the rectangle. You could first find the area of the square. Since you would also know the area of the rectangle, you could find the width of the rectangle.

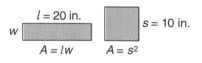

150

A shorter method is to combine the formulas for the area of a rectangle and the area of a square. For these figures, A is the same in $A = lw$ and $A = s^2$. You can solve the equation $lw = s^2$.

Finding the Dimension that Makes Two Figures Equal

Example: Find the width of the rectangle pictured on page 150.

Step 1. Since the areas are equal, write an equation with lw equal to s^2.

$$lw = s^2$$

Step 2. Substitute 20 for l and 10 for s. Then solve for w.

$$20w = 10^2$$
$$20w = 100$$

The width of the rectangle is 5 inches.

$$w = 5 \text{ inches}$$

B. Use the information given to find the missing dimension. You may use a calculator.

5. The area of the rectangle equals the area of the square. What is the width of the rectangle?

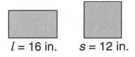

$l = 16$ in. $s = 12$ in.

6. The perimeter of the square and the perimeter of the rectangle are equal. Find the length of the rectangle.

$s = 16$ m $w = 9$

7. The combined floor area of the two rooms shown in the drawing is 260 square feet. What is the width of the entrance hall?

12 ft.
locker room → 10 ft.
15 ft. — w
entrance hall

8. The two grain containers have the same volume. What is the height of the taller container?

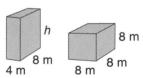

h 8 m
8 m   8 m
4 m   8 m

Making Connections: Choosing Dimensions

Alfonso has to design a container. There are three requirements for the design: (1) The shape must be a rectangular solid. (2) The longest measurement must not be over 12 feet. (3) The volume must be 400 cubic feet. To come up with a design, Alfonso decided to make a table of values for length, width, height, and volume.

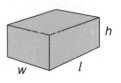

1. Complete the table at right. The values for Container A are done as an example.

2. Which of the containers meet *all* the requirements?

	length	width	height	volume
Container A	8 ft.	5 ft.	10 ft.	400 ft.^{3}
Container B	8 ft.		8 ft.	400 ft.^{3}
Container C	5 ft.	5 ft.		400 ft.^{3}
Container D		4 ft.	5 ft.	400 ft.^{3}
Container E	10 ft.		10 ft.	400 ft.^{3}

Equations and Geometric Figures

You can use algebra to show the relationship that exists between parts of geometric figures.

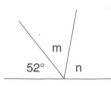

Ratio is a useful tool for expressing the size of angles. The ratio of ∠m to ∠n in the illustration is 3:5. Remember that if two unknown numbers have a ratio of 3:5, they can be represented by $3x$ and $5x$.

Using Ratio with Angles

Example: Find the measurements of ∠m and ∠n in the drawing above.

Step 1. Since the sum of the three angles is 180°, write an equation with the three angles adding up to 180°.

$$52° + 3x + 5x = 180°$$
$$52° + 8x = 180°$$
$$8x = 128°$$

Step 2. Simplify and solve the equation.

$$x = 16°$$

Step 3. Substitute the value of x into the expressions for the size of each angle.

$$∠m = 3(16°) = 48°$$
$$∠n = 5(16°) = 80°$$
$$\mathbf{∠m = 48° \text{ and } ∠n = 80°}$$

A. Solve each problem.

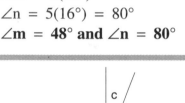

1. For the angles in the diagram, ∠d is 10° greater than ∠c. Find the measurement of each angle. (*Hint:* Let $x = ∠c$.)

2. In the illustration the ratio of ∠a to ∠b is 3:4. Find the number of degrees in each angle.

Using Algebraic Expressions with Perimeter

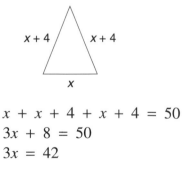

Example: The perimeter of the triangle in the diagram is 50 inches. Find the length of each side.

Step 1. Write an equation with the three sides totaling 50.

$$x + x + 4 + x + 4 = 50$$
$$3x + 8 = 50$$
$$3x = 42$$

Step 2. Simplify and solve the equation. The base is 14 inches.

$$x = \mathbf{14 \text{ inches}}$$

Step 3. Substitute the value for x into the expression showing the length of the two long sides. Each long side is 18 inches.

$$x + 4 =$$
$$14 + 4 = \mathbf{18 \text{ inches}}$$

B. Solve each problem. Use any formulas on pages 223–224 that you need.

3. The perimeter of this equilateral triangle is 102 feet. Find the length of each side.

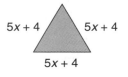

4. The triangle in the illustration has an area of 72 square yards. The base and the height are equal. Find the length of each.

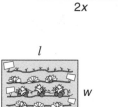

5. In an isosceles triangle, each of the equal sides is twice the length of the base. Which of the following represents that isosceles triangle?

(1) $2x$ \ $2x$ / $2x$
(2) x \ x / x
(3) $2x$ \ $2x$ / x
(4) x \ x / $2x$

6. The illustration shows a vegetable garden. The length of the garden is 2 feet more than the width. Sue has 100 feet of fencing that will just fit the garden. Find both the length and the width.

7. The plan shows a fenced-in playground. The ratio of the length to the width is $\frac{9}{5}$. The length of fencing surrounding the park is 560 feet. Find both the length and the width of the playground.

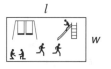

8. The drawing shows the floor plan for a workshop. The floor is 40 feet long and has an area of 800 square feet. What is the ratio of the length to the width?

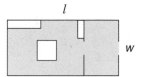

9. **Investigate** Choose a length and a width for a rectangle, such as 5 inches and 3 inches.

a. *Add* the same number, starting with 1, to both the length and the width. The first enlargement is $l + 1$ by $w + 1$, the next is $l + 2$ by $w + 2$, etc. Are each of these enlargements similar to the original?

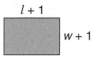

b. *Multiply* both the length and the width by the same number starting with 2. The first enlargement is $2l$ by $2w$, the next is $3l$ by $3w$, etc. Are each of these enlargements similar to the original?

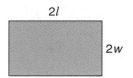

Setting Up Solutions

A **set-up solution** shows the operations and values needed to solve a problem. It does not give a final answer. For example, if Al makes $8 an hour and Sally makes $9, the set-up solution for the sum of their hourly wages is $8 + $9.

Set-up solutions are common on multiple-choice tests. A set-up solution tests your knowledge of the process involved in finding a solution.

For another look at order of operations, turn to page 221.

Choosing a Set-Up Solution

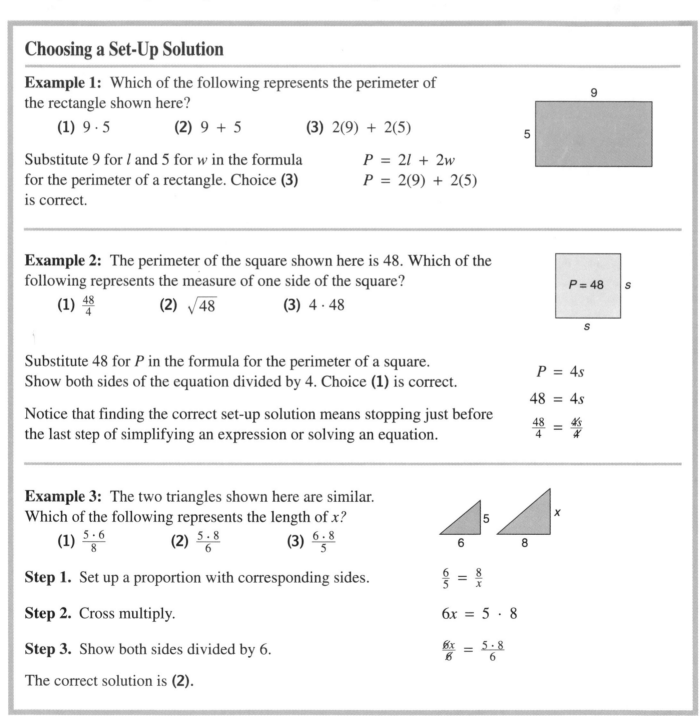

Example 1: Which of the following represents the perimeter of the rectangle shown here?

    (1) $9 \cdot 5$ **(2)** $9 + 5$ **(3)** $2(9) + 2(5)$

Substitute 9 for l and 5 for w in the formula for the perimeter of a rectangle. Choice **(3)** is correct.

$$P = 2l + 2w$$
$$P = 2(9) + 2(5)$$

Example 2: The perimeter of the square shown here is 48. Which of the following represents the measure of one side of the square?

    (1) $\frac{48}{4}$ **(2)** $\sqrt{48}$ **(3)** $4 \cdot 48$

Substitute 48 for P in the formula for the perimeter of a square. Show both sides of the equation divided by 4. Choice **(1)** is correct.

Notice that finding the correct set-up solution means stopping just before the last step of simplifying an expression or solving an equation.

$$P = 4s$$
$$48 = 4s$$
$$\frac{48}{4} = \frac{\cancel{4}s}{\cancel{4}}$$

Example 3: The two triangles shown here are similar. Which of the following represents the length of $x?$

    (1) $\frac{5 \cdot 6}{8}$ **(2)** $\frac{5 \cdot 8}{6}$ **(3)** $\frac{6 \cdot 8}{5}$

Step 1. Set up a proportion with corresponding sides. $\frac{6}{5} = \frac{8}{x}$

Step 2. Cross multiply. $6x = 5 \cdot 8$

Step 3. Show both sides divided by 6. $\frac{\cancel{6}x}{\cancel{6}} = \frac{5 \cdot 8}{6}$

The correct solution is **(2)**.

Choose the correct solution to each problem. Use any formulas on pages 223–224 that you need.

1. Which of the following represents the area of the triangle?

   (1) $\frac{13}{9}$　　　　**(2)** $13 \cdot 9$　　　　**(3)** $2 \cdot 13 \cdot 9$　　　　**(4)** $\frac{1}{2} \cdot 13 \cdot 9$

   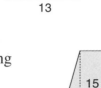

2. The area of the parallelogram is 180 square centimeters. Which of the following represents the base?

   (1) 180　　　**(2)** $\frac{180}{15}$　　　**(3)** $\frac{180}{2}$　　　**(4)** $\frac{15}{180}$

   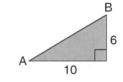

3. Which of the following represents the length of hypotenuse AB in the right triangle?

   (1) $\frac{10 + 6}{2}$　　　**(2)** $\sqrt{10^2 + 6^2}$　　　**(3)** $10 + 6$　　　**(4)** $10^2 + 6^2$

4. Which of the following represents the number of degrees in $\angle x$?

   (1) $180 - 81$　　　**(2)** $33 + 48$　　　**(3)** $90 - 81$　　　**(4)** $\frac{48}{33}$

5. Mel enlarged the picture shown here to be 20 inches long. Which of the following expresses the width of his enlargement?

   (1) $5 \cdot 7 \cdot 20$　　**(2)** $\frac{5 \cdot 7}{20}$　　**(3)** $\frac{7 \cdot 20}{5}$　　**(4)** $\frac{5 \cdot 20}{7}$

6. The illustration shows the lot where Ann will build a house. If the perimeter of the lot is 360 feet, which of the following represents the width?

   (1) $\frac{360}{4}$　　**(2)** $360 - 100$　　**(3)** $\frac{360 - 200}{2}$　　**(4)** $\frac{360}{100}$

7. The wheel has a circumference of 10 feet. Which of the following is an expression for the radius of the wheel?

   (1) $\frac{10}{2\pi}$　　　**(2)** $\frac{10\pi}{2}$　　　**(3)** $\frac{\pi}{10}$　　　**(4)** $10\pi^2$

8. **Multiple Solutions** The volume of the rectangular container is 1,000 cubic feet. Which of the following is *not* an expression for the height of the container?

   (1) $\frac{1,000}{20 \cdot 10}$　　**(2)** $\frac{1,000}{200}$　　**(3)** $\frac{1,000}{20}$　　**(4)** $\frac{100}{20}$

Mixed Review

A. For problems 1–4, tell whether the figures in each pair are similar.

1.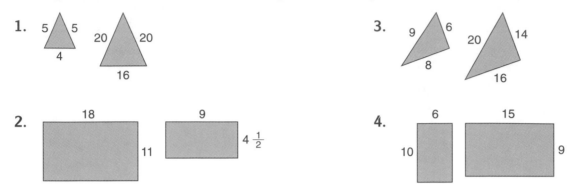

2.

3.

4.

B. In problems 5–8, the figures in each pair are similar. Find each measurement labeled *x*.

5.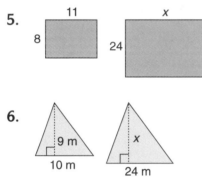

7.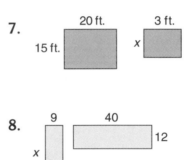

6.

Hint: Think of the heights of similar figures as corresponding sides.

8.

C. Solve each problem.

9. A 6-foot man casts a shadow 5 feet long. At the same time, a tree casts a shadow 60 feet long. How tall is the tree?

6 ft.

5 ft.   60 ft.

11. The rectangle and the square pictured here have the same area. What is the width of the rectangle?

w

l = 25 yd.   *s* = 20 yd.

10. The perimeter of the square tabletop shown here is 96 inches. Find the area of the top of the table.

P = 96 in.

12. The cube in the illustration has a surface area of 384 square inches. What is the length of each edge?

13. The combined area of the two rooms in the drawing is 360 square feet. What is the width of the larger room?

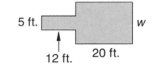

14. Which of the following correctly shows the labels for a rectangle whose length and width are in the ratio of 5:3?

(1) 3x / 3x   **(2)** 5x / 3x   **(3)** 5x / 5x   **(4)** 8x / 5x

15. The diagram shows the floor plan of a classroom. The ratio of the length of the room to the width is 5:4. The perimeter of the room is 90 feet.

  a. Find the length and width of the room.

  b. Find the area of the room.

  c. The state requires that there be at least 16 square feet of floor space for every student. Find the maximum number of students the classroom will hold.

P = 90 ft.

D. Choose the correct solution to each problem.

16. The area of the square in the illustration is 200 square centimeters. Which of the following represents the length in centimeters of one side of the square?

  (1) $\sqrt{200}$ **(2)** $\frac{200}{2}$ **(3)** $\frac{200}{4}$ **(4)** $\sqrt{50}$

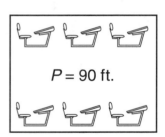

A = 200 cm²

17. The snapshot shown here was enlarged to have a length of 24 inches. If the enlargement is similar to the original, which of the following represents the new width in inches?

  (1) $3 \cdot 5 \cdot 24$ **(2)** $\frac{3 \cdot 5}{24}$ **(3)** $\frac{3 \cdot 24}{5}$ **(4)** $\frac{5 \cdot 24}{3}$

3 in.

5 in.

18. The diagram shows the frame for a door. The distance around the frame is 20 feet. Which of the following represents the height (length) of the door in feet?

  (1) $\frac{20}{3}$ **(2)** $\frac{20}{6}$ **(3)** $\frac{26}{2}$ **(4)** $\frac{20 - 6}{2}$

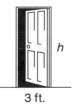

h

3 ft.

The Coordinate System

Look at the city map at right with streets intersecting at regular intervals. You can use the intersections to locate buildings. On the map, the city hall is at the intersection of Ash and Monroe.

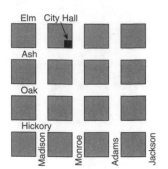

A **rectangular coordinate system** functions in the same way. A coordinate system is made up of two perpendicular lines that intersect at zero. The horizontal line is the **x-axis.** The vertical line is the **y-axis.** The point where the lines intersect is the **origin.**

Every point on the system represents an **ordered pair** of numbers (*x,y*). The *x*-coordinate, which always comes first, tells how far a point lies to the left or right of the origin. The *y*-coordinate tells how far a point lies above or below the origin.

Identifying Points on the Coordinate System

Example 1: What are the coordinates of point P? P is 3 units left of the origin and 5 units above the origin. (Notice that values to the left of 0 on the *x*-axis are negative.) The coordinates are **(–3,5).**

Example 2: What are the coordinates of point R? R is 2 units right of the origin and 1 unit below. (Notice that values below 0 on the *y*-axis are negative.) The coordinates are **(2,–1).**

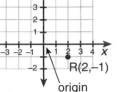

A. Use the points on this rectangular coordinate system to tell the coordinates for problems 1–6.

1. A = (*x,y*) = (,)   3. C =   5. E =

2. B = (*x,y*) = (– ,)   4. D =   6. F =

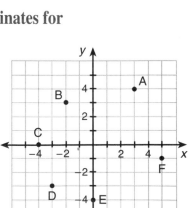

B. Use the rectangular coordinate system in Part A to draw the points described in problems 7–12.

7. G = (–4,2)   9. I = (–5,–2)   11. K = (2,4)

8. H = (–3,0)   10. J = (3,–3)   12. L = (0,5)

Finding the Distance between Two Points

Example 1: What is the distance from A to B?

Method 1. A is 3 units right of the y-axis, and B is 4 units left. The total distance is $3 + 4 = 7$.

Method 2. Find the absolute value of the difference between the x-values of each pair: $|3 - (-4)| = |3 + 4| = 7$ or $|-4 - 3| = |-7| = 7$

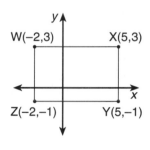

Example 2: What is the distance from A to C?

Method 1. A is 2 units above the x-axis, and C is 2 units below. The total distance is $2 + 2 = 4$.

Method 2. Find the absolute value of the difference between the y-values of each pair: $|2 - (-2)| = |2 + 2| = 4$ or $|-2 - 2| = |-4| = 4$

C. Use figure WXYZ to solve problems 13 and 14.

13. What is the distance WX?

14. What is the distance WZ?

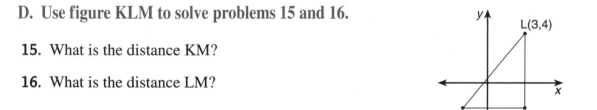

D. Use figure KLM to solve problems 15 and 16.

15. What is the distance KM?

16. What is the distance LM?

Making Connections: Reading Temperatures

The vertical axis tells the temperature in degrees Fahrenheit, and the horizontal axis tells the time of day. Use the graph to answer these questions.

1. By how many degrees did the temperature rise from 6 A.M. to 8 A.M?

2. What is the difference between the high and the low temperatures on the graph?

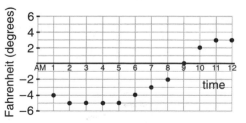

Distances on the Coordinate System

In the last lesson, you found distances between points. The distances were parallel to either the x-axis or the y-axis. For example, the distance between R and U is $|-3 - 4| = |-7| = 7$. The distance between R and S is $|-1 - 4| = |-5| = 5$. Notice that RU corresponds to the length of rectangle RSTU, and RS corresponds to the width. You can use these distances to calculate perimeter and area.

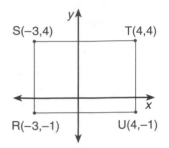

Finding Perimeter and Area on the Coordinate System

Example: Find both the perimeter and the area of the rectangle pictured above.

Step 1. Substitute 7 for l and 5 for w in the formula $P = 2l + 2w$.
$P = 2 \cdot 7 + 2 \cdot 5$
$P = 14 + 10$
$P = $ **24 units**

Step 2. Substitute 7 for l and 5 for w in the formula $A = lw$.
$A = 7 \cdot 5$
$A = $ **35 square units**

A. Use figure ABCD to solve problems 1–5.

1. What is the length (horizontal distance) of figure ABCD?

2. What is the width (vertical distance) of figure ABCD?

3. What is the shape of the figure?

4. What is the perimeter of the figure?

5. What is the area of the figure?

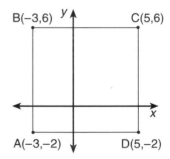

B. Use figure STU to solve problems 6–8.

6. What is the base of the triangle (distance SU)?

7. What is the height of the triangle (the perpendicular distance from point T to base SU)?

8. What is the area of the triangle?

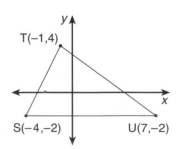

For the figure at the right, the distance between F and G is $|4 - (-2)| = |4 + 2| = 6$. The distance between E and G is $|-5 - 3| = |-8| = 8$. Line EF is not parallel to either the *x*-axis or the *y*-axis. You can use the Pythagorean theorem to find the distance from E to F.

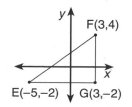

Using the Pythagorean Theorem with the Coordinate System

Example: What is the distance between E and F?

Use the Pythagorean theorem. $c^2 = a^2 + b^2$, so $c = \sqrt{a^2 + b^2}$

Find the length of hypotenuse EF. $EF = \sqrt{6^2 + 8^2}$

The vertical leg is 6, and the horizontal leg is 8. $EF = \sqrt{36 + 64}$

Solve the Pythagorean theorem. $EF = \sqrt{100}$

The length of hypotenuse EF is 10. $\mathbf{EF = 10}$

C. Use **figure JKLM** to solve problems 9–13.

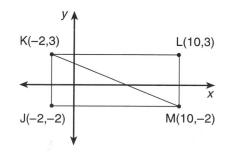

9. What is the length?

10. What is the width?

11. What is the perimeter?

12. What is the area?

13. What is the diagonal distance from K to M?

Making Connections: Accident Reports

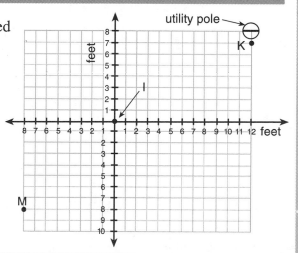

The diagram shows the point where a car and truck bumped into each other. The point of impact is I. The point where Kathy's car finally stopped is K. The point where Mike's truck finally stopped is M.

Use the diagram to calculate the following distances.

1. the distance between the two vehicles when they stopped

2. Kathy's distance from the utility pole when she stopped

Making a Table of Patterns

So far in this book, each equation you have solved had one solution. For example, the solution to the equation $y + 2 = 6$ is $y = 4$. The only value of y that makes the equation true is $y = 4$.

For some equations, there are an infinite number of solutions. Think about the equation $y = x - 1$. For every value of x, there is a value of y that makes the equation true.

When $x = 5$, $y = 5 - 1 = 4$.
When $x = 3$, $y = 3 - 1 = 2$.
When $x = 0$, $y = 0 - 1 = -1$.

A. Solve each problem.

1. Use $y = 3x$ to find y
   a. when $x = 5$, $y = 3(5) = $
   b. when $x = 1$
   c. when $x = -2$

2. Use $y = x + 6$ to find y
   a. when $x = 2$
   b. when $x = 0$
   c. when $x = -4$

Making a Table of Solutions to an Equation

Example: For the equation $y = x + 3$, find the value of y when $x = 4$, when $x = 2$, and when $x = -2$. Then make a table of the values.

Step 1. Substitute 4 for x in $y = x + 3$. $y = 4 + 3 = 7$
When $x = 4$, $y = \mathbf{7}$.

Step 2. Substitute 2 for x in $y = x + 3$. $y = 2 + 3 = 5$
When $x = 2$, $y = \mathbf{5}$.

Step 3. Substitute -2 for x in $y = x + 3$. $y = -2 + 3 = 1$
When $x = -2$, $y = \mathbf{1}$.

Step 4. Make a table with the values of x and y.

x	y
4	7
2	5
-2	1

Together, each value of x and the corresponding value of y describe a point on the rectangular coordinate system. The table above describes three points (4,7), (2,5), and (-2,1).

To make a **graph** of an equation, plot the points on a coordinate system and connect them with a line. Equations whose solutions lie in a straight line are called **linear equations.**

Graphing an Equation

Example: Make a graph of the equation $y = x + 3$.

Plot the three points (4,7), (2,5), and (–2,1) on a coordinate system, and connect the points. The line forms the **graph of the equation** $y = x + 3$. Notice that the graph is a straight line. Every point on the line is a solution to the equation $y = x + 3$.

B. For problems 3–5, first complete the table of values for each equation. Then plot each set of points on the coordinate system and connect them.

3. $y = x + 5$

x	y
2	
0	
–3	

4. $y = x - 2$

x	y
6	
3	
–2	

5. $y = 2x$

x	y
3	
1	
–1	

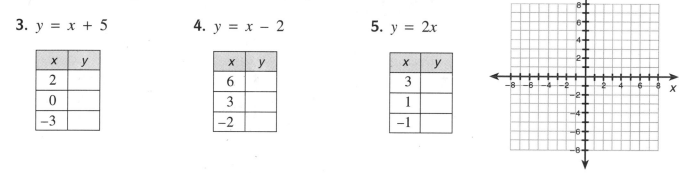

Making Connections: Graphing Complementary Angles

The equation $x° + y° = 90°$ represents pairs of complementary angles.

Fill in the chart for the corresponding values of y. Then plot the points on the coordinate system and connect them.

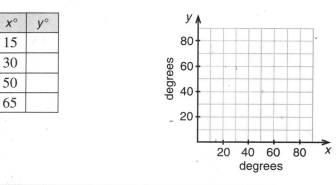

x°	y°
15	
30	
50	
65	

Graphing Multistep Linear Equations

In the last lesson, you filled out tables and made graphs for one-step equations.
The same steps work for longer equations.

Graphing a Multistep Linear Equation

Example: Make a graph of the equation $y = 2x + 1$. Find corresponding values of y
for $x = 4, x = 1$, and $x = -2$.

Step 1. Substitute each value of x to find the corresponding value of y.

When $x = 4, y = 9$. $y = 2(4) + 1 = 8 + 1 = 9$

When $x = 1, y = 3$. $y = 2(1) + 1 = 2 + 1 = 3$

When $x = -2, y = -3$. $y = 2(-2) + 1 = -4 + 1 = -3$

Step 2. Make a table with the values of x and y.

x	y
4	9
1	3
-2	-3

Step 3. Plot the points (4,9), (1,3), and (-2,-3) on the coordinate plane, and connect them with a straight line.

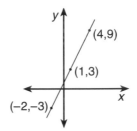

A. **Complete the table of values for each equation. Then plot each set of points on the coordinate system and connect them.**

1. $y = 2x - 5$

x	y
4	2
1	-3
-1	5

2. $y = 4x + 1$

x	y
0	
2	
-3	

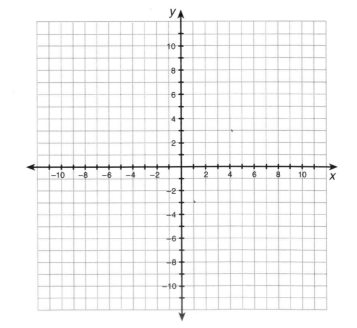

3. $y = \frac{1}{2}x + 3$

x	y
4	
2	
−2	

4. $y = -3x + 1$

x	y
−2	
1	
3	

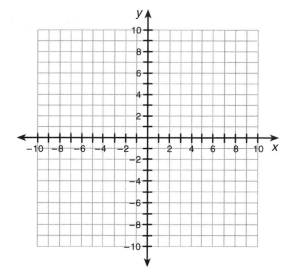

To find out whether a point is a solution to an equation, substitute one value into the equation. The result should equal the other value.

Checking Whether a Point Is a Solution to an Equation

Example: Are the points (5,4) and (8,9) solutions to $y = x - 1$?

Step 1. Substitute 5 for x in $y = x - 1$. When $x = 5$, $y = 5 - 1 = 4$
$y = 4$. Point (5,4) **is** a solution.

Step 2. Substitute 8 for x in $y = x - 1$. When $x = 8$, $y = 8 - 1 = 7$
the value of y is 7. Point (8,9) **is not** a solution.

B. Substitute to solve each problem.

5. Is (2,11) a solution to the equation $y = 6x - 1$?

6. Is (5,8) a solution to the equation $x + y = 13$?

7. Is (1,10) a solution to the equation $y = 5x + 4$?

Making Connections: Graphing Messenger Rates

A local company delivers packages to surrounding areas. The equation $y = .75x + 2$ represents the cost in dollars and cents of carrying a package x miles. Fill in the corresponding y-values on the chart. Then plot the points on the coordinate system and connect them.

x	y
1	
2	
3	

Slope and Intercept

Slope refers to the amount of incline or slant or steepness. Ski runs, most roofs, and the graphs of linear equations have slope.

Slope is the ratio of the **rise** to the **run** of an incline. The slope of the ramp shown here is $\frac{4}{20}$ or $\frac{1}{5}$. This means that for every foot of vertical distance (rise), there are 5 feet of horizontal distance (run).

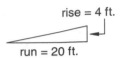
rise = 4 ft.
run = 20 ft.

▶ To calculate the slope of a line on the coordinate system, use slope $(m) = \frac{y_2 - y_1}{x_2 - x_1}$ where (x_1, y_1) and (x_2, y_2) are two points on the coordinate system.

Calculating Slope

Example 1: What is the slope of the line that passes through points A and B?
Point A (1,2) is (x_1, y_1) and point B (7,6) is (x_2, y_2).

Substitute these values into the formula for slope and simplify. The slope is $\frac{2}{3}$.

$$m = \frac{6-2}{7-1} = \frac{4}{6} = \frac{2}{3}$$

Example 2: What is the slope of the line that passes through points C and D?
Point C (2,4) is (x_1, y_1) and point D (5,1) is (x_2, y_2).

Substitute these values into the formula for slope and simplify. The slope is –1.

$$m = \frac{1-4}{5-2} = \frac{-3}{3} = -1$$

A line that *rises* from *left to right* has **positive slope.**

A line that *falls* from *left to right* has **negative slope.**

A. Calculate the slope for each pair of coordinates.

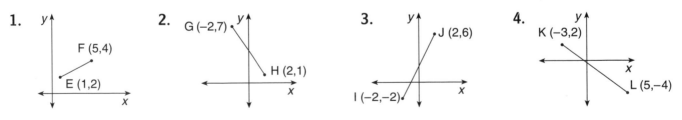

1. F (5,4) E (1,2)

2. G (−2,7) H (2,1)

3. J (2,6) I (−2,−2)

4. K (−3,2) L (5,−4)

5. The slope, or **pitch,** of a roof is based on *rise over run.*
The roof shown here has a pitch of $\frac{3}{9}$ or 3 in 9.
Would a roof with a pitch of 9 in 12 have a steeper slope?
Describe ways to support your answer.

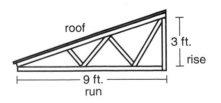
roof
3 ft.
rise
9 ft.
run

The illustration shows the graph of the equation $y = x + 3$. The graph crosses the y-axis at $(0,3)$. This point is called the **y-intercept.** The graph crosses the x-axis at $(-3,0)$. This point is called the **x-intercept.**

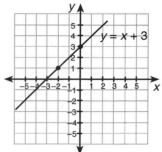

B. Use the graph at the right to solve problems 6 and 7.

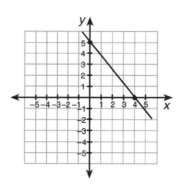

6. What are the coordinates of the y-intercept?

7. What are the coordinates of the x-intercept?

Notice that the y-intercept has an x-coordinate of 0. To find the y-intercept of any equation, substitute 0 for x, and solve the equation for y.

Finding a y-Intercept

Example: Find the y-intercept for $3x + y = 15$.
Substitute 0 for x, and solve the equation for y. $\qquad 3(0) + y = 15$
The y-intercept is **(0,15).** $\qquad\qquad\qquad\qquad\qquad y = 15$

An x-intercept has a y-coordinate of 0. To find the x-intercept of any equation, substitute 0 for y, and solve the equation for x.

Finding an x-Intercept

Example: Find the x-intercept for $3x + y = 15$.
Substitute 0 for y, and solve the equation for x. $\qquad 3x + 0 = 15$
$\qquad\qquad\qquad\qquad\qquad\qquad\qquad\qquad\qquad\qquad\qquad 3x = 15$
The x-intercept is **(5,0).** $\qquad\qquad\qquad\qquad\qquad\qquad x = 5$

C. Find the coordinates of each y-intercept and x-intercept.

8. $y = 2x - 1$

    y-intercept =

    x-intercept =

9. $2x + y = 5$

    y-intercept =

    x-intercept =

10. $y = \frac{1}{2}x + 3$

    y-intercept =

    x-intercept =

Linear Equations and Graphs

The problems in this lesson give you a chance to put linear equations to use.

A. Manolo has been driving at an average speed of **40 miles per hour.**
   Use this information for problems 1–4.

1. Fill in the blanks on the following table. The first two have been
   completed as examples.

hours	0	1	2	3	4
distance	0	40	___	___	___

2. Which of the following expresses the relationship between the distance Manolo
   travels (d) and the hours that he drives (h)?

   (1) $d = \frac{h}{40}$ **(2)** $d = 40h$ **(3)** $d = 40 + h$ **(4)** $h = 40d$

3. Which of the following graphs expresses the relationship between the hours
   Manolo drives and the distance he travels?

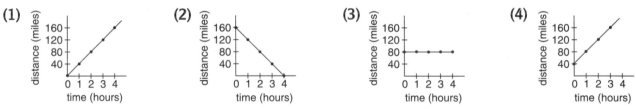

4. The coordinates (h,d), where h is hours and d is distance, represent points on the
   graph of the equation. If the graph were extended, could the point (5,100) be on
   the graph? Tell why or why not.

B. The equation **100 $=$ 2l + 2w** represents lengths and widths of rectangles
   with perimeters of 100. Use the equation to solve problems 5–8.

5. Fill in the blanks on the following table. The first one has been
   completed as an example.

   $100 = 2l + 2(5)$
   $100 = 2l + 10$
   $90 = 2l$
   $45 = l$

   w | $P = 100$

   l

w	5	10	15	20	25
l	45	___	___	___	___

6. Which of the following graphs best represents the equation?

(1) 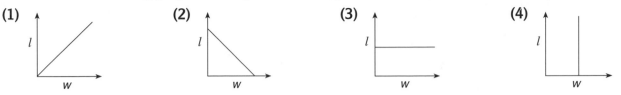   (2)   (3)   (4)

7. Each pair of values (w,l) from problem 5 represents a point on the coordinate system.

  a. Use two points from the table, $(10,\_\_)$ and $(20,\_\_)$, to calculate the slope of the graph.

  b. Is the slope of the graph positive or negative?

8. At what point do you think the graph would cross the vertical (l) axis? Can that point represent the length and width of a rectangle?

Making Connections: Renting Equipment

To rent a small power sander at Ricky's Rentals, a customer must pay $20 for the first 2 hours plus $5 for each hour thereafter. For example, to rent the sander for 3 hours, a customer pays $20 + $5(1) = $25.

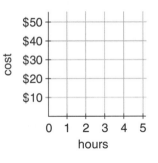

1. Fill in the cost blanks on the following table. The first two blanks have been completed as examples.

hours	2	3	4	5
cost	20	25	___	___

2. Plot the points on the coordinate system.

3. Which of the following best expresses the relationship between cost (c) and number of hours over 2 hours (h) for renting the sander?

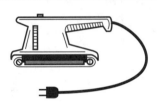

  (1) $c = 5h$ **(3)** $c = 20h + 5$

  (2) $c = 20h$ **(4)** $c = 5h + 20$

4. Is the value $(8,55)$ a solution to the equation?

5. What is the cost of renting the sander for 6 hours?

6. Is the slope of the graph positive or negative? Describe the relationship between hours and cost as shown on the graph.

A. For problems 1 and 2, tell whether the figures in each pair are similar.

1.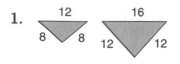

2.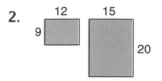

B. In problems 3 and 4, the figures in each pair are similar. Find the length of each side labeled *x*.

3.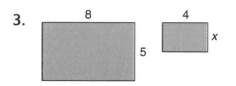

4.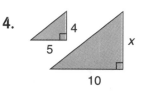

C. For problems 5 and 6, choose the correct solution.

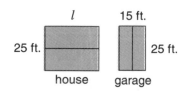

5. The combined floor area of the house and garage is 1,125 square feet. Find the length of the house.

    (1) 25 feet   **(3)** 35 feet

    (2) 30 feet   **(4)** 40 feet

6. Enlarge the poster so it has a width of 60 inches. Which of the following represents the new length (height) in inches?

    (1) $\frac{30 \cdot 60}{20}$ **(3)** $\frac{20 \cdot 30}{60}$

    (2) $\frac{20 \cdot 60}{30}$ **(4)** $20 \cdot 30 \cdot 60$

D. Use the coordinate system to solve problems 7–13.

7. What are the coordinates of Point A?

8. What are the coordinates of Point B?

9. What are the coordinates of Point C?

10. What is the distance from Point A to Point B?

11. What is the distance from Point B to Point C?

12. What is the diagonal distance from Point A to Point C?

13. What is the area of figure ABCD?

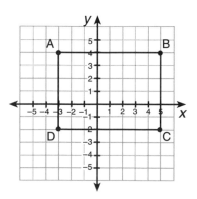

E. The graph shows the relationship between the time a hiker walks and the distance she travels. Use the graph to solve problems 14–16.

14. As t increases, does d increase or decrease?

15. Is the slope of the graph positive or negative?

16. What are the coordinates of the y-intercept of the graph?

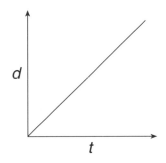

Working Together

Do the following with a partner or with a group of other students.

1. Work in small groups. Collect advertisements for photo enlargements or photos reproduced as posters. Measure the length and width of a regular-size photo. Determine whether the enlargements advertised are similar in shape and size to the originals. Compare your findings with those of other groups.

2. Work with a partner. Take a yardstick and a tape measure out of doors on a sunny day. Hold the yardstick vertically with one end resting on the ground and measure the length of its shadow. Also measure the length of the shadow of some tall object, such as a building or a tree. Use proportion to calculate the height of the object.

3. Make a rectangular coordinate grid. Along the vertical axis, put distance in miles, and along the horizontal axis put time in hours. Use the grid to show the distance you can drive at different average speeds, for example, 20 miles per hour, 40 miles per hour, and 60 miles per hour. Discuss with other students how the distance formula $d = rt$ works like a linear equation.

4. Stairs are made of *treads,* the horizontal part that you step on, and *risers,* the vertical part. Measure the height of a riser, the vertical distance from one step to the next. Also measure the tread from the front to the back. Compare the ratios of risers to treads. Discuss how the slope of a linear equation is similar to the construction of a stair. Make a list of places you see slopes in daily life.

Posttest

Solve the following problems. Use any formulas on pages 223–224 that you need.

1. To mix a color of paint, Jaime used 6 gallons of blue paint and 4 gallons of gray paint. What is the ratio of gray paint to blue paint?

   (1) 6:10

   (2) 6:4

   (3) 3:5

   (4) 2:3

   (5) 2:5

2. The formula for converting Celsius to Fahrenheit temperature is $F = \frac{9}{5}C + 32$. What Fahrenheit temperature corresponds to 40° Celsius?

   (1) 122°F

   (2) 104°F

   (3) 86°F

   (4) 72°F

   (5) 40°F

Problem 3 refers to the drawing below.

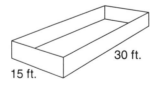

30 ft.

15 ft.

3. The capacity of the pool is 3,600 cubic feet. What is the depth of the pool?

   (1) 20 feet

   (2) 15 feet

   (3) 12 feet

   (4) 10 feet

   (5) 8 feet

4. Mike drove a truck at an average speed of 50 miles per hour. Jorge drove his car at an average speed of 65 miles per hour. They started at the same time and headed in the same direction. How far apart were they in three hours?

   (1) 15 miles

   (2) 30 miles

   (3) 45 miles

   (4) 60 miles

   (5) 115 miles

Problem 5 refers to the drawing below.

c

29°

5. What is the measurement of ∠c?

   (1) 29°

   (2) 61°

   (3) 71°

   (4) 119°

   (5) 151°

6. Which of the following equals $\frac{20 - 24}{18 - 10}$?

   (1) $-\frac{1}{2}$

   (2) $+\frac{2}{3}$

   (3) $-\frac{3}{4}$

   (4) -1

   (5) -2

Problem 7 refers to the drawing below.

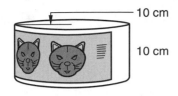

10 cm

10 cm

7. What is the volume in cubic centimeters of the cylindrical container?

(1) 3.14

(2) 31.4

(3) 314

(4) 3,140

(5) 31,400

Problem 8 refers to the diagram below.

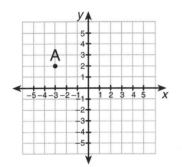

8. What are the coordinates of point A?

(1) (2,3)

(2) (−2,−3)

(3) (−2,3)

(4) (−3,2)

(5) (2,−3)

9. What is the solution for p in the equation $7p + 4 = 2p − 11$?

(1) 3

(2) −3

(3) 5

(4) −5

(5) $−\frac{5}{3}$

Problem 10 refers to the drawing below.

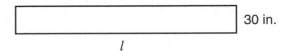

30 in.

l

10. The drawing shows the surface of a countertop. The ratio of the length to the width is 15:2. Find the length.

(1) 90 inches

(2) 175 inches

(3) 225 inches

(4) 450 inches

(5) 900 inches

11. A circular reflecting pond has a diameter of 40 feet. Which of the following is closest to the length of fencing required to surround the pond?

(1) 80 feet

(2) 110 feet

(3) 130 feet

(4) 180 feet

(5) 250 feet

Problem 12 refers to the drawing below.

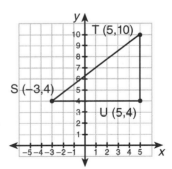

12. What is the distance from S to T?

(1) 6

(2) 8

(3) 10

(4) 12

(5) 15

Problem 13 refers to the drawing below.

13. In isosceles triangle ABC, ∠a measures 28°. What is the measurement of ∠b?

    (1) 28°
    (2) 56°
    (3) 118°
    (4) 124°
    (5) 152°

14. Which of the following is the same as $12m - 5 - m + 6$?

    (1) $11m + 1$
    (2) $12m - 1$
    (3) $12m + 11$
    (4) $11m - 11$
    (5) $11m + 11$

Problem 15 refers to the drawing below.

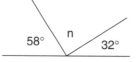

15. What kind of angle is ∠n?

    (1) acute
    (2) right
    (3) obtuse
    (4) vertical
    (5) straight

16. Choose the expression that shows *two more than seven times a number is thirty.*

    (1) $2 = 7d + 30$
    (2) $7d + 2 + 30$
    (3) $2(7d) = 30$
    (4) $\frac{7d}{2} = 30$
    (5) $7d + 2 = 30$

Problems 17–19 refer to the following diagram.

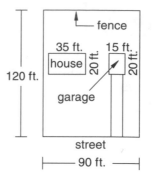

17. A footing is a concrete base poured around the edge of a structure. What is the total length of footings needed for the house and the garage?

    (1) 70 feet
    (2) 110 feet
    (3) 150 feet
    (4) 180 feet
    (5) 200 feet

18. What is the combined ground floor area of both the house and the garage?

    (1) 1,200 square feet
    (2) 1,000 square feet
    (3) 850 square feet
    (4) 700 square feet
    (5) 300 square feet

19. Which of the following is closest, in meters, to the distance from the street to the fence at the back of the property? (3 ft. = 0.914 m)

    (1) 27
    (2) 31
    (3) 37
    (4) 41
    (5) 47

Problem 20 refers to the drawing below.

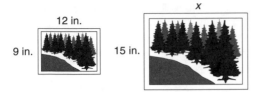

12 in.

9 in.

x

15 in.

20. The drawing shows a picture and an enlargement. Which of the following represents the length of the enlargement if it has the same shape as the original?

(1) $\frac{12 \cdot 15}{9}$

(2) $\frac{9 \cdot 15}{12}$

(3) $9 \cdot 12 \cdot 15$

(4) $9 + 12 + 15$

(5) $\frac{15}{9 \cdot 12}$

Problem 21 refers to the drawing below.

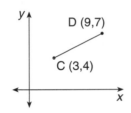

D (9,7)

C (3,4)

21. What is the slope of the line that connects points C and D?

(1) $\frac{7}{9}$

(2) $\frac{6}{9}$

(3) $\frac{1}{2}$

(4) 1

(5) −1

22. What is the solution to the inequality $9m - 4 > 5$?

(1) $m < 1$

(2) $m > 1$

(3) $m > \frac{1}{2}$

(4) $m < \frac{1}{2}$

(5) $m > 3$

Problem 23 refers to the drawing below.

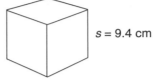

$s = 9.4$ cm

23. Which of the following represents the cube's surface area in square centimeters?

(1) $(9.4)^2$

(2) $4(9.4)$

(3) $(9.4)^3$

(4) $3(9.4)$

(5) $6(9.4)^2$

24. When $y = 5$, what is the value of x in $2x - y = 7$?

(1) 1

(2) 2

(3) 4

(4) 6

(5) 8

Problem 25 refers to the drawing below.

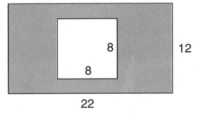

8

8

12

22

25. Which of the following represents the area of the shaded part of the figure?

(1) $22 \cdot 12 - 8^2$

(2) $22 \cdot 12 \cdot 8$

(3) $22 \cdot 12 + 8$

(4) $22 \cdot 12 - 2 \cdot 8$

(5) $22^2 - 8^2$

1. **(4) 2:3**

    gray:blue = 4:6 = 2:3

2. **(2) 104°**

    $F = \frac{9}{5}C + 32$

    $F = \frac{9}{5}(40) + 32$

    $F = 72 + 32$

    $F = 104$

3. **(5) 8 feet**

    $V = lwh$

    $3,600 = 30 \cdot 15h$

    $3,600 = 450h$

    $8 = h$

4. **(3) 45 miles**

    $d = rt = 65 \cdot 3 = 195$ mi.

    $d = rt = 50 \cdot 3 = 150$ mi.

    difference = 45 mi.

5. **(2) 61°**

    $90° - 29° = 61°$

6. **(1) $-\frac{1}{2}$**

    $\frac{20 - 24}{18 - 10}$

    $-\frac{4}{8} = -\frac{1}{2}$

7. **(4) 3,140**

    $V = \pi r^2 h$

    $V = 3.14 \cdot 10^2 \cdot 10$

    $V = 3,140$

8. **(4) (–3,2)**

9. **(2) –3**

    $7p + 4 = 2p - 11$

    $5p = -15$

    $p = -3$

10. **(3) 225 inches**

    $\frac{\text{length}}{\text{width}} \frac{15}{2} = \frac{l}{30}$

    $2l = 450$

    $l = 225$

11. **(3) 130 feet**

    $C = \pi d$

    $C = 3.14 \cdot 40$

    $C = 125.6$, which is close to 130

12. **(3) 10**

    $ST = \sqrt{8^2 + 6^2}$

    $ST = \sqrt{100}$

    $ST = 10$

13. **(4) 124°**

    $180° - 28° - 28° = 124°$

14. **(1) $11m + 1$**

15. **(2) right**

    $\angle n = 180° - 58° - 32° = 90°$

16. **(5) $7d + 2 = 30$**

17. **(4) 180 feet**

    $2(35) + 2(20) + 2(20) + 2(15) = 180$

18. **(2) 1,000 square feet**

    $35(20) + 20(15) = 1,000$

19. **(3) 37**

    $\frac{120}{3} = 40$

    $40(0.914) = 36.56$, which is close to 37

20. **(1) $\frac{12 \cdot 15}{9}$**

    $\frac{9}{12} = \frac{15}{x}$

    $\frac{9x}{9} = \frac{12 \cdot 15}{9}$

21. **(3) $\frac{1}{2}$**

    $\frac{7 - 4}{9 - 3} = \frac{3}{6} = \frac{1}{2}$

22. **(2) $m > 1$**

    $9m - 4 > 5$

    $9m > 9$

    $m > 1$

23. **(5) $6(9.4)^2$**

    6 times the area of one face

24. **(4) 6**

    $2x - 5 = 7$

    $2x = 12$

    $x = 6$

25. **(1) $22 \cdot 12 - 8^2$**

    $A = lw - s^2$

    $A = 22 \cdot 12 - 8^2$

Posttest Evaluation Chart

Make note of any problems you answered incorrectly. Review the skill area for each of those problems, using the unit number given.

Problem Number	Skill Area	Unit
1	Using ratio	2
2	Using formulas	1
3	Finding missing dimensions	5
4	Solving motion problems	2
5	Identifying pairs of angles	3
6	Multiplying and dividing signed numbers	1
7	Finding volume	4
8	Identifying points on the coordinate system	5
9	Solving two-step equations	2
10	Using proportion	2
11	Finding circumference	4
12	Finding distance on the coordinate system (Pythagorean theorem)	5
13	Using the properties of triangles	3
14	Simplifying expressions	1
15	Measuring angles	3
16	Writing a number sentence	1
17	Finding perimeter	4
18, 25	Finding area	4
19	Converting measurements	3
20	Setting up solutions	5
21	Finding slope	5
22	Solving inequalities	2
23	Finding surface area	4
24	Substituting	1

Answer Key

Unit 1

When Do I Use Algebra? p. 13

1. arithmetic (specific)
2. algebra (general)
3. algebra (general)
4. arithmetic (specific)

Talk About It

Discussion will vary.

Writing Expressions pp. 14–15

Part A

1. $9 + $2
2. 220 − 15
3. 12° + 8° *or* 8° + 12°
4. 3 + 6
5. $299 − $50

Part B

Answers will vary.

6. $25(5) *or* $25 · 5 *or* $25 × 5
7. $\frac{28}{7}$ *or* 28 ÷ 7 *or* $7\overline{)28}$
8. $\frac{$240}{2}$ *or* $240 ÷ 2 *or* $2\overline{)$240}$
9. $\frac{$36}{3}$ *or* $36 ÷ 3 *or* $3\overline{)$36}$
10. 10($1.149) *or* 10 · $1.149 *or* 10 × $1.149

Part C

11. 36 + 12; A + B
12. 36 − 12; A − B
13. 36(12) *or* 12(36); A(B) *or* B(A)
14. $\frac{12}{36}$; $\frac{B}{A}$

Powers and Roots pp. 16–17

Part A

1. 64
2. 144
3. 9
4. 400
5. 8
6. 64
7. 1,000
8. 1
9. 16
10. 225
11. 49
12. 729

Part B

$2^2 = 4$	$5^2 = 25$	$8^2 = 64$	$11^2 = 121$	$14^2 = 196$
$3^2 = 9$	$6^2 = 36$	$9^2 = 81$	$12^2 = 144$	$15^2 = 225$
$4^2 = 16$	$7^2 = 49$	$10^2 = 100$	$13^2 = 169$	$20^2 = 400$

Part C

13. 8
14. 10
15. 5
16. 9
17. 7
18. 12
19. 2
20. 3

Part D

21. **(1)** 6 and 7
22. **(2)** 2 and 3
23. **(2)** 10 and 11
24. Discussion will vary.

Order of Operations pp. 18–19

Part A

1. 3 · 10 + 5 · 2
   30 + 10
   40
2. 8 + 3 − 5
   11 − 5
   6
3. $\sqrt{36}$ − 3
   6 − 3
   3
4. $\frac{12}{2} - \frac{10}{2}$
   6 − 5
   1
5. $(9 + 6)^2$
   $(15)^2$
   225
6. $\frac{8 + 12}{5 - 3}$
   $\frac{20}{2}$
   10
7. 4(7 − 1)
   4(6)
   24
8. $2 · 7^2$
   2 · 49
   98
9. $\frac{20 - 4}{8}$
   $\frac{16}{8}$
   2
10. 5(6 + 3) − 12
    5(9) − 12
    45 − 12
    33
11. $3 · 5^2 + 10$
    3 · 25 + 10
    75 + 10
    85
12. $10(3 + 9)^2$
    $10(12)^2$
    10(144)
    1,440
13. 3 · 8 − (5 + 7)
    3 · 8 − 12
    24 − 12
    12
14. $\frac{15}{12 - 7}$
    $\frac{15}{5}$
    3
15. $6(5 - 1)^2$
    $6(4)^2$
    6(16)
    96

Part B

16. **(2)** 40 − 12
17. **(2)** 6 + 3 + 8
18. **(1)** 9(4)
19. **(3)** (7)(3)
20. **(1)** $\frac{21}{3}$
21. **(1)** 4 + 3

Making Connections: Counting Money p. 19

1. 3($1) + 2($5) + 4($10)
2. $3 + $10 + $40
   $53

Perimeter and Area pp. 20–21

Part A

1. **16**
   $3 + 5 + 3 + 5$ or $2(3 + 5)$
2. **50**
   $10 + 10 + 10 + 10 + 10$ or $5(10)$
3. **78**
   $14 + 25 + 14 + 25$ or $2(14 + 25)$
4. **28**
   $7 + 7 + 7 + 7$ or $4(7)$
5. **35**
   $6 + 6 + 10 + 13$
6. **48**
   $12 + 16 + 20$

Part B

7. A   9. P   11. A   13. A
8. P   10. A   12. P

Part C

14. 48 square units   17. 202 square units
15. 81 square units   18. 102 square units
16. 2.25 square units   19. 0.36 square units

The Number Line pp. 22–23

Part A

1. $8 < 15$ 4. $2 > -6$ 7. $5 = 5$
2. $-10 > -12$ 5. $-1 = -1$ 8. $-11 > -12$
3. $-3 > -4$ 6. $9 > -3$ 9. $-8 < -6$

Part B

10. A $|-5| = 5$
    B $|-3| = 3$
    C $|-1.5|$ or $\left|-1\frac{1}{2}\right| = 1.5$ or $1\frac{1}{2}$
    D $|+2| = 2$
    E $|+3.5|$ or $\left|+3\frac{1}{2}\right| = 3.5$ or $3\frac{1}{2}$
    F $|+5| = 5$

11. **a.** A and F are both 5 units from 0.
    b. A and F have the same absolute value.

12. Discussion will vary. The total distance from A to D is 7. Different ways to find the total distance between points: count the number of units between points or add the absolute values of the points. Adding absolute values gives the distance between a negative and a positive number.

Making Connections: Keeping Score p. 23

Contestant: Answer	A	B
A: correct	200	
B: correct		200
B: wrong		–100
A: wrong	–100	
B: correct		200
A: wrong	–100	
Score	0	300

Adding and Subtracting Signed Numbers pp. 24–25

Part A

1. $+3 + (+4) = 7$ or $3 + 4 = 7$
2. $-3 + (-4) = -7$ or $-3 - 4 = -7$
3. $+7 + (-6) = 1$ or $7 - 6 = 1$
4. $-7 + (+5) = -2$ or $-7 + 5 = -2$

Part B

5. add, +11   11. find the difference, +5
6. add, –14   12. add, –19
7. add, –15   13. find the difference, +13
8. find the difference, +6   14. add, –23
9. find the difference, –3   15. add, +24
10. find the difference, –11   16. find the difference, –14

Part C

17. +6   22. +22
18. +1   23. +15
19. –21   24. –9
20. +15   25. +1
21. –5   26. $-3 + (+5) = +2$ or $-3 - (-5) = +2$

Multiplying and Dividing Signed Numbers pp. 26–27

Part A

1. +32   3. +54   5. –48   7. –34   9. –135
2. –63   4. +800   6. +60   8. +125

Part B

10. –3   12. +8   14. +1   16. +25   18. –10
11. –4   13. –25   15. –3   17. +2

Part C

19. $15 - 8 = \textbf{7}$ 22. $-2(6)^2 = -2(36) = \textbf{–72}$
20. $-8(5) = \textbf{–40}$ 23. $(7)(-7) = \textbf{–49}$
21. $-6 + 5 = \textbf{–1}$ 24. $\frac{(-5)}{(5)} = \textbf{–1}$

Making Connections: Gains and Losses p. 27

1. $+4 \cdot +2 = +8$ or 8 pounds *more* than now

2. $-4 \cdot +2 = -8$ or 8 pounds less than now

3. $+4 \cdot -2 = -8$ or 8 pounds less than now

Expressions and Variables pp. 28–29

Part A

1. $3x + 7$

2. $8m + 9$

3. $2 + 5c$

Part B

4. (1) $y - 7$

5. (2) $2p + 8$

6. (1) $3\sqrt{c}$

7. (2) $\frac{9m}{5}$

8. (1) $10(y - 1)$

9. (3) $(6n)^2$

Part C

10. $A = 14m$

    $P = 2m + 28$

11. $A = r^2$

    $P = 4r$

12. $A = 5(2m + 1)$

    $P = 2(2m + 1) + 10$

Part D

13. $w + \$2$ or $\$2 + w$

14. $\frac{p}{2}$

15. $e + 5$ or $5 + e$

16. $2v$ or $v + v$

Substitution pp. 30–31

Part A

1. a. $2(6) = \mathbf{12}$

   b. $2(15) = \mathbf{30}$

2. a. $\frac{8}{2} = \mathbf{4}$

   b. $\frac{12}{2} = \mathbf{6}$

3. a. $(6 + 4)^2 = 10^2 = \mathbf{100}$

   b. $(11 + 4)^2 = 15^2 = \mathbf{225}$

4. a. $18 + \frac{1}{2}(18) - 6 = 18 + 9 - 6 = \mathbf{21}$

   b. $24 + \frac{1}{2}(24) - 6 = 24 + 12 - 6 = \mathbf{30}$

5. a. $\sqrt{16} + 2(16) = 4 + 32 = \mathbf{36}$

   b. $\sqrt{25} + 2(25) = 5 + 50 = \mathbf{55}$

6. a. $9(-5 - 2) = 9(-7) = \mathbf{-63}$

   b. $9(-9 - 2) = 9(-11) = \mathbf{-99}$

Part B

7. $P = a + a + 1 + a + 2 = 8 + 8 + 1 + 8 + 2$
   $= \mathbf{27}$

8. $P = 2x + 2y = 2(7) + 2(11) = 14 + 22 = \mathbf{36}$

9. $P = 4c = 4(3.5) = \mathbf{14}$

Part C

10. $A = nm = 12(9) = \mathbf{108}$ **square units**

11. $A = c(c + 6) = 20(20 + 6) = 20(26) =$
    520 square units

12. $A = w^2 = 20^2 = \mathbf{400}$ **square units**

Part D

13. $7 \cdot 4 - 5 = 28 - 5 = \mathbf{23}$

14. $\frac{24}{3} - \frac{8}{2} = 8 - 4 = \mathbf{4}$

15. $8 \cdot 3^2 = 8 \cdot 9 = \mathbf{72}$

16. $\frac{10 + 5}{10 - 5} = \frac{15}{5} = \mathbf{3}$

Making Connections: Sales Tax p. 31

$.05 \cdot \$25 = \mathbf{\$1.25}$

Finding Patterns in Algebra pp. 32–33

Part A

1. 9

2. 32

3. –13

4. 7

5. $1\frac{1}{4}$ or 1.25

6. –400

Part B

7. any figure with 6 sides

8.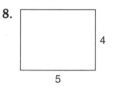

Part C

×	−2	−1	0	+1	+2
−1	+2	+1	0	−1	−2
−2	+4	+2	0	−2	−4
−3	+6	+3	0	−3	−6
−4	+8	+4	0	−4	−8
−5	+10	+5	0	−5	−10

Part D

Squares						
length of one side	1	2	3	4	5	6
perimeter	4	8	12	16	20	24
area	1	4	9	16	25	36

Part E

9. $1.75

10. **$5.50**

    Each increase is $.75 per pound.
    ($4.75 + $.75 = $5.50)

11. **$4.00**

    Since 4.5 pounds is more than 4 pounds, the cost is
    that of a 5-pound package.

Part F

12. **$55.00**

   $20.00 + $17.50 + $17.50 = $55.00

13. $(-2)(+2)(-2)(+2)(-2) = -32$

   $(-2)(+2)(-2)(+2)(-2)(+2) = -64$

   When multiplying more than two signed numbers, the answer is positive when there are an even number (2, 4, 6, etc.) of minus signs. The answer is negative when there are an odd number (1, 3, 5, etc.) of minus signs.

Mixed Review pp. 34–35

Part A

1. **(3)** $6 + 30$ 2. **(1)** $\frac{30}{6}$

Part B

3. 196   4. 32   5. 81

Part C

6. **(3)** 17   7. **(2)** 23   8. **(2)** 100

Part D

9. 45   10. 38   11. 32.8

Part E

12. $5 < 25$ 13. $6 > -6$ 14. $14 = +14$

Part F

15. 6   18. −14   21. 30   24. 13

16. −19   19. −22   22. 15   25. $-\frac{2}{3}$

17. −8   20. 9   23. −7   26. −9

Part G

27. $A = 5l$ 29. $A = 6(7a + 5)$

28. $A = 8(m - 1)$

Part H

30. $4(7) - 3 = 28 - 3 =$ **25**

31. $\frac{120}{6} + 5 = 20 + 5 =$ **25**

32. $(-2)(5) + 5^2 = -10 + 25 =$ **15**

33. $5(1 - 4) = 5(-3) =$ **−15**

Part I

34. 243   35. −16

Part J

36. $w + \$.50$

37. n = number of items and p = original price

   cost at original price $= np$

   cost at reduced price $= n(p - \$.50)$

Simple Formulas and Substitution pp. 36–37

Part A

1. $c = 6 \cdot \$1.25$ 3. $c = 2 \cdot \$7.80$

   $c =$ **$7.50** $c =$ **$15.60**

2. $c = 4 \cdot \$13.20$ 4. $c = \frac{1}{2} \cdot \$6.80$

   $c =$ **$52.80** $c =$ **$3.40**

Part B

5. $r = \frac{c}{n}$ 6. $n = \frac{c}{r}$

   $r = \frac{\$8.94}{6}$ $n = \frac{\$6.95}{\$1.39}$

   $r =$ **$1.49** $n =$ **5**

Part C

7. $d = rt$ 9. $t = \frac{d}{r}$

   $d = 55 \cdot 3$ $t = \frac{1,275}{425}$

   $d =$ **165 miles** $t =$ **3 hours**

8. $d = rt$ 10. $r = \frac{d}{t}$

   $d = 2.5 \cdot 5$ $r = \frac{180}{4}$

   $d =$ **12.5 miles** $r =$ **45 miles per hour**

Part D

11. $A = \frac{1}{2}bh$ 13. $A = \frac{1}{2}(b + B)h$

   $A = \frac{1}{2} \cdot 13 \cdot 8$ $A = \frac{1}{2}(14 + 26)12$

   $A =$ **52 square units** $A = \frac{1}{2}(40)12$

12. $A = bh$ $A =$ **240 square units**

   $A = 24 \cdot 10$

   $A =$ **240 square units**

Part E

14. $y = \frac{180}{9}$

   $y =$ **20 square yards**

15. Explanations will vary. Here is one good approach. First choose a number of items and a rate. For example, choose 5 gallons and $2 for the price of a gallon of milk. With the formula $c = nr$, you get $c = 5 \cdot \$2 = \$10$ for the total cost. Then substitute $10 and $2 in $n = \frac{c}{r}$ to get 5 gallons. Also substitute 10 and 5 in $r = \frac{c}{n}$ to get $2 per gallon.

Using a Calculator pp. 38–39

Part A

1. 84   4. 529   7. 7   10. 0.0225

2. 6   5. 42   8. 32   11. 86

3. 9   6. 34   9. 2,250

Part B

12. 41.5   13. 36   14. 12.2

Part C

15. 91 square units

16. 73.96 square units

17. 22.8 square units

Part D

18. **18**
   30 − 12 = 18

19. **57**
   21 + 36 = 57

20. **187**
   7 + 180 = 187

21. **53**
   65 − 12 = 53

22. **6.25**
   $(2.5)^2 = 6.25$

23. **40**
   54 − 14 = 40

Part E

24. **322 miles**
   3.5 × 92 = 322

25. **\$7.53** *or* **\$7.54**
   2.8 × \$2.69 = \$7.532

26. Answers will vary.

The Distributive Property pp. 40–41

Part A

1. 10
2. 90
3. 63
4. 27
5. 90
6. yes
7. Answers will vary.

Part B

8. **(2)** $4 \cdot 7 + 4 \cdot 11$

9. **(1)** $9 \cdot 8 - 9 \cdot 3$

10. **(3)** $2a + 2 \cdot 13$

11. **(3)** $8(3 + 6)$

12. **(2)** $15(9 - 4)$

Part C

13. $A = 4(7 + 2)$ *or* $A = 4(7) + 4(2)$

14. $A = 6(3 + 5)$ *or* $A = 6(3) + 6(5)$

15. $A = 7(8 + 1)$ *or* $A = 7(8) + 7(1)$

Making Connections: Finding Averages p. 41

$a = \frac{1}{2}(78 + 86)$

$a = \frac{1}{2}(164)$

$a = \mathbf{82}$

or

$a = \frac{1}{2}(78) + \frac{1}{2}(86)$

$a = 39 + 43$

$a = \mathbf{82}$

Simplifying Expressions pp. 42–43

Part A

1. $3x$
2. $-5k$
3. $-2t + 5$
4. $11a - 3$
5. $13 + 6m$
6. $25 - 6y$
7. $-k - 8m$
8. $6c + 8d$
9. $-8s + t$

Part B

10. $x + 3$; because the expression for that side is 3 more than x and 1 more than $x + 2$

11. $P = x + x + 2 + x + 3$

12. $P = 3x + 5$ (*Note:* $3x$ is the same as $x \cdot 3$)

13. $P = 3(8) + 5 = 24 + 5 = \mathbf{29}$

14. $P = 3(25) + 5 = 75 + 5 = \mathbf{80}$

Part C

15. $P = m + m + 1 + m + m + 1$

16. $P = 4m + 2$ (*Note:* $4m$ is the same as $m \cdot 4$)

17. $P = 4(4.5) + 2 = 18 + 2 = \mathbf{20}$

18. $P = 4(18) + 2 = 72 + 2 = \mathbf{74}$

Part D

19. $P = c + c + c + c$

20. $P = 4c$ (*Note:* $4c$ is the same as $c \cdot 4$)

21. $4c = 24$; ***Think:*** What times 4 equals 24?; $24 \div 4 = 6$; $c = \mathbf{6}$

22. $A = 6 \cdot 6 = \mathbf{36}$ **square units**

Scientific Notation pp. 44–45

Part A

1. **(2)** $\mathbf{1.9 \times 10^4}$
   This is the only choice that shows the product of a power of 10 and a number from 1 to 10.

2. **(1)** 7.35×10^5

3. **(3)** 6.4×10^6

Part B

4. 3.5×10^6

5. 4.85×10^5

6. 5.6×10^7

7. 7.5×10^4

8. 9.2×10^5

9. 1.3×10^8

Part C

10. 81,000

11. 930,000,000

12. 40,000,000

13. 2,500,000

14. 6,000,000,000

15. 380,000

Making Connections: Earth Measurements p. 45

1. $239{,}000 = 2.39 \times 10^5$

2. $93{,}000{,}000 = 9.3 \times 10^7$

3. $197{,}000{,}000 = 1.97 \times 10^8$

4. $67{,}000 = 6.7 \times 10^4$

5. Answers will vary.

Celsius and Fahrenheit Thermometers pp. 46–47

Part A

1. 50°F
2. 95°F
3. 5°F
4. –58°F
5. 104°F
6. 212°F

Part B

7. 58°F
8. –10°F
9. 78°F

Part C

10. 15°C
11. 45°C
12. **–20°C**

   $C = \frac{5}{9}(-4 - 32) = \frac{5}{9}(-36) = -20$

13. **–30°C**

   $C = \frac{5}{9}(-22 - 32) = \frac{5}{9}(-54) = -30$

14. 35°C
15. **–10°C**

   $C = \frac{5}{9}(14 - 32) = \frac{5}{9}(-18) = -10$

Part D

Specific Temperatures	Fahrenheit	Celsius
Boiling point of water (at sea level)	212°F	100°C
Healthy body temperature	98.6°F	37°C
Comfortable room temperature	68°F	20°C
Freezing point of water (at sea level)	32°F	0°C
Temperature at which scales are equal	–40°F	–40°C
The coldest temperature recorded in the United States outside Alaska	–70°F	–56.7°C

Writing a Number Sentence pp. 48–49

Part A

1. (2) $6n = 30$
2. (3) $y - 12 = 19$
3. (1) $\frac{c}{5} > 14$
4. (3) $p - 8 = 20$
5. (1) $2r - 1 = 15$
6. (2) $10a + 3 = 39$

Part B

Answers may vary slightly but should be similar to the ones below.

7. Twelve decreased by a number is five.
8. Five times a number is greater than twelve, or the product of five and a number is more than twelve.
9. Five less than twelve times a number is one.

Part C

10. (3) $x + 21 = 4$
11. (1) $2y + 49 = 15$
12. (3) $67 + 5m = 7$
13. (1) $80 + 3n = 5$
14. Discussion will vary. "Seven less than" suggests subtracting 7 from a number, as in $10 - 7$. "Seven is less than" suggests an inequality, as in $7 < 9$.

Unit 1 Review pp. 50–51

Part A

1. –84
2. –21
3. $\frac{3}{10}$
4. 11
5. 16
6. –35

Part B

7. (3) $8 \cdot 9 - 8 \cdot 1$
8. (1) $10c + 30$

Part C

9. $P = n - 6 + n - 6 + n - 6 + n - 6$

   $P = 4n - 24$

10. $P = a + a + 4 + a + a + 4$

   $P = 4a + 8$

Part D

11. $A = (m + 5)(m + 5) \ or \ (m + 5)^2$

   $A = (16 + 5)^2 = 21^2 =$ **441 square units**

12. $A = x(x + 8) \ or \ x^2 + 8x$

   $A = 15(15 + 8) = 15(23) =$ **345 square units**

Part E

13. 1.13×10^9
14. 142,000,000

Part F

15. **59°F**

   $F = \frac{9}{5}(15) + 32 = 27 + 32 = 59$

16. **–22°F**

   $F = \frac{9}{5}(-30) + 32 = -54 + 32 = -22$

17. **10°C**

   $C = \frac{5}{9}(50 - 32) = \frac{5}{9}(18) = 10$

18. **–5°C**

   $C = \frac{5}{9}(23 - 32) = \frac{5}{9}(-9) = -5$

19. $2a + 17 = 49$ *or* $49 - 17 = 2a$ *or* $49 - 2a = 17$

20. $m + 12 = 90$ *or* $90 - 12 = m$ *or* $90 - m = 12$

21. $7x + 3 = 80$ *or* $80 - 7x = 3$ *or* $80 - 3 = 7x$

Working Together

Answers will vary.

Unit 2

How Do I Use Algebra? p. 53

Talk About It

Answers will vary. Perhaps the easiest way to tell whether an item can be solved for one exact value is to use examples. For item 1, you could find the exact length of the rectangle if you knew the width. For item 2, you could find John's weight when he loses 15 pounds if you knew his current weight.

Solving Equations pp. 54–55

Part A

1. $m + 5 = 14$
$14 - 5 = m$
$m = 9$

2. $c + 18 = 25$
$25 - 18 = c$
$c = 7$

3. $y + 4 = 30$
$30 - 4 = y$
$y = 26$

Part B

4. $a = 2$
5. $y = 17$
6. $p = -12$
7. $50 = r$
8. $9 = m$

9. $-2 = s$
10. $v = 48$
11. $26 = c$
12. $n = 8$

Part C

13. $9w = 72$
$w = 8$

14. $3l = 45$
$l = 15$

15. $8l = 88$
$l = 11$

Part D

16. $4x = 20$
$x = 5$

17. $8y = 24$
$y = 3$

18. $32 = 12 + 9 + c$
$32 = 21 + c$
$11 = c$

19. Answers will vary.

Addition and Subtraction Equations pp. 56–57

Part A

1. $c = 120$

2. $w = -15$

3. $100 = u$

4. $\$19.65 = p$

5. $\$79.90 = t$

6. $d = 0.4$

Part B

7. $f + 94 = 284$
$f = 190$

8. $e + 14 = 40$
$e = 26$

Part C

9. $18.6 = a + 6.8 + 7.3$
$18.6 = a + 14.1$
$4.5 = a$

10. $22 = 4\frac{3}{4} + b + 7\frac{1}{4}$
$22 = 12 + b$
$10 = b$

11. $39.4 = 17.1 + 8.7 + c$
$39.4 = 25.8 + c$
$13.6 = c$

Part D

12. $w + \$1.25 = \$10.00$
$w = \$8.75$

13. $t - 6 = -5$
$t = +1°F$

14. $m + \$40 = \$150$
$m = \$110$

15. Yes. Adding (-7) gives the same result as subtracting 7. Discussion will vary.

Multiplication and Division Equations pp. 58–59

Part A

1. $a = 9$
2. $c = 45$
3. $d = -8$
4. $a = 74$
5. $e = -30$
6. $\frac{1}{2} = g$ *or* $0.5 = g$

7. $n = -72$
8. $w = -12$
9. $r = 4$
10. $r = 50$
11. $s = -1$
12. $6 = t$

Part B

13. $17.5 = 2.5l$

    $7 = l$

14. $70 = 14w$

    $5 = w$

15. $0.72 = 0.9w$

    $0.8 = w$

Part C

16. $9a = 90$

    $a = 10$

17. $8m - 3m = 45$

    $5m = 45$

    $m = 9$

18. $48 = 17c - c$

    $48 = 16c$

    $3 = c$

19. $10 = 7x + 13x$

    $10 = 20x$

    $\frac{1}{2} = x$

Making Connections: Unit Pricing p. 59

Corn Crunchies—0.118125 rounds up to $.12 per oz.

Fruity Flakes—0.10875 rounds up to $.11 per oz.

Bananas & Bran—0.1495 rounds up to $.15 per oz.

Mighty Mix—0.1291666 rounds up to $.13 per oz.

Fruity Flakes has the lowest unit price.

Equations and Multiple Operations pp. 60–61

Part A

1. $m = 6$
2. $r = 80$
3. $s = 4$
4. $a = 2$
5. $4 = n$
6. $2 = y$
7. $36 = b$
8. $10 = x$
9. $x = \frac{1}{2}$ or 0.5
10. $t = 8$
11. $r = -2$
12. $1 = a$

Part B

13. $2c + 9 = 41$

    $2c = 32$

    $c = 16$

14. $5a + 4 = 39$

    $5a = 35$

    $a = 7$

15. $4x + 3 = 55$

    $4x = 52$

    $x = 13$

Part C

16. $3m - 5 + 7m + 12 = 87$

    $10m + 7 = 87$

    $10m = 80$

    $m = 8$

17. $46 = x + 5 + 2x - 1 + 3x$

    $46 = 6x + 4$

    $42 = 6x$

    $7 = x$

18. $2a + 4 = 60$

    $2a = 56$

    $a = 28$ years

19. $\$60x + \$140 = \$500$

    $\$60x = \$360$

    $x = 6$ weeks

20. The solution is **$x = 31.$**

If you first subtract 51 from both sides, you get $-x = -31$. Since you are looking for x, not $-x$, multiply both sides of $-x = -31$ by -1. The result is **$x = 31.$**

You could also first subtract 20 from both sides. Then add x to both sides. Again the answer is **$x = 31$:**

$51 - x = 20$

$31 - x = 0$

$31 - x + x = 0 + x$

$31 = x$

Another way to solve the equation is to first add x to both sides. Then subtract 20 from both sides. Again the answer is **31.**

$51 - x = 20$

$51 - x + x = 20 + x$

$51 = 20 + x$

$51 - 20 = 20 + x - 20$

$31 = x$

In each case, two steps are required, and the solution is 31.

Simplifying Equations pp. 62–63

Part A

1. $c = -3$
2. $y = 4$
3. $a = 6$
4. $n = 3$
5. $30 = r$
6. $1 = p$
7. $8 = s$
8. $5 = w$
9. $b = -4$
10. $z = \frac{1}{2}$ or 0.5
11. $t = 6$
12. $e = 8$

Part B

13. $7p + 3 = 2p + 48$

$5p = 45$

$p = 9$

14. $4d + 1 = 2d + 21$

$2d = 20$

$d = 10$

Part C

15. $y = 7$

16. $m = 11$

17. $d = 6$

18. $s = 15$

19. $4 = w$

20. $1 = n$

21. $3 = p$

22. $2 = r$

Part D

23. $5(x + 4) = 85$

$5x + 20 = 85$

$5x = 65$

$x = 13$

24. a. $7a - 4 = 2a + 11$

$7a = 2a + 15$

$5a = 15$

$a = 3$

b. $7a - 4 = 2a + 11$

$7a - 15 = 2a$

$-15 = -5a$

$3 = a$

c. $7a - 4 = 2a + 11$

$5a - 4 = 11$

$5a = 15$

$a = 3$

d. $7a - 4 = 2a + 11$

$-4 = -5a + 11$

$-15 = -5a$

$3 = a$

e. Discussion will vary.

Using Substitution pp. 64–65

1. $5a - 12 = 43$

$5a = 55$

$a = 11$

2. $4s + 3(-3) = -1$

$4s - 9 = -1$

$4s = 8$

$s = 2$

3. $3x + x + y + 3x + x + y = 52$

$4x + 10 + 4x + 10 = 52$

$8x + 20 = 52$

$8x = 32$

$x = 4$

$l = 4 + 10 = 14$

$w = 3(4) = 12$

Part B

4. $9m - 4 = 68$

$9m = 72$

$m = 8$

$t = 2(8) = 16$

5. $17 = \frac{1}{2}r + 11$

$6 = \frac{1}{2}r$

$12 = r$

$s = 3(12) = 36$

6. $4(n - 6) = 20$

$n - 6 = 5$

$n = 11$

$p = 7(11) = 77$

Part C

7. $2(2s + 1) + 5s = 29$

$4s + 2 + 5s = 29$

$9s = 27$

$s = 3$

$r = 2(3) + 1 = 6 + 1 = 7$

8. $3c - 2(c - 3) = 14$

$3c - 2c + 6 = 14$

$c = 8$

$d = 8 - 3 = 5$

9. $5p + 4(2p + 5) = 98$

$5p + 8p + 20 = 98$

$13p = 78$

$p = 6$

$t = 2(6) + 5 = 12 + 5 = 17$

10. $2(b + 3) + 5b = -22$

$2b + 6 + 5b = -22$

$7b = -28$

$b = -4$

$a = -4 + 3 = -1$

Making Connections: Formulas as Equations p. 65

1. $c = nr$

$\frac{c}{n} = \frac{nr}{n}$

$\frac{c}{n} = r$

2. $P = 4s$

$\frac{P}{4} = \frac{4s}{4}$

$\frac{P}{4} = s$

3. $A = lw$

$\frac{A}{w} = \frac{lw}{w}$

$\frac{A}{w} = l$

4. $A = s^2$

$\sqrt{A} = s$

Using Formulas pp. 66–67

1. $P = 2l + 2w$

$P - 2w = 2l$

$\frac{P - 2w}{2} = l$

$l = \frac{P - 2w}{2} = \frac{17 - 2(3.5)}{2} = \frac{17 - 7}{2} = \frac{10}{2} = 5$

2. $c = nr$

$r = \frac{c}{n} = \frac{\$156}{20} = \$7.80$

3. $\frac{a + b + c + d}{4} = m$

$a + b + c + d = 4m$

$d = 4m - a - b - c$

$d = 4(80) - 74 - 92 - 75$

$d = 320 - 241$

$d = 79$

4. $F = \frac{9}{5}C + 32$

$F - 32 = \frac{9}{5}C$

$\frac{5}{9}(F - 32) = C$

$C = \frac{5}{9}(F - 32) = \frac{5}{9}(104 - 32) = \frac{5}{9}(72) = 40°C$

5. $d = rt$

$t = \frac{d}{r}$

$t = \frac{18}{3} = 6$

$6 + 1\frac{1}{2} = 7\frac{1}{2}$ **hours**

6. $i = prt$

$r = \frac{i}{pt}$

$r = \frac{216}{3,600 \cdot 1} = 0.06 = 6\%$

7. $P = a + b + c$

$c = P - a - b$

$c = 22 - 7 - 8$

$c = 22 - 15 = 7$

8. $c = nr$

$n = \frac{c}{r}$

$n = \frac{\$100}{\$11.99} = 8.34$ or **8 CDs**

9. The inverse of raising a number to the second power is finding the square root. $s = \sqrt{A}$; $\sqrt{196} = 14$

Solving Inequalities pp. 68–69

Part A

1. $x < 1$

2. $n > 20$

3. $a \geq 7$

4. $m < 13$

5. $2 > c$

6. $10 \leq y$

Part B

7. $x \leq 4$

    (1) –3

    (2) 0

    (3) 2

    (4) 4

8. $x > 12$

    (4) 14

    (5) 20

    (6) 25

Part C

9. $2x + 3 < 13$

$2x < 10$

$x < 5$

10. $3m + 5 < 23$

$3m < 18$

$m < 6$

11. $a + 7 + a + 4 < 17$

$2a + 11 < 17$

$2a < 6$

$a < 3$

Part D

12. $n < 43$

13. $n < 8$

14. $5n - 43$

15. $5n - 37$

16. $n < 11$

17. $5n - 55$

Part E

18. $20w > 100$

$w > 5$

6 is the smallest whole number for which the inequality is true.

19. **(3)** $360 \leq x \leq 840$

30% of $1,200 = .3(1,200) = 360$

70% of $1,200 = .7(1,200) = 840$

20. **a.** $5 < 9$ is true.

    b. $-1 < 3$ is true.

    c. $18 < 42$ is true.

    d. $-6 < -14$ is not true.

Remember that if you multiply any inequality by a negative number, you should reverse the direction of the inequality sign. When you multiply $3 < 7$ by -2, you should get $-6 > -14$.

Mixed Review pp. 70–71

Part A

1. $g + 27 = 63$

   $g = \mathbf{36}$

2. $b + 11.4 = 70.1$

   $b = \mathbf{58.7}$

3. $c + 19.3 = 40$

   $c = \mathbf{20.7}$

4. $3(a + 3) = 60$

   $3a + 9 = 60$

   $3a = 51$

   $a = \mathbf{17}$

5. $9c + 16 = 2c + 72$

   $7c = 56$

   $c = \mathbf{8}$

6. $3x + 12 = 40 + x$

   $2x = 28$

   $x = \mathbf{14}$

Part B

7. $18.6 = m - 3.4$

   $\mathbf{22 = m}$

8. $8x = -6$

   $x = -\frac{3}{4}$ or $\mathbf{-0.75}$

9. $\frac{c}{3} = -1.1$

   $c = \mathbf{-3.3}$

10. $7s - s - 3 = 27$

    $6s = 30$

    $s = \mathbf{5}$

11. $5a - 1 = -21$

    $5a = -20$

    $a = \mathbf{-4}$

12. $19 = \frac{a}{2} + 13$

    $6 = \frac{a}{2}$

    $\mathbf{12 = a}$

13. $2(w - 1) + 9 = 5$

    $2w - 2 + 9 = 5$

    $2w + 7 = 5$

    $2w = -2$

    $w = \mathbf{-1}$

14. $6e + 5 = 2e + 13$

    $4e = 8$

    $e = \mathbf{2}$

15. $y + 9 = 5(y - 3)$

    $y + 9 = 5y - 15$

    $24 = 4y$

    $\mathbf{6 = y}$

Part C

16. $12(m + 8) = 216$

    $12m + 96 = 216$

    $12m = 120$

    $m = 10$

    $l = 10 + 8 = \mathbf{18}$

17. $2x + x + 5 + x + 6 = 47$

    $4x + 11 = 47$

    $4x = 36$

    $x = 9$

    Sides are $2(9) = \mathbf{18}$; $9 + 5 = \mathbf{14}$; and $9 + 6 = \mathbf{15}$.

18. $9x - y = -17$

    $9x - 8 = -17$

    $9x = -9$

    $x = \mathbf{-1}$

19. $3d - 13 = 23$

    $3d = 36$

    $d = \mathbf{12}$

    $e = \frac{2}{3}(12) = \mathbf{8}$

20. $4m + 5n = 57$

    $4m + 5(2m + 3) = 57$

    $4m + 10m + 15 = 57$

    $14m = 42$

    $m = \mathbf{3}$

    $n = 2(3) + 3 = 6 + 3 = \mathbf{9}$

21. $t = \frac{i}{pr} = \frac{296}{(1{,}850 \cdot .08)} = \frac{296}{148} = \mathbf{2\ years}$

22. $3 \cdot m = \frac{a + b + c}{3} \cdot 3$

    $3m = a + b + c$

    $3m - a - b = c$

    $3(100) - 74 - 110 = 300 - 184 = \mathbf{\$116}$

23. $\frac{9}{5}C = \frac{5}{9}(F - 32) \cdot \frac{9}{5}$

$\frac{9}{5}C = F - 32$

$\frac{9}{5}C + 32 = F$

$\frac{9}{5}(60) + 32 = 108 + 32 = \mathbf{140°F}$

24. $r = \frac{c}{n} = \frac{\$12.25}{2.5} = \mathbf{\$4.90 \ per \ pound}$

25. $t = \frac{d}{r} = \frac{22}{4} = \mathbf{5\frac{1}{2} \ hours} \ or \ \mathbf{5.5 \ hours}$

Part D

26. $\frac{1}{4}x - 7 > 3$

$\frac{1}{4}x > 10$

$\mathbf{x > 40}$

27. $-9 < 2x - 1$

$-8 < 2x$

$\mathbf{-4 < x}$

28. $3(p - 2) \le -30$

$3p - 6 \le -30$

$3p \le -24$

$\mathbf{p \le -8}$

29. $19 \ge 10c + 3 - 2c$

$19 \ge 8c + 3$

$16 \ge 8c$

$\mathbf{2 \ge c}$

Part E

30. $2c + 9 < 43$

$2c < 34$

$\mathbf{c < 17}$

31. $12l > 192$

$l > 16$

The smallest whole number for l is 17.

Lists and Diagrams pp. 72–73

Part A

1. a. n

b. $n + 6$

c. $n - 3$

d. $2(n + 6)$

e. $n + n + 6 \ or \ 2n + 6$

f. $n + 6 - n \ or \ 6$

2. a. x

b. $4x$

c. $x + 4x \ or \ 5x$

d. $x + 5$

e. $4x - 9$

f. $3(4x) \ or \ 12x$

Part B

3.

	Anna	Luba
age now	x	x + 3
age last year	x − 1	(x − 1) + 3
age in 10 years	x + 10	x + 3 + 10 or x + 13
age y years ago	x − y	x + 3 − y

4.

	Juan	Sara
age now	2x	x
age in 6 years	2x + 6	x + 6
age 2 years ago	2x − 2	x − 2
age y years ago	2x − y	x − y

5.

	Tom	Linda
age now	x	40 − x
age next year	x + 1	40 − x + 1 or 41 − x
age 4 years ago	x − 4	40 − x − 4 or 36 − x
age in y years	x + y	40 − x + y

6.

	Alma	Tony
age now	x + 23	x
age 5 years ago	x + 23 − 5 or x + 18	x − 5
age in y years	x + 23 + y	x + y
age z years ago	x + 23 − z	x − z

Part C

7. $5n$

8. $25q$

9. $50h$

10. $10x$

11. $20y$

12. $100z$

Part D

13. c

14. b

15. d

16. Answers will vary. For the arrows in illustration a, two travelers start from the same spot, head off in opposite directions, and then both turn around and head back to their starting point.

Algebra Word Problems pp. 74–77

Part A

Note: You may have used different approaches than the ones shown here. However, you should have gotten the same pairs of numbers for problems 1 and 2 and the same answers for problems 3 and 4.

1. **a.** (2) x and $21 - x$

   b. smaller number $= x$

   larger number $= 21 - x$

   $3x = 21 - x - 1$

   $4x = 20$

   $x = \mathbf{5}$

   $21 - x = 21 - 5 = \mathbf{16}$

   If $x =$ larger number and $21 - x =$ smaller number, $x = 16$ and $21 - x = 21 - 16 = 5$.

2. **a.** (3) x and $100 - x$

   b. $2x = 3(100 - x)$

   $2x = 300 - 3x$

   $5x = 300$

   $x = \mathbf{60}$

   $100 - x = 100 - 60 = \mathbf{40}$

3. Rosie's hourly wage $= x$

   Carlos's hourly wage $= 4x - 1$

   $8(x + 4x - 1) = 232$

   $8x + 32x - 8 = 232$

   $40x = 240$

   $x = 6$

   Rosie's wage is **$6**.

   Carlos gets $4(6) - 1 = 24 - 1 = \mathbf{\$23}$.

4. Gus's gas $= x$

   Antonio's gas $= x + 1$

   Sam's gas $= 2(x + 1)$

   $x + x + 1 + 2(x + 1) = 39$

   $2x + 1 + 2x + 2 = 39$

   $4x + 3 = 39$

   $4x = 36$

   $x = 9$

   Gus's gas $= x = \mathbf{9\ gallons}$

   Antonio's gas $= x + 1 = 9 + 1 = \mathbf{10\ gallons}$

   Sam's gas $= 2(x + 1) = 2(9 + 1) = \mathbf{20\ gallons}$

Part B

5. **a.**

	age now	age in 9 years
Greg	x	x + 9
Dorothy	3x + 2	3x + 2 + 9 or 3x + 11

b. $x + 9 + 3x + 2 + 9 = 60$

$4x + 20 = 60$

$4x = 40$

$x = 10$

Greg is **10**.

Dorothy is $3(10) + 2 = \mathbf{32}$.

c. In 9 years, Greg will be $10 + 9 = \mathbf{19}$, and Dorothy will be $32 + 9 = \mathbf{41}$.

d. The sum of their ages in 9 years will be $19 + 41 = \mathbf{60}$.

6.

	age now	age 8 years ago
Annabel	x	x − 8
Laurie	34 − x	34 − x − 8 or 26 − x

$x - 8 = \frac{1}{2}(34 - x - 8)$

$x - 8 = \frac{1}{2}(26 - x)$

$2(x - 8) = 26 - x$

$2x - 16 = 26 - x$

$3x = 42$

$x = 14$

Annabel is **14**.

Laurie is $34 - 14 = \mathbf{20}$.

7.

	age now	age x years ago
Gordons' house	35	35 − x
Romans' house	25	25 − x

$35 - x = 2(25 - x)$

$35 - x = 50 - 2x$

$2x + 35 - x = 50 - 2x + 2x$

$x + 35 - 35 = 50 - 35$

$x = \mathbf{15\ years\ ago}$

8.

	years on job now	years on job in 2 years
Cal	x	x + 2
Phil	x + 6	x + 6 + 2 or x + 8

$x + 2 + x + 6 + 2 = 50$

$2x + 10 = 50$

$2x = 40$

$x = 20$

Cal has worked **20 years** at the shop. Phil has worked $20 + 6 = \mathbf{26\ years}$ at the shop.

Part C

9. **a.** $d = 45t$

    ⟶

    $d = 55t$

    ⟶

  b. The distance between them is the difference between $55t$ (Dave's distance) and $45t$ (Frank's distance).

    $55t - 45t = d$

  c. $55t - 45t = d$

    $10t = 25$

    $t = 2\frac{1}{2}$ **hours** *or* **2.5 hours**

10.   Jed Alicia

    ⟵ • ⟶

  Jed drives $d = rt$.

  Alicia drives $d = (r + 10)t$.

  The distance between them is the sum of the two distances.

  $rt + (r + 10)t = 318$

  $3r + (r + 10)3 = 318$

  $3r + 3r + 30 = 318$

  $6r = 288$

  $r = 48$

  Jed's rate = **48 miles per hour**

  Alicia's rate = 48 + 10 = **58 miles per hour**

11.

By 10:00 both have gone $16 \cdot 1 = 16$ miles.

By 11:00 both have gone $16 \cdot 2 = 32$ miles.

By noon each has gone another 16 miles, but in opposite directions.

At noon they are $16 + 16 = $ **32 miles apart.**

Part D

12. **a.** **(4)** $9 - q$ **c.** **(2)** 135

    b. **(1)** $25q$ **d.** number of quarters = q

                          number of dimes = $9 - q$

                          $25q + 10(9 - q) = 135$

                          $25q + 90 - 10q = 135$

                          $15q = 45$

                          $q = 3$

                        Mark has **3 quarters.**

                        Mark has $9 - 3 = $ **6 dimes.**

13. number of quarters = q

    number of nickels = $12 - q$

    $25q + 5(12 - q) = 160$

    $25q + 60 - 5q = 160$

    $20q = 100$

    $q = 5$

    She used **5 quarters** and $12 - 5 = $ **7 nickels.**

    (You may have used a different approach to solve this problem, but you should have gotten the same answer.)

14. number of nickels = n

    number of quarters = $2n$

    number of dimes = $3n$

    $5n + 25(2n) + 10(3n) = 340$

    $5n + 50n + 30n = 340$

    $85n = 340$

    $n = 4$

    Al has **4 nickels,** $2(4) = $ **8 quarters,** and $3(4) = $ **12 dimes.**

15. number of $10 bills = n

    number of $5 bills = $3n$

    number of $20 bills = $2n - 1$

    $5(3n) + 10n + 20(2n - 1) = 175$

    $15n + 10n + 40n - 20 = 175$

    $65n = 195$

    $n = 3$

    She deposited **3 $10 bills,** $3(3) = $ **9 $5 bills,** and $2(3) - 1 = $ **5 $20 bills.**

16. **Answers will vary.**

Percents and Equations pp. 78–79

Part A

1. $\frac{1}{4}(80) = x$

    $20 = x$

    x represents the **part.**

2. $\frac{1}{2}n = 16$

    $n = 32$

    n represents the **whole.**

3. $300p = 120$

    $p = \frac{120}{300} = \frac{2}{5} = .40 = $ **40%**

    p represents the **percent.**

4. $\frac{1}{3}(45) = y$

   15 = y

   y represents the **part**.

5. $64p = 48$

   $p = \frac{48}{64} = \frac{3}{4} = \textbf{75\%}$

   p represents the **percent**.

6. $.2c = 30$

   c = 150

   c represents the **whole**.

7. $170p = 17$

   $p = \frac{17}{170} = \frac{1}{10} = \textbf{10\%}$

   p represents the **percent**.

8. $.06(400) = t$

   24 = t

   t represents the **part**.

9. $.3w = 75$

   w = 250

   w represents the **whole**.

Part B

10. **(3)** $d + .06d$

11. $c = d + .06d$

    $\$25.44 = d + .06d$

    $\$25.44 = 1.06d$

    \$24 = d

12. **a.** $\$12h + .1t$

    b. $\$12(8) + .1(\$780) = \$96 + \$78 = \textbf{\$174}$

    c. $\$12(8) + .1t = \$300$

    $\$96 + .1t = \$300$

    $.1t = \$204$

    t = \$2,040

    d. $\$12h + .1(\$5,400) = \$960$

    $\$12h + \$540 = \$960$

    $\$12h = \$420$

    h = 35 hours

13. The area of the patio now is $40 \times 20 = 800$ square units.

    The new area should be $800 + .6(800) = 800 + 480 = 1,280$ square units.

    The new length should be $1,280 = 20l$

    $64 = l$

    The length of the extension will be $64 - 40 = \textbf{24.}$

    (You may have used a different approach to solve this problem, but you should have gotten the same answer.)

14. **a.** $c = p - .3p$

    b. $c = \$94 - .3(\$94)$

    $c = \$94 - \$28.20$

    c = \$65.80

15. If s is the supplier's price, the price p that Sabrina charges her customers is $p = s + .4s \; or \; p = 1.4s$

    $\$28 = 1.4s$

    \$20 = s

16. Answers will vary, but it is unusual to find more than 50% off. "100% off" would mean that the entire price was taken off—in other words, the item was free. "110% off" might mean that you would be paid to take the item.

Using Ratio pp. 80–81

Part A

1. won:lost = $8:6 = \textbf{4:3}$

2. Total number played is $8 + 6 = 14$.

   won:played = $8:14 = \textbf{4:7}$

3. Marla:Sandra = $\$1,000:\$750 = \textbf{4:3}$

4. food:pay = $350:2,100 = \textbf{1:6}$

Part B

5. $l:w = \textbf{17:4}$

6. $a:b:c = \textbf{6:9:10}$

7. $l:w = \textbf{11.2:3.1}$

Part C

8. number of men $= 3x$

   number of women $= 4x$

   $3x + 4x = 56$

   $7x = 56$

   $x = 8$

   number of women $= 4(8) = \textbf{32}$

9. Al:Boris:Cassidy $= \$2,000:\$5,000:\$8,000 = 2:5:8$

   Al's share $= 2x$

   Boris's share $= 5x$

   Cassidy's share $= 8x$

   $2x + 5x + 8x = \$4,500$

   $15x = \$4,500$

   $x = \$300$

   Boris gets $5(\$300) = \textbf{\$1,500}$

10. length $= 3x$

width $= 2x$

$P = 2l + 2w$

$200 = 2(3x) + 2(2x)$

$200 = 6x + 4x$

$200 = 10x$

$20 = x$

length $= 3(20) =$ **60**

width $= 2(20) =$ **40**

Making Connections: Population Density p. 81

X Town $\frac{150 \text{ people}}{\text{square mile}}$

Y County $\frac{96.7 \text{ people}}{\text{square mile}}$

NY City $\frac{23,624.6 \text{ people}}{\text{square mile}}$

U.S. $\frac{71.4 \text{ people}}{\text{square mile}}$

Using Proportion pp. 82–83

Part A

1. $6x = 90$

   $x =$ **15**

2. $4a = 36$

   $a =$ **9**

3. $2c = 56$

   $c =$ **28**

4. $m =$ **45**

5. $5w = 24$

   $w = 4\frac{4}{5}$

6. $y =$ **14**

7. $3n = 10$

   $n = 3\frac{1}{3}$

8. $7r = 24$

   $r = 3\frac{3}{7}$

9. $10e = 84$

   $e = 8\frac{2}{5}$

Part B

10. $\frac{9}{12} = \frac{36}{l}$

    $9l = 432$

    $l =$ **48**

11. $\frac{4}{15} = \frac{w}{60}$

    $15w = 240$

    $w =$ **16**

12. $\frac{10}{18} = \frac{90}{l}$

    $10l = 1,620$

    $l =$ **162**

Part C

13. $\frac{\text{sugar}}{\text{flour}} \quad \frac{2}{3} = \frac{6}{x}$

    $2x = 18$

    $x =$ **9 cups of flour**

14. $5 + 3 = 8$

    $\frac{\text{in favor}}{\text{total}} \quad \frac{5}{8} = \frac{x}{400}$

    $8x = 2,000$

    $x =$ **250 in favor**

15. $\frac{\text{inches}}{\text{miles}} \quad \frac{1}{15} = \frac{2.5}{x}$

    $x =$ **37.5 miles**

16. Answers will vary.

Different Ways to Solve Problems pp. 84–85

1. **a.** Bill's amount $= x$

   Fred's amount $= 3x$

   $x + 3x = 80,000$

   $4x = 80,000$

   $x = 20,000$

   Bill gets **\$20,000.**

   Fred gets $3(20,000) =$ **\$60,000.**

   b. Bill:Fred $= 1:3$

   total: $1 + 3 = 4$

   $\frac{\text{Bill}}{\text{total}} \quad \frac{1}{4} = \frac{x}{80,000}$

   $4x = 80,000$

   $x = 20,000$

   Bill gets **\$20,000.**

   Fred gets $80,000 - 20,000 =$ **\$60,000.**

2. **a.** $r = \frac{d}{t} = \frac{156}{3} = 52$ miles per hour

   $d = rt = 52 \cdot 10 =$ **520 miles**

   b. $\frac{\text{miles}}{\text{hours}} \quad \frac{156}{3} = \frac{x}{10}$

   $3x = 1,560$

   $x =$ **520 miles**

3. **a.** $r = \frac{c}{n} = \frac{\$32.50}{5} = \$6.50$ per pound

   $c = nr = 18 \cdot \$6.50 =$ **\$117**

   b. $\frac{\text{cost}}{\text{weight}} \quad \frac{\$32.50}{5} = \frac{x}{18}$

   $5x = 585$

   $x =$ **\$117**

4. **a.**

   Mike: $d = rt = 15 \cdot 4 = 60$ miles

   Nick: $d = rt = 55 \cdot 4 = 220$ miles

   The distance between them is $220 - 60 =$ **160 miles.**

   b. In 1 hour they are $55 - 15 = 40$ miles apart.

   $\frac{\text{miles apart}}{\text{hours}} \quad \frac{40}{1} = \frac{x}{4}$

   $x =$ **160 miles**

5. a. $\frac{1{,}050 \text{ bushels}}{30 \text{ acres}} = 35$ bushels per acre

   100 acres $\cdot \frac{35 \text{ bushels}}{\text{acre}} = $ **3,500 bushels**

   b. $\frac{\text{bushels}}{\text{acres}}$ $\frac{1{,}050}{30} = \frac{x}{100}$

   $30x = 105{,}000$

   $x = $ **3,500 bushels**

6. a. $A = lw = 25 \cdot 16 = 400$

   For the square $s^2 = 400$

   $s = \sqrt{400}$

   $s = $ **20**

   b. $lw = s^2$

   $25 \cdot 16 = s^2$

   $400 = s^2$

   $\sqrt{400} = s$

   20 $= s$

7. a. $\frac{\text{miles}}{\text{inches}}$ $\frac{150}{2.5} = \frac{x}{1}$

   $2.5x = 150$

   $x = 60$

   The scale is **1 inch = 60 miles.**

   b. Each $\frac{1}{2}$ inch is $\frac{150}{5} = 30$ miles.

   $1\frac{1}{2}$ inches is $3(30) = $ **90 miles.**

8. a. One person gets x.

   The other person gets $4x$.

   $x + 4x = 50$

   $5x = 50$

   $x = 10$

   One person gets **10 pounds.**

   The other person gets $4(10) = $ **40 pounds.**

   b. $4 + 1 = 5$

   $\frac{\text{larger share}}{\text{total}}$ $\frac{4}{5} = \frac{x}{50}$

   $5x = 200$

   $x = 40$

   The larger share is **40 pounds.**

   The smaller share is $50 - 40 = $ **10 pounds.**

9. a. $\frac{\$120}{8 \text{ hours}} = \frac{\$15}{\text{hour}}$

   In 20 hours he gets $15 \cdot 20 = $ **\$300.**

   b. $\frac{\text{money}}{\text{hours}}$ $\frac{120}{8} = \frac{x}{20}$

   $8x = 2{,}400$

   $x = $ **\$300**

10. a. $\frac{\text{taxes}}{\text{assessed value}} = \frac{3{,}000}{120{,}000} = \frac{\$0.025}{\$1 \text{ assessed value}}$ *or* $\frac{\$25}{\$1{,}000 \text{ assessed value}}$

   $0.025(\$85{,}000) = $ **\$2,125** *or* $25(\$85) = $ **\$2,125**

   b. $\frac{\text{taxes}}{\text{assessed value}}$ $\frac{3{,}000}{120{,}000} = \frac{x}{85{,}000}$

   $120{,}000x = 255{,}000{,}000$

   $x = $ **\$2,125**

Unit 2 Review pp. 86–87

Part A

1. $\frac{2}{3}c = 24$

   $c = $ **36**

2. $30.2 = m + 4.9$

   25.3 $= m$

3. $\frac{x}{4} = -12$

   $x = $ **−48**

4. $a - 9.6 = -5$

   $a = $ **4.6**

5. $7n + 12 = 5$

   $7n = -7$

   $n = $ **−1**

6. $3 = \frac{1}{2}w - 9$

   $12 = \frac{1}{2}w$

   24 $= w$

7. $4(p + 3) = 20$

   $4p + 12 = 20$

   $4p = 8$

   $p = $ **2**

8. $9y + 5 = 3y - 19$

   $6y = -24$

   $y = $ **−4**

9. $8p - p = 17 + 18$

   $7p = 35$

   $p = $ **5**

10. $3d - 2 \leq 19$

   $3d \leq 21$

   $d \leq $ **7**

11. $2(b - 6) > 4$

   $2b - 12 > 4$

   $2b > 16$

   $b > $ **8**

12. $3 < r + 5$

   −2 $< r$

Part B

13. $3(x + 1) + 4 = 40$

   $3x + 3 + 4 = 40$

   $3x + 7 = 40$

   $3x = 33$

   $x = $ **11**

14. $3c + 26 = 74$

   $3c = 48$

   $c = $ **16**

Part C

15. $3a + 2(5a + 1) = 41$

   $3a + 10a + 2 = 41$

   $13a = 39$

   $a = $ **3**

16. $d = 4m - a - b - c$

$d = 4(200) - 163 - 191 - 212$

$d = 800 - 566$

$d = \mathbf{234}$

17. **(3) 3:2**

Kate's age:Sophie's age $= 60{:}40 = 3{:}2$

18. 90 minutes is $\frac{90}{60} = 1\frac{1}{2}$ hours.

Andrea: $d = 60 \cdot 1\frac{1}{2}$

Tomás: $d = 40 \cdot 1\frac{1}{2}$

The distance between them is the difference in the distances that they drive.

$d = 60 \cdot 1\frac{1}{2} - 40 \cdot 1\frac{1}{2}$

$d = 90 - 60 = \mathbf{30\ miles}$

19. The area of the deck now is $18 \cdot 15 = 270$ square feet.

After the new section is built, the area will be $270 + .4(270) = 270 + 108 = 378$.

If the measurement of the other side is l, $378 = 18l$.

21 feet $= l$

20. $2 + 3 = 5$

$\frac{\text{owners}}{\text{total}}\quad \frac{3}{5} = \frac{x}{420}$

$5x = 1{,}260$

$x = \mathbf{252\ owners}$

21. **(4)** $7 - q$

Working Together

Answers will vary.

Unit 3

How Do I Recognize Geometry? p. 89

Talk About It

Answers will vary.

Points, Lines, and Angles pp. 90–91

Part A

1. (2)   2. (2)   3. (1)

Part B

4. c

   a

   b

5. Angle a is the smallest, because the amount of rotation of the sides is least. (*Note:* The length of the sides has nothing to do with the size of the angle. In fact, angle b is the largest.)

6. a. acute   **d.** obtuse

   b. right   **e.** straight

   c. acute

Protractors pp. 92–93

Part A

1. c

   b

   d

   a

Part B

2. $\angle WYZ = 135° - 49° = \mathbf{86°}$

3. **$\angle AOD$ is an obtuse angle of 115°.**

$25° + 30° + 60° = 115°$

$\angle BOD$ is a right angle of 90°.

$30° + 60° = 90°$

$\angle AOC$ is an acute angle of 55°.

$25° + 30° = 55°$

4. Let x represent $\angle$b and $2x$ represent $\angle$a.

$x + 2x = 126$

$3x = 126$

$x = \mathbf{42°} = \mathbf{\angle b}$

$\mathbf{\angle a = 2(42) = 84°}$

5. Each hour represents $\frac{1}{12}$ of 360° or 30°. Or think about 15 minutes after the hour: $90° \div 3 = 30°$ for each hour mark.

a. 2:00 has $2(30) = \mathbf{60°}$.

b. 3:00 has $3(30) = \mathbf{90°}$.

c. 5:00 has $5(30) = \mathbf{150°}$.

d. 6:00 has $6(30) = \mathbf{180°}$.

6. At 12:30, the hour hand of the clock is halfway between 12:00 and 1:00, and the minute hand is at 6:00. The hands are open to $5\frac{1}{2}(30) = 165°$.

Pairs of Angles pp. 94–95

Part A

1. **a.** 69°   **c.** 45°   **e.** 85.5°

   b. 1°   **d.** 82°

2. a. 159°

  b. 30°

  c. 135°

  d. 89°

  e. 64.5°

Part B

3. a. $\angle$s

  b. $\angle$n and $\angle$r

  c. $\angle$n = 68°, $\angle$s = 112°, and $\angle$r = 68°

4. supplementary

5. equal

6. a. $\angle$BOA or $\angle$AOB

  b. $\angle$COA or $\angle$AOC

Making Connections: Understanding Street Patterns p. 95

1. $\angle$c and $\angle$g

2. $\angle$b, $\angle$d, $\angle$f, and $\angle$h

3. $\angle$f, $\angle$d, and $\angle$b

Rulers, Yardsticks, and Tape Measures pp. 96–97

1. a. $2\frac{1}{4}$ inches

  b. $1\frac{7}{8}$ inches

  c. 4.5 centimeters

  d. 3.2 centimeters

2. x = part underground; $6x$ = part above ground

$x + 6x = 56$

$7x = 56$

$x =$ **8 feet underground**

You can also solve the problem using ratio and proportion:

$\frac{6}{1} = \frac{56 - x}{x}$

$6x = 56 - x$

$7x = 56$

$x =$ **8 feet underground**

3. Answers may vary, but they should be close to $6\frac{1}{2}$ inches.

4. $3x + 4x + 5x = 96$

$12x = 96$

$x = 8$ cm

The smallest side is $3(8) =$ **24 centimeters.**

The next longest side is $4(8) =$ **32 centimeters.**

The longest side is $5(8) =$ **40 centimeters.**

5. Let x = width and $4x$ = length.

$2(x) + 2(4x) = 120$

$2x + 8x = 120$

$10x = 120$

$x = 12$ ft.

The length is $4x = 4(12) =$ **48 feet**

6. Answers may vary.

  a. inches or centimeters

  b. feet or yards or meters

  c. inches or feet or meters

  d. miles or kilometers

Changing Units of Measure pp. 98–99

Part A

1. a. smaller to larger; 48 in. = $48\left(\frac{1}{12}\text{ ft.}\right) =$ **4 feet**

  b. larger to smaller; 2 mi. = 2(5,280 ft.) = **10,560 feet**

  c. larger to smaller; 20 yd. = 20(3 ft.) = **60 feet**

  d. smaller to larger; 9 in. = $9\left(\frac{1}{12}\text{ ft.}\right) = \frac{3}{4}$ **foot**

  e. larger to smaller; $1\frac{1}{2}$ yd. = $1\frac{1}{2}(3\text{ ft.}) = 4\frac{1}{2}$ **feet**

Part B

2. a. 75 cm = 75(0.01 m) = **0.75 meter**

  b. 2 km = 2(1,000 m) = **2,000 meters**

  c. 875 mm = 875(0.001 m) = **0.875 meter**

  d. 105 cm = 105(0.01 m) = **1.05 meters**

  e. 20 cm = 20(0.01 m) = **0.2 meter**

Part C

3. a. $P = 2(12) + 2(10)$

    $= 24 + 20$

    $=$ **44 inches**

  b. 44 in. = $44\left(\frac{1}{12}\text{ ft.}\right) = 3\frac{2}{3}$ **feet**

  c. 44 in. = 44(2.54 cm) = **111.76 centimeters**

4. 100 yd. $\approx$ 100(0.914 m) = **91.4 meters**

5. a. 70 in. = 70(2.54 cm) = **177.8 centimeters**

  b. 177.8 cm = 177.8(0.01 m) = **1.778 meters**

  c. 70 in. = $\frac{70}{12} =$ **5 feet 10 inches**

6. A 5-mile run is longer because a mile is greater than a kilometer. Therefore, it would take more kilometers to represent the same distance in miles.

Making Connections: Converting Metric to English p. 99

$1 \text{ cm} \approx \dfrac{1}{3} \text{ in.}$
$1 \text{ cm} \approx \dfrac{1}{30} \text{ ft.}$
$1 \text{ m} \approx 1 \text{ yd.}$
$1 \text{ km} \approx \dfrac{1}{2} \text{ mi.}$

1. $7{,}420 \text{ km} \approx 7{,}420 \left(\frac{1}{2} \text{ mi.}\right) = \textbf{3,710 miles}$

2. $90 \text{ cm} \approx 90 \left(\frac{1}{3} \text{ in.}\right) = \textbf{30 inches}$

Mixed Review pp. 100–101

Part A

1. a. **(3)** perpendicular
   b. **(2)** right
2. a. **(2)** right
   b. **(3)** perpendicular
3. **(3)** horizontal and parallel
4. **(1)** acute

Part B

5. 55°; acute
6. 130°; obtuse

Part C

7. 77°; acute
8. right (The measurement is 90°.)
9. 135°; obtuse

Part D

10. 90°
11. **63.5°**
    $90° - 26.5° = 63.5°$
12. **51°**
    $180° - 129° = 51°$

Part E

13. $\angle g$
14. $\angle e$ and $\angle g$
15. a. **44°**
    $180° - 136° = 44°$
    b. **136°**
    Vertical angles are equal.

Part F

16. 3 centimeters
17. 2.5 centimeters
18. $P = 2(2.5) + 2(3)$
    $= 5 + 6$
    $= \textbf{11 centimeters}$

Part G

19. $2.5(2.54 \text{ cm}) = \textbf{6.35 centimeters}$
20. $2{,}900(1.6 \text{ km}) = \textbf{4,640 kilometers}$

Properties of Quadrilaterals pp. 102–103

Part A

1. ZY *or* YZ
2. XY and WZ
3. XZ and WY
4. Y

Part B

5. a. rectangle
   b. trapezoid
   c. square
   d. parallelogram

Part C

6. Since a rectangle has 4 right angles, the sum of the angles is $4(90°) = \textbf{360°.}$

7. a. square, rectangle, rhombus, and parallelogram
   b. square and rectangle
   c. square, rectangle, rhombus, and parallelogram
   d. square and rhombus

8. $5x + 6x + 4x + 9x = 72$
   $24x = 72$
   $x = 3$
   $AD = 9(3) = \textbf{27}$

9. a. rhombus
   b. $P = 5 + 5 + 5 + 5 = \textbf{20 inches}$ *or* $4(5) = \textbf{20 inches}$
   c. If angle P gets smaller, the perimeter stays the same.

10. a. Yes, a rectangle is also a parallelogram, because a rectangle has opposite sides equal and two pairs of parallel sides.
    b. Yes, a square is also a rhombus, because a square has four equal sides and opposite sides parallel.

11. Answers will vary. Some windowpanes and the notes included in compact disks are squares. Sunlight shining through windows often makes parallelograms on floors. A diamond on a playing card is sometimes a rhombus.

Properties of Circles pp. 104–105

Part A

1. diameter
2. radius
3. 10 inches
4. 13 centimeters

Part B

5. $d = 2r$

6. $r = \frac{d}{2}$ or $r = \frac{1}{2}d$

7. $\pi = \frac{C}{d}$

8. Since $d = 2r$, $C = 2\pi r$ or $2r\pi$.

Part C

9. $C = \pi d$

   $C = 3.14(10)$

   $C = \textbf{31.4 inches}$

10. $C = \pi d$

   $C = 3.14(4)$

   $C = \textbf{12.56 inches}$

11. $C = \pi d$

   $C = 3.14(16)$

   $C = \textbf{50.24 inches}$

12. Draw 2 diameter lines. Insert the hole for the straw where the lines intersect. In other words, the center of the lid is at half the distance of the diameter.

Making Connections: Lines of Symmetry p. 105

1. **(2)** and **(4)**

2. **(1)**, **(2)**, and **(3)**

3. a.   b.   c.   d.

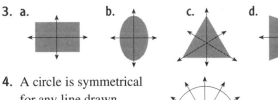

4. A circle is symmetrical for any line drawn through its center.

Properties of Triangles pp. 106–107

Part A

1. right

2. isosceles

3. equilateral

4. equilateral

Part B

5. a. 30°, 60°, 80° cannot form a triangle because the sum is 170°.

    c. 40°, 50°, 100° cannot form a triangle because the sum is 190°.

6. a. $\angle R = 180 - 90 - 40 = \textbf{50°}$

    b. $x + 2x + 114 = 180$

       $3x + 114 = 180$

       $3x = 66$

       $x = \textbf{22°} = \angle\textbf{N}$

       $\angle M = 2(22) = \textbf{44°}$

    c. $x + 2x + 3x = 180$

       $6x = 180$

       $x = \textbf{30°} = \angle\textbf{T}$

       $\angle Y = 2(30) = \textbf{60°}$

       $\angle P = 3(30) = \textbf{90°}$

7. The sum of the two acute angles is $180 - 90 = \textbf{90°}$.

8. No. If there are two right angles, there is no measurement left for the third angle since $90° + 90° = 180°$. An angle does not exist at 0°.

9. Side BC is the longest because it is opposite $\angle$A, which is the largest angle.

10. $\angle$H is the largest angle because it is opposite GI, the longest side.

11. Let x represent the vertex angle.

    $65 + 65 + x = 180$

    $130 + x = 180$

    $x = \textbf{50°} = \angle\textbf{H}$

12. Let x represent each base angle.

    $x + x + 42 = 180$

    $2x + 42 = 180$

    $2x = 138$

    $x = \textbf{69°} = \textbf{each base angle}$

13. Combination b (7, 8, 16) cannot be a triangle because the sum of the sides 7 inches and 8 inches long is not long enough for the third side, 16 inches.

    Combination c (4, 5, 9) cannot be a triangle because the sum of the sides 4 and 5 inches long is exactly the length of the third side, 9 inches.

    The *sum* of any two sides must be greater than the third side.

The Pythagorean Theorem pp. 108–109

Part A

1. $a^2 + b^2 = c^2$

    $16^2 + 12^2 = c^2$

    $256 + 144 = c^2$

    $400 = c^2$

    $\sqrt{400} = c$

    $\textbf{20 inches} = c$

2. $a^2 + b^2 = c^2$

    $7^2 + 24^2 = c^2$

    $49 + 576 = c^2$

    $625 = c^2$

    $\sqrt{625} = c$

    $\textbf{25} = c$

3. $a^2 + b^2 = c^2$

$300^2 + 400^2 = c^2$

$90{,}000 + 160{,}000 = c^2$

$250{,}000 = c^2$

$\sqrt{250{,}000} = c$

$500 \text{ yd.} = c$

Distance walking along the edge: $300 + 400 = 700$ yd. Yards saved: $700 - 500 = \textbf{200 yards}$

Part B

4. $a^2 + b^2 = c^2$

$5^2 + b^2 = 13^2$

$25 + b^2 = 169$

$b^2 = 144$

$b = \sqrt{144}$

$b = \textbf{12 centimeters}$

5. $a^2 + b^2 = c^2$

$8^2 + b^2 = 10^2$

$64 + b^2 = 100$

$b^2 = 36$

$b = \sqrt{36}$

$b = \textbf{6 inches}$

6. $a^2 + b^2 = c^2$

$90^2 + 90^2 = c^2$

$8{,}100 + 8{,}100 = c^2$

$16{,}200 = c^2$

$\sqrt{16{,}200} = c$

$\textbf{127.3 feet} = c$

Making Connections: Pythagorean Triples p. 109

1. The numbers in each column are multiples of the first number in the column. For example, 3, 6, and 9 are all multiples of 3. Each row also shows a pattern. Values 3, 4, and 5 are each 1 unit more than the value before it. Values 6, 8, and 10 are 2 units apart. Values 9, 12, and 15 are 3 units apart.

a	*b*	*c*
3	4	5
6	8	10
9	12	15
12	16	20
15	20	25

2.

a	*b*	*c*
5	12	13
10	24	26
15	36	39
20	48	52

Understanding Maps pp. 110–111

Part A

1. a. 27 miles

$2\frac{1}{4} \cdot 12 = 27$

d. 15 miles

$1\frac{1}{4} \cdot 12 = 15$

b. 24 miles

$2 \cdot 12 = 24$

e. 21 miles

$12\left(\frac{3}{4} + 1\right) = 9 + 12 = 21$

c. 18 miles

$1\frac{1}{2} \cdot 12 = 18$

2. $a^2 + b^2 = c^2$

$9^2 + 12^2 = c^2$

$81 + 144 = c^2$

$225 = c^2$

$\sqrt{225} = c$

15 miles $= c$

You can also measure the hypotenuse:

$1\frac{1}{4} \cdot 12 = \textbf{15 miles}$

3. (2) $x > 27$ miles

Part B

4. (3) 500 feet

The approximate length of the water main running from the east side of Elm Street to the west side of Spruce Avenue on the map is $2\frac{1}{2}$ in. Since 1 in. $= 200$ ft., the actual distance is $2\frac{1}{2}(200) = 500$ feet.

5. (2) 1,200 feet

Approximate distances may vary. The approximate distance from the police department to the fire station on the map is $4\frac{3}{4}$ in. $+ 1\frac{1}{4}$ in. $= 6$ in. Since 1 in. $= 200$ ft., the actual distance is $6(200) = 1{,}200$ feet.

6. $a^2 + b^2 = c^2$

$200^2 + 400^2 = c^2$

$40{,}000 + 160{,}000 = c^2$

$200{,}000 = c^2$

$\sqrt{200{,}000} = c$

$447.2 \approx c$

To the nearest 10 feet, this is **450 feet.**

You can also measure the hypotenuse:

$2\frac{1}{4} \cdot 200 = \textbf{450 feet}$

7. The shortest way to get from the corner of Maple and First to the fire station is to take the diagonal walk through the walkway. Then walk down Second Street to the fire station. The hypotenuse (about 450 ft.) is shorter than the sum of the two legs (400 ft. + 200 ft. = 600 ft.)

Unit 3 Review pp. 112–113

Part A

1. 65°
3. 42°
2. 127°
4. 120°

Part B

5. d
8. b
6. a
9. e
7. c
10. f

Part C

11. $2\frac{3}{4}$ inches

12. 4.2 centimeters

Part D

13. (3) street

14. $a^2 + b^2 = c^2$

$30^2 + 40^2 = c^2$

$900 + 1{,}600 = c^2$

$2{,}500 = c^2$

$\sqrt{2{,}500} = c$

50 feet $= c$

Part E

15. $d = 2r = 2(20 \text{ ft.}) =$ **40 feet**

16. $C = \pi d = 3.14(40) = 125.6 \text{ ft.} =$
126 feet to the nearest foot

Part F

17. Let x represent the vertex angle.

$48 + 48 + x = 180$

$96 + x = 180$

$x = 84°$

18. $l = 9\frac{1}{2}(2.54) = 24.13 =$
24 centimeters to the nearest centimeter

$w = 4(2.54) = 10.16 =$
10 centimeters to the nearest centimeter

19. (3) **45 miles**

The distance between Centerville and the bridge is $1\frac{1}{2}$ inches on the map.

$1\frac{1}{2}(30) = 45$ miles

Working Together

1–2. Answers will vary.

3. The illustration below shows a series of isosceles triangles each with a base of 2 inches. Each triangle is labeled with a number at the vertex. As the base angles get smaller, the triangles get "flatter." The perimeter gets smaller and closer to 4 inches.

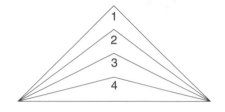

Unit 4

How Do I Use Geometry? p. 115

Talk About It

Discussion will vary.

Perimeter and Circumference Formulas pp. 116–117

Part A

1. $P = 2l + 2w$

$P = 2(12) + 2(5)$

$P = 24 + 10$

$P =$ **34 feet**

2. $P = 4s$

$P = 4(16)$

$P =$ **64 centimeters**

3. $P = s_1 + s_2 + s_3$

$P = 8 + 8 + 10$

$P =$ **26 inches**

4. $P = s_1 + s_2 + s_3 + s_4 + s_5 + s_6$

$P = 5 + 5 + 4 + 5 + 5 + 4$

$P =$ **28 inches**

Part B

5. $C = \pi d$

$C = 3.14(100)$

$C =$ **314 meters**

6. $C = 2\pi r$

$C = 2 \cdot 3.14 \cdot \frac{1}{2}$

$C =$ **3.14 inches**

7. $C = \pi d$

$C = 3.14(9)$

$C =$ **28.26 yards**

Part C

8. $P = s_1 + s_2 + s_3$

   $P = s + s + (s + 2)$

   $P = 3s + 2$

9. $P = 3(8) + 2$

   $P = 24 + 2$

   $P = 26$ centimeters

10. $P = 2l + 2w$

    $P = 2(2w) + 2w$

    $P = 4w + 2w$

    $P = 6w$

11. $P = 6(10)$

    $P = 60$ inches

12. a. $C = \pi d$

    $C = 3.14(10)$

    $C = 31.4$ centimeters

    b. $P = 4s$

    $P = 4(10)$

    $P = 40$ centimeters

13. a. (3) $s \approx 7$

    $s = \sqrt{5^2 + 5^2}$

    $s = \sqrt{25 + 25}$

    $s = \sqrt{50} \approx \sqrt{49} = 7$

    b. $P = 4s$

    $P \approx 4(7)$

    $P \approx 28$ centimeters

14. a. (2) $d + \frac{1}{2}\pi d$

    It expresses the diameter plus half the circumference.

    b. $49 + \frac{1}{2}\left(\frac{22}{7} \cdot 49\right) = 49 + \frac{1}{2}(154) = 49 + 77 =$ **126 feet**

15. a. $120 = 2l + 2(25)$

    $120 = 2l + 50$

    $70 = 2l$

    35 feet $= l$

    b. $120 = 2l + 2(20)$

    $120 = 2l + 40$

    $80 = 2l$

    40 feet $= l$

    c. $120 = 2l + 2(15)$

    $120 = 2l + 30$

    $90 = 2l$

    45 feet $= l$

    d. $120 = 2l + 2(10)$

    $120 = 2l + 20$

    $100 = 2l$

    50 feet $= l$

Solving Complex Perimeter Problems pp. 118–119

Part A

1. $b = 20 + 3 =$ **23**

   $r = 9 + 6 =$ **15**

   $P = 23 + 15 + 20 + 6 + 3 + 9$

   $P = 76$ units

2. $x = 16 - 9 =$ **7**

   $y = 12 - 8 =$ **4**

   $P = 12 + 16 + 8 + 7 + 4 + 9$

   $P = 56$ units

3. $c = 12 - 4 =$ **8**

   $d = 12 - 5 =$ **7**

   $P = 12 + 12 + 7 + 4 + 5 + 8$

   $P = 48$ units

4. $u = 9 + 10 =$ **19**

   $t = 25 - 10 =$ **15**

   $P = 25 + 19 + 10 + 10 + 15 + 9$

   $P = 88$ units

Part B

5. missing vertical side $= 20 - 9 = 11$ ft.

   missing horizontal side $= 26 - 14 = 12$ ft.

   $P = 26 + 20 + 14 + 11 + 12 + 9$

   $P = 92$ feet

6. You do not know exactly where the diving area is placed. However, the total horizontal dimensions are $2(60) = 120$ ft. The left and right sides add up to $2(30) = 60$ ft. The perimeter includes 2 additional 8-foot stretches, or $2(8) = 16$ ft. The perimeter is $120 + 60 + 16 =$ **196 feet.**

7. a. small vertical side $= 10 - 7 = 3$ ft.

   small horizontal side $= 12 - 8 = 4$ ft.

   $c = \sqrt{3^2 + 4^2}$

   $c = \sqrt{9 + 16}$

   $c = \sqrt{25}$

   $c = 5$ feet

   b. $P = 12 + 7 + 5 + 8 + 10$

   $P = 42$ feet

Part C

8. c

9. d

10. b

11. a

Part D

12. The perimeter includes 2 half circles (or 1 circle) and 2 lengths of 40 inches each.

    $P = \pi d + 40 + 40$

    $P = 3.14 \cdot 30 + 80 = 94.2 + 80 =$ **174.2 inches**

13. The total length along which diners will sit is:

    $6 + 3 + 6 + 6 + 3 + 6 = 30$ ft.

    At 2 feet per diner, the tables accommodate $\frac{30}{2} =$ **15 people.**

14. As the figure is drawn,
$$P = 3 + 5 + 6 + 2 + 9 + 7 = 32.$$

When 3 becomes 4 and 2 becomes 3,
$$P = 4 + 4 + 5 + 3 + 9 + 7 = 32.$$

The perimeter does not change.

Area Formulas pp. 120–121

Part A

1. $A = lw$

$A = 7 \cdot 3$

$A =$ **21 square meters**

2. $A = \frac{1}{2}bh$

$A = \frac{1}{2} \cdot 12 \cdot 10$

$A =$ **60 square feet**

3. $A = bh$

$A = 14 \cdot 9$

$A =$ **126 square centimeters**

4. $A = s^2$

$A = 11^2$

$A = 11 \cdot 11$

$A =$ **121 square centimeters**

Part B

5. $A = s^2$

$400 = s^2$

$\sqrt{400} = s$

20 meters $= s$

6. $A = lw$

$180 = 30w$

6 centimeters $= w$

7. $A = \frac{1}{2}bh$

$96 = \frac{1}{2} \cdot 12h$

$96 = 6h$

16 inches $= h$

8. $A = bh$

$300 = b \cdot 15$

20 meters $= b$

Part C

9. $A = \pi r^2$

$A = 3.14 \cdot 3^2$

$A = 3.14 \cdot 9$

$A =$ **28.26 square inches**

10. $A = \pi r^2$

$A = 3.14 \cdot 100^2$

$A = 3.14 \cdot 10,000$

$A =$ **31,400 square meters**

11. $r = \frac{1}{2}d$

$r = 1$ in.

$A = \pi r^2$

$A = 3.14(1)^2$

$A = 3.14(1)$

$A =$ **3.14 square inches**

Part D

12. (1) πr^2

13. (2) r^2

14. (3) $4r^2$

The large square is made up of 4 small squares. Each small square has an area of r^2. Therefore, the area of the large square is $4r^2$.

Part E

15. $A = lw$

$A = 110 \cdot 90$

$A =$ **9,900 square feet**

16. a. (3) $\frac{1}{2}\pi r^2$

The area is half the area of a circle.

b. $\frac{1}{2}\pi r^2 = \frac{1}{2} \cdot 3.14(2)^2 = \frac{1}{2} \cdot 3.14 \cdot 4 = 3.14 \cdot 2 =$ **6.28 square feet**

17. When $w = 1$ in., $A = 12(1) = 12$ in.^{2}

When $w = \frac{1}{2}$ in., $A = 12\left(\frac{1}{2}\right) = 6$ in.^{2}

When $w = \frac{1}{4}$ in., $A = 12\left(\frac{1}{4}\right) = 3$ in.^{2}

When $w = \frac{1}{8}$ in., $A = 12\left(\frac{1}{8}\right) = \frac{12}{8} = 1\frac{4}{8} = 1\frac{1}{2}$ or 1.5 in.^{2}

When $w = \frac{1}{16}$ in., $A = 12\left(\frac{1}{16}\right) = \frac{12}{16} = \frac{3}{4}$ or 0.75 in.^{2}

Each area is half of the preceding area.

Solving Complex Area Problems pp. 122–123

Part A

1. larger rectangle $A = lw = 9 \cdot 5 = 45$ yd.^{2}

smaller rectangle $A = lw = 4 \cdot 3 = 12$ yd.^{2}

sum $= 45 + 12 =$ **57 square yards**

2. square $A = s^2 = 8^2 = 64$ cm^2

semicircle $A = \frac{1}{2}\pi r^2 = \frac{1}{2} \cdot 3.14 \cdot 4^2 = 3.14 \cdot 8 = 25.12$ cm^2

sum $= 64 + 25.12 =$ **89.12 square centimeters**

3. triangle $A = \frac{1}{2}bh = \frac{1}{2} \cdot 25 \cdot 10 = 125$ ft.^{2}

rectangle $A = lw = 25 \cdot 20 = 500$ ft.^{2}

sum $= 125 + 500 =$ **625 square feet**

Part B

4. rectangle $A = 25 \cdot 20 = 500$ ft.^{2}

   triangle $A = \frac{1}{2} \cdot 10 \cdot 25 = 125$ ft.^{2}

   difference $= 500 - 125 =$ **375 square feet**

5. larger rectangle $A = 5 \cdot 9 = 45$ yd.^{2}

   smaller rectangle $A = 3 \cdot 4 = 12$ yd.^{2}

   difference $= 45 - 12 =$ **33 square yards**

6. square $A = 8 \cdot 8 = 64$ cm^2

   semicircle $A = \frac{1}{2} \cdot 3.14 \cdot 4^2 = 25.12$ cm^2

   difference $= 64 - 25.12 =$
   38.88 square centimeters

Part C

All of the figures will have the same area. No matter how the measurements are broken up, the distributive property guarantees that the perimeter and area of the figure will remain the same.

7. Area $A = 5 \cdot 4 = 20$ ft.^{2}

   Area $B = 10 \cdot 8 = 80$ ft.^{2}

   sum $=$ **100 square feet**

8. Area $C = 12 \cdot 5 = 60$ ft.^{2}

   Area $D = 8 \cdot 5 = 40$ ft.^{2}

   sum $=$ **100 square feet**

9. Area $E = 5 \cdot 4 = 20$ ft.^{2}

   Area $F = 8 \cdot 5 = 40$ ft.^{2}

   Area $G = 8 \cdot 5 = 40$ ft.^{2}

   sum $=$ **100 square feet**

10. Area $H = 12 \cdot 10 = 120$ ft.^{2}

    Area $I = 5 \cdot 4 = 20$ ft.^{2}

    difference $=$ **100 square feet**

Part D

11. large area $= 80 \cdot 45 = 3,600$ ft.^{2}

    pool area $= 60 \cdot 25 = 1,500$ ft.^{2}

    difference $=$ **2,100 square feet**

12. **(3) $7s^2$**

    There are 5 squares, each with an area of s^2. Together, the two half squares at the top have the same area as one square. Together, the two half squares at the bottom also have the same area as one square. The total area is $5s^2 + s^2 + s^2 = 7s^2$.

13. $7s^2 = 7(10)^2 = 7(100) =$ **700 square centimeters**

14. **(1) $10s^2$**

15. $10s^2 = 10(3)^2 = 10(9) =$ **90 square inches**

16. Estimates will vary.

    a. $P = 9 + 8 + 2 + 3 + 7 + 5 =$ **34 feet**

    $A = 9 \cdot 8 - 7 \cdot 3 = 72 - 21 =$ **51 square feet**

    b. $P = 9 + 8 + 4 + 3 + 5 + 5 =$ **34 feet**

    $A = 9 \cdot 8 - 5 \cdot 3 = 72 - 15 =$ **57 square feet**

    c. $P = 9 + 8 + 6 + 3 + 3 + 5 =$ **34 feet**

    $A = 9 \cdot 8 - 3 \cdot 3 = 72 - 9 =$ **63 square feet**

    The perimeter stays the same from room to room, but the area gets bigger. Plan c has the greatest area.

Solid Figures pp. 124–125

Part A

1. $V = lwh$

   $V = 10 \cdot 6 \cdot 4$

   $V =$ **240 cubic meters**

2. $V = lwh$

   $V = 7 \cdot 4 \cdot 1$

   $V =$ **28 cubic inches**

3. $V = lwh$

   $V = 7 \cdot 4 \cdot 2$

   $V =$ **56 cubic inches**

Part B

4. $V = s^3$

   $V = 5^3 = 5 \cdot 5 \cdot 5$

   $V =$ **125 cubic centimeters**

5. $V = s^3$

   $V = 1^3 = 1 \cdot 1 \cdot 1$

   $V =$ **1 cubic yard**

6. $V = s^3$

   $V = 12^3 = 12 \cdot 12 \cdot 12$

   $V =$ **1,728 cubic inches**

Part C

7. $V = lwh$

   $V = 40 \cdot 20 \cdot 2$

   $V =$ **1,600 cubic inches**

8. $V = lwh$

   $V = 30 \cdot 20 \cdot 10$

   $V =$ **6,000 cubic feet**

9. cube: $V = s^3 = 6^3 = 216$ ft.^{3}

   rectangular solid: $V = lwh = 8 \cdot 6 \cdot 4 = 192$ ft.^{3}

   The cube-shaped crate has a larger volume.

10. $V = lwh$

    $V = 16 \cdot 4 \cdot \frac{1}{2}$

    $V =$ **32 cubic feet**

11. When $s = 3$ in., $V = 3^3 = 27$ in.^{3}

When $s = 6$ in., $V = 6^3 = 216$ in.^{3}

The new volume is 8 (that is, 2^3) times as big as the old volume. $\frac{216}{27} = 8$

Volume Formulas pp. 126–127

Part A

1. $V = \pi r^2 h$

$V = 3.14 \cdot 4^2 \cdot 9$

$V = 3.14 \cdot 16 \cdot 9$

$V = $ **452.16 cubic centimeters**

2. $V = s^3$

$V = (3)^3$

$V = (3)(3)(3)$

$V = $ **27 cubic meters**

3. $V = \pi r^2 h$

$V = 3.14 \cdot 5^2 \cdot 12$

$V = 3.14 \cdot 25 \cdot 12$

$V = $ **942 cubic inches**

4. $V = \pi r^2 h$

$V = 3.14 \cdot 4^2 \cdot 12$

$V = 3.14 \cdot 16 \cdot 12$

$V = $ **602.88 cubic feet**

5. $V = \pi r^2 h$

$V = 3.14 \cdot 6^2 \cdot 5$

$V = 3.14 \cdot 36 \cdot 5$

$V = $ **565.2 cubic feet**

6. $V = lwh$

$V = 12 \cdot 8 \cdot 2$

$V = $ **192 cubic feet**

Part B

7. **a.** $V = lwh$

$120 = 10 \cdot 6h$

$120 = 60h$

2 centimeters $= h$

b. $300 = 10 \cdot 6h$

$300 = 60h$

5 centimeters $= h$

8. 4 in. $= \frac{4}{12} = \frac{1}{3}$ ft.

$V = lwh$

$V = 16 \cdot 12 \cdot \frac{1}{3}$

$V = $ **64 cubic feet**

9. **a.** $V = \pi r^2 h$

$r = \frac{1}{2}d = \frac{1}{2}(8) = 4$

$V = 3.14 \cdot 4^2 \cdot 20$

$V = 3.14 \cdot 16 \cdot 20$

$V = $ **1,004.8 cubic feet**

b. $7.5(1,004.8) = $ **7,536 gallons**

10. **No,** the can holds more than the box.

can: $V = \pi r^2 h$

$V = 3.14 \cdot 5^2 \cdot 12$

$V = 3.14 \cdot 25 \cdot 12$

$V = 942$ in.^{3}

box: $V = lwh$

$V = 15 \cdot 12 \cdot 5$

$V = 900$ in.^{3}

942 in.$^3 > 900$ in.^{3}

Making Connections: Finding Capacity p. 127

container: $V = lwh$

$V = 30 \cdot 20 \cdot 20$

$V = 12,000$ in.^{3}

$\frac{12,000}{230} \approx 52.2$ gal.

Choice **(4)** 50 gallons is correct.

Surface Area pp. 128–129

1. **(4)** $6s^2$

2. **a.** $6(10)^2 = 6(100) = $ **600 square centimeters**

   b. $V = s^3 = 10^3 = 10 \cdot 10 \cdot 10 = $ **1,000 cubic centimeters**

3. front $A = 15 \cdot 10 = 150$ ft.^{2}

back $A = 15 \cdot 10 = 150$ ft.^{2}

left $A = 15 \cdot 5 = 75$ ft.^{2}

right $A = 15 \cdot 5 = 75$ ft.^{2}

top $A = 10 \cdot 5 = 50$ ft.^{2}

bottom $A = 10 \cdot 5 = 50$ ft.^{2}

total A = **550 square feet**

4. $V = lwh$

$V = 15 \cdot 10 \cdot 5 = $ **750 cubic feet**

5. front $A = 2 \cdot 1 = 2$ ft.^{2}

back $A = 2 \cdot 1 = 2$ ft.^{2}

left $A = 3 \cdot 1 = 3$ ft.^{2}

right $A = 3 \cdot 1 = 3$ ft.^{2}

top $A = 3 \cdot 2 = 6$ ft.^{2}

bottom $A = 3 \cdot 2 = 6$ ft.^{2}

total A = **22 square feet**

6. $V = lwh$

   $V = 3 \cdot 2 \cdot 1 =$ **6 cubic feet**

7. Choice **(2)** is correct. Only choice **(2)** has six faces.

8. front $A = 8 \cdot 3 = 24$ ft.^{2}

   back $A = 8 \cdot 3 = 24$ ft.^{2}

   left $A = 11 \cdot 3 = 33$ ft.^{2}

   right $A = 11 \cdot 3 = 33$ ft.^{2}

   bottom $A = 11 \cdot 8 = 88$ ft.^{2}

   total $A =$ **202 square feet**

   (Notice that the truck bed has no top.)

9. $A = 6s^2 = 6(1)^2 = 6(1)(1) =$ **6 square inches**

10. **a.** front $A = 24 \cdot 16 = 384$ cm^2

    back $A = 24 \cdot 16 = 384$ cm^2

    left $A = 24 \cdot 6 = 144$ cm^2

    right $A = 24 \cdot 6 = 144$ cm^2

    top $A = 16 \cdot 6 = 96$ cm^2

    bottom $A = 16 \cdot 6 = 96$ cm^2

    total $A =$ **1,248 square centimeters**

    b. $V = lwh$

    $V = 16 \cdot 6 \cdot 24 =$ **2,304 cubic centimeters**

Making Connections: Finding the Surface Area of a Cylinder p. 129

1. **(4)** πd

   The length l is the circumference of the circle.

2. $A = lw$, where $l = \pi d$ and $w = h$

   $A = (\pi d)h$

3. $A = \pi r^2$

4. To find the total surface area of the cylinder, add the area of the rectangle to the total area of both circular bases.

Mixed Review pp. 130–131

Part A

1. $P = 3 + 3 + 5 + 5 + 4 + 4$

   $P =$ **24 inches**

2. right side $= 3 + 9 = 12$

   bottom $= 5 + 6 = 11$

   $P = 9 + 5 + 3 + 6 + 12 + 11$

   $P =$ **46 meters**

3. small horizontal line $= 20 - 11 = 9$

   small vertical line $= 18 - 4 = 14$

   $P = 20 + 18 + 11 + 14 + 9 + 4$

   $P =$ **76 feet**

Part B

4. $A = bh$

   $A = 20 \cdot 15$

   $A =$ **300 square centimeters**

5. right side $= 12 + 18 = 30$

   area of small rectangle on left: $A = lw = 15 \cdot 12 = 180$ ft.^{2}

   area of large rectangle on right: $A = lw = 30 \cdot 20 = 600$ ft.^{2}

   total $= 180 + 600 =$ **780 square feet**

   You may have used a different approach to solve this problem, but you should have gotten the same answer.

6. area of large rectangle: $A = lw = 60 \cdot 40 = 2,400$ m^2

   area of half circle: $A = \frac{1}{2}\pi r^2 = \frac{1}{2} \cdot 3.14(10)^2 = 157$ m^2

   difference $= 2,400 - 157 =$ **2,243 square meters**

Part C

7. $V = lwh$

   $V = 20 \cdot 14 \cdot 2$

   $V =$ **560 cubic feet**

8. $V = \pi r^2 h$

   $V = 3.14(10)^2 \cdot 12$

   $V =$ **3,768 cubic inches**

9. $V = s^3$

   $V = 15^3$

   $V =$ **3,375 cubic centimeters**

Part D

10. **(2)** is correct. Only choice **(2)** shows 6 faces.

11. top $A = 8 \cdot 5 = 40$ in.^{2}

    bottom $A = 8 \cdot 5 = 40$ in.^{2}

    left $A = 5 \cdot 2 = 10$ in.^{2}

    right $A = 5 \cdot 2 = 10$ in.^{2}

    front $A = 8 \cdot 2 = 16$ in.^{2}

    back $A = 8 \cdot 2 = 16$ in.^{2}

    total $A =$ **132 square inches**

12. $V = lwh$

    $V = 8 \cdot 5 \cdot 2$

    $V =$ **80 cubic inches**

Part E

13. a. $P = 2l + 2w$

   $P = 2(3w) + 2w$

   $P = 6w + 2w$

   $P = 8w$

   $P = 8(7)$

   $P = \textbf{56 feet}$

   b. $A = lw$

   $A = 21 \cdot 7$

   $A = \textbf{147 square feet}$

   c. $21 + 7 + 7 = \textbf{35 feet}$

   d. $\frac{147}{50} = 2.94 \approx \textbf{3 cans of stain}$

14. a. area of lot: $A = lw = 120 \cdot 80 = 9{,}600$ ft.^{2}

   area of house: $A = lw = 35 \cdot 20 = 700$ ft.^{2}

   area of driveway: $A = lw = 30 \cdot 10 = 300$ ft.^{2}

   area of yard: $9{,}600 - 700 - 300 =$ **8,600 square feet**

   b. $\frac{8{,}600}{1{,}000} = 8.6 \approx \textbf{9 bags of grass seed}$

15. **(2)** $3r^2 + \frac{1}{4}\pi r^2$

   The area is three small squares, each with side r, and one-fourth of a circle with radius r.

16. $h = \frac{6}{12} = \frac{1}{2}$ ft.

   $V = lwh$

   $V = 18 \cdot 18 \cdot \frac{1}{2}$

   $V = \textbf{162 cubic feet}$

17. $V = \pi r^2 h$

   $V = 3.14(2)^2 \cdot 1$

   $V = \textbf{12.56 cubic feet}$

18. $12.56(7.5) = \textbf{94.2 gallons}$

Seeing Geometric Figures pp. 132–133

Part A

1. rectangle

2. a. $l = 14$ ft. and $w = 9$ ft.

   b. $l = 7$ ft. and $w = 3$ ft.

   c. $l = 5$ ft. and $w = 3$ ft.

3. $A = lw = 5 \cdot 3 = \textbf{15 square feet}$

4. $A = lw = 7 \cdot 3 = \textbf{21 square feet}$

5. wall: $A = lw = 14 \cdot 9 = 126$ ft.^{2}

   wall area not including window and door:
   $126 - 21 - 15 = \textbf{90 square feet}$

Part B

6. 19 feet

7. 6 feet

8. $A = \pi r^2$

   $A = 3.14 \cdot 6^2$

   $A = 3.14 \cdot 36$

   $A = \textbf{113.04 square feet}$

9. $A = lw$

   $A = 94 \cdot 50$

   $A = \textbf{4,700 square feet}$

10. $P = 2l + 2w$

   $P = 2(94) + 2(50)$

   $P = 188 + 100$

   $P = \textbf{288 feet}$

11. $c^2 = a^2 + b^2$

   $c^2 = 10^2 + 15^2$

   $c^2 = 100 + 225$

   $c = \sqrt{325}$

   $c \approx \textbf{18 feet}$

Part C

12. **10 feet**

   $20 \div 2 = 10$

13. $A = \pi r^2$

   $A = 3.14(10)^2$

   $A = 3.14(100)$

   $A = \textbf{314 square feet}$

14. $V = \pi r^2 h$

   $V = 314(5)$

   $V = \textbf{1,570 cubic feet}$

Part D

15. **(4)** rectangular solid

16. $V = lwh$

   $V = 30 \cdot 22 \cdot 4$

   $V = \textbf{2,640 cubic centimeters}$

17. front $A = 30 \cdot 22 = 660$

   back $A = 30 \cdot 22 = 660$

   side $A = 30 \cdot 4 = 120$

   total $A = \textbf{1,440 square centimeters}$

Part E

18. **(1)** cylinder

19. **(4)** $3.14 \cdot 5^2 \cdot 14$

20. **(3)** πdh

   The surface area of the part with the label is the circumference (πd) times the height (h).

21. $2(\pi r^2) + (\pi dh)$

Choosing Perimeter, Area, or Volume pp. 134–135

Part A

1. a. perimeter

   b. $P = 2l + 2w$

   $P = 2(12) + 2(10)$

   $P = 24 + 20$

   $P = 44$ ft.

   Phil needs $44 - 3 = \textbf{41 feet of molding.}$

2. a. area

   b. $A = lw$

   $A = 9 \cdot 3$

   $A =$ **27 square feet**

3. a. volume

   b. $V = lwh$

   $V = 10 \cdot 6 \cdot 4$

   $V =$ **240 cubic feet**

4. a. area

   b. $A = lw$

   $A = 50 \cdot 30$

   $A = 1{,}500$ in.^{2}

   Each tile is $2 \cdot 2 = 4$ in.^{2}

   Marta needs $\frac{1{,}500}{4} =$ **375 tiles**

Part B

5. a. cubic feet

   b. 4 in. $= \frac{4}{12} = \frac{1}{3}$ ft.

   $V = lwh$

   $V = 6 \cdot 6 \cdot \frac{1}{3}$

   $V =$ **12 cubic feet**

6. a. square feet

   b. $A = lw$

   $A = 12 \cdot 9$

   $A =$ **108 square feet**

7. a. cubic feet

   b. truck bed: $V = lwh$

   $V = 10 \cdot 8 \cdot 4$

   $V =$ **320 cubic feet**

   c. box: $V = 2^3 = 8$ ft.^{3}

   Boris can load $\frac{320}{8} =$ **40 boxes.**

Making Connections: Comparing Perimeter and Area p. 135

1.

Shape	Perimeter	Area
A	18 yd.	20 yd.^{2}
B	42 yd.	20 yd.^{2}
C	18 yd.	14 yd.^{2}

2. B

3. C

4. A and C

5. A and B

6. (2)

Long, thin shapes tend to have relatively large perimeters and small areas.

Drawing a Picture pp. 136–137

1.

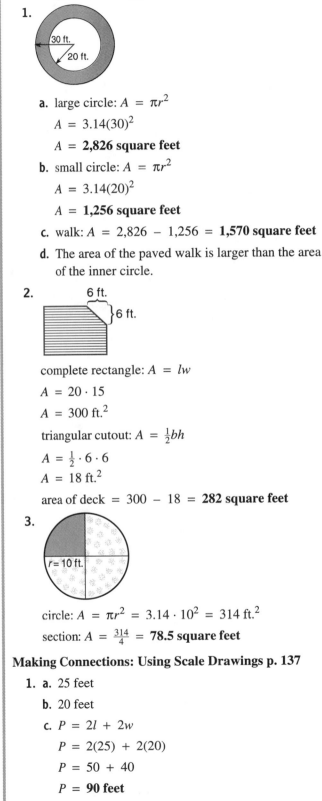

a. large circle: $A = \pi r^2$

   $A = 3.14(30)^2$

   $A =$ **2,826 square feet**

b. small circle: $A = \pi r^2$

   $A = 3.14(20)^2$

   $A =$ **1,256 square feet**

c. walk: $A = 2{,}826 - 1{,}256 =$ **1,570 square feet**

d. The area of the paved walk is larger than the area of the inner circle.

2.

complete rectangle: $A = lw$

$A = 20 \cdot 15$

$A = 300$ ft.^{2}

triangular cutout: $A = \frac{1}{2}bh$

$A = \frac{1}{2} \cdot 6 \cdot 6$

$A = 18$ ft.^{2}

area of deck $= 300 - 18 =$ **282 square feet**

3.

circle: $A = \pi r^2 = 3.14 \cdot 10^2 = 314$ ft.^{2}

section: $A = \frac{314}{4} =$ **78.5 square feet**

Making Connections: Using Scale Drawings p. 137

1. a. 25 feet

   b. 20 feet

   c. $P = 2l + 2w$

   $P = 2(25) + 2(20)$

   $P = 50 + 40$

   $P =$ **90 feet**

   d. No. You would also need to know the height of the roof to find its area.

2. **a.** 90 feet

   b. 60 feet

   c. $P = 2l + 2w$

   $P = 2(90) + 2(60)$

   $P = 180 + 120$

   $P = $ **300 feet**

   d. $A = lw$

   $A = 90 \cdot 60 = $ **5,400 square feet**

3. **a.** 24 feet

   b. 12 feet

   c. $C = \pi d$

   $C = 3.14 \cdot 24$

   $C = $ **75.36 feet**

   d. $A = \pi r^2$

   $A = 3.14(12)^2$

   $A = $ **452.16 square feet**

4. **a.** $V = \pi r^2 h$

   $V = 3.14(12)^2 \cdot 4$

   $V = 1,808.64$ to the nearest cubic foot $=$ **1,809 cubic feet**

   b. $1,809(7.5) = $ **13,567.5 gallons**

Renovating a Room pp. 138–139

Part A

1. $P = 2(16) + 2(12)$

   $P = 32 + 24$

   $P = $ **56 feet**

2. $3 + 3 = $ **6 feet**

3. $56 - 6 = $ **50 feet**

4. $A = 16 \cdot 12 = $ **192 square feet**

Part B

5. $A = 7 \cdot 3 = $ **21 square feet**

6. $A = 7 \cdot 4 = $ **28 square feet**

7. $A = 16 \cdot 8 = $ **128 square feet**

8. $128 - 28 - 21 = $ **79 square feet**

9. $P = 2(7) + 2(4)$

   $P = 14 + 8$

   $P = $ **22 feet**

Part C

10. 4

11. $A = 12 \cdot 5 = $ **60 square feet**

12. $A = 16 \cdot 8 = $ **128 square feet**

13. $A = 128 - 60 = $ **68 square feet**

Part D

14. $A = 7 \cdot 3 = $ **21 square feet**

15. 1

16. $A = 5 \cdot 3 = $ **15 square feet**

17. $A = 12 \cdot 8 = $ **96 square feet**

18. $96 - 21 - 15 = $ **60 square feet**

Part E

19. 2

20. $A = 6 \cdot 5 = $ **30 square feet** (for two windows)

21. $A = 12 \cdot 8 = $ **96 square feet**

22. $96 - 30 = $ **66 square feet**

Part F

23. $A = 16 \cdot 12 = $ **192 square feet**

24. $A = 8 \cdot 2 = $ **16 square feet**

25. $192 - 16 = $ **176 square feet**

Part G

26. $4 + 1 + 2 = $ **7**

27. $128 + 128 + 96 + 96 = $ **448 square feet**

28. $79 + 68 + 60 + 66 = $ **273 square feet**

29. Drawings will vary.

Using the Cost Formula pp. 140–141

Type of Work	Quantity (n)	Unit	Unit Price (r)	Total
1. new interior door	1	EA	$300	$300
2. new exterior door	1	EA	350	350
3. new window (26)	7	EA	375	2,625
4. framing around pass-through (9)	22	LF	7	154
5. new gypsum board walls (28)	273	SF	3	819
6. new gypsum board ceiling (23)	192	SF	4	768
7. light fixtures (24)	2	EA	80	160
8. new hardwood floor (4)	192	SF	6	1,152
9. baseboard molding (3)	50	LF	3	150
10. painting walls (27)	448	SF	.80	358.40
11. painting ceiling (23)	192	SF	1	192
12. electrical work (4)	192	SF	4	768
13. plumbing for radiators	—	LS	400	400
14. Total (before tax)				$8,196.40

Part B

Subtotal from line 14	$8,196.40
15. Contingencies (10%)	819.64
16. Overhead and profit (20%)	1,639.28
17. Total (not including tax)	$10,655.32

Making Connections: Multiplying Units p. 141

1. $\dfrac{30\ \cancel{\text{ft}}}{1} \cdot \dfrac{\$7}{1\ \cancel{\text{ft}}} = \dfrac{\$210}{1} = $ **$210**

2. $\dfrac{120\ \cancel{\text{ft}^2}}{1} \cdot \dfrac{\$6}{1\ \cancel{\text{ft}^2}} = \dfrac{\$720}{1} = $ **$720**

Unit 4 Review pp. 142–143

Part A

1. **(3)** volume
2. **(1)** flat figure
3. **(4)** surface area

Part B

4. left side $= 7 + 5 = 12$

   small horizontal side $= 13 - 10 = 3$

   $P = 13 + 5 + 3 + 7 + 10 + 12$

   $P = $ **50 meters**

5. $P = 7 + 7 + 5 + 5 + 8$

   $P = $ **32 inches**

6. The perimeter is $\frac{3}{4}$ of a circumference and 2 sides of a square. The diameter is $2(12) = 24$ cm.

   $\frac{3}{4}C = \frac{3}{4}\pi d$

   $= \frac{3}{4}(3.14)(24)$

   $= 56.52$ cm

   $P = 56.52 + 12 + 12 = $ **80.52 centimeters**

Part C

7. horizontal side at right is $18 - 8 = 10$ in.

   rectangle at left: $A = lw = 11 \cdot 8 = 88$ in.^{2}

   rectangle at right: $A = lw = 10 \cdot 8 = 80$ in.^{2}

   total $= $ **168 square inches**

8. large rectangle: $A = lw = 20 \cdot 15 = 300$ ft.^{2}

   small square: $A = s^2 = 6^2 = 36$ ft.^{2}

   difference: $A = $ **264 square feet**

9. The area is $\frac{3}{4}$ of a circle plus a square.

   circle: $\frac{3}{4}A = \frac{3}{4}\pi r^2$

   $= \frac{3}{4}(3.14)(8)^2$

   $= \frac{3}{4}(3.14)(64)$

   $= 150.72$ cm^2

   square: $A = s^2 = (8)^2 = 64$ cm^2

   total: $A = $ **214.72 square centimeters**

Part D

10. $V = lwh$

    $V = 20 \cdot 9 \cdot 3$

    $V = $ **540 cubic centimeters**

11. $V = \pi r^2 h$

    $V = 3.14(1)^2(3)$

    $V = $ **9.42 cubic meters**

12. $V = s^3$

    $V = 8^3$

    $V = $ **512 cubic feet**

Part E

13. $A = 6s^2$

    $A = 6(3)^2$

    $A = 6(9)$

    $A = $ **54 square inches**

14. $P = 2l + 2w$

    $P = 2(80) + 2(25)$

    $P = 160 + 50$

    $P = $ **210 feet**

15. **(1)** $18 \cdot 14 \cdot \$7$

Working Together

Answers will vary.

Unit 5

How Can Algebra and Geometry Work Together?
p. 145

Talk About It

Answers will vary.

Similar Figures pp. 146–147

Part A

1. **No,** the figures are not similar.

   Ratio of long sides $= \frac{8}{5}$

   Ratio of middle sides $= \frac{7}{4}$

   Ratio of short sides $= \frac{6}{3} = \frac{2}{1}$

2. **Yes,** the figures are similar.

   Ratio of long sides $= \frac{9}{6} = \frac{3}{2}$

   Ratio of short sides $= \frac{6}{4} = \frac{3}{2}$

3. **Yes,** the figures are similar.

   Ratio of long sides $= \frac{4}{8} = \frac{1}{2}$

   Ratio of short sides $= \frac{1\frac{1}{2}}{3} = \frac{1}{2}$

4. **Yes,** the figures are similar.

   Ratio of long sides $= \frac{18}{6} = \frac{3}{1}$

   Ratio of middle sides $= \frac{15}{5} = \frac{3}{1}$

   Ratio of short sides $= \frac{12}{4} = \frac{3}{1}$

Part B

5. Length of mat $= 12 + 3 + 3 = 18$ in.

   Width of mat $= 10 + 3 + 3 = 16$ in.

   Ratio of lengths $= 18:12 = 3:2$

   Ratio of widths $= 16:10 = 8:5$

   The picture and the mat are not similar figures.

   The picture and the mat do not have to be similar for the picture to fit in the mat.

6. Figures A and B are similar because the ratio of the length to the width for each is 3:2. Figure C is a parallelogram. It is not similar to the other two figures because its shape is different.

7. The two courts are not similar. The ratio of the length to the width for the high school court is $84:50 = 42:25$. The ratio of the length to the width for the college court is $94:50 = 47:25$. You can tell the figures are not similar without calculating because two sides in each figure are equal while the other sides are not.

8. **a.** $15:10 = $ **3:2**

   b. $9:6 = $ **3:2**

   c. $12:8 = $ **3:2**

   d. Yes, the triangles are similar.

9. **No.** The ratio of the length to the width of the original is $5:3\frac{1}{2}$.

   The ratio of the length to the width of the enlargement is $10:8 = 5:4$.

10. **a.** All squares are similar because they have the same shape and proportions.

    b. All equilateral triangles are similar because they have the same shape and proportions.

    c. Not all right triangles are similar because they do not all have the same shape and proportions.

    d. Not all isosceles triangles are similar because they do not all have the same shape and proportions.

Using Proportion with Similar Figures
pp. 148–149

Part A

1. $\frac{7}{4} = \frac{y}{12}$

   $4y = 84$

   $y = $ **21**

2. $\frac{12}{20} = \frac{18}{y}$

   $12y = 360$

   $y = $ **30**

3. $\frac{3}{5} = \frac{y}{30}$

   $5y = 90$

   $y = $ **18**

4. $\frac{6}{y} = \frac{10}{9}$

   $10y = 54$

   $y = $ **5.4** *or* $5\frac{2}{5}$

Part B

5. **a.** $\frac{5}{9} = \frac{30}{x}$

   $5x = 270$

   $x = $ **54**

   b. $\frac{5}{8} = \frac{30}{x}$

   $5x = 240$

   $x = $ **48**

   c. $\frac{5}{13} = \frac{30}{x}$

   $5x = 390$

   $x = $ **78**

6. $\frac{20}{35} = \frac{x}{140}$

   $35x = 2,800$

   $x = $ **80 feet**

7. $\frac{5}{2} = \frac{40}{x}$

   $5x = 80$

   $x = $ **16 feet**

8. $\frac{4}{3} = \frac{x}{36}$

   $3x = 144$

   $x = $ **48 feet**

9. $\frac{32}{24} = \frac{x}{6}$

   $24x = 192$

   $x = $ **8 inches**

Making Connections: Finding the Size of Reductions p. 149

1. **a.** $.75(8) = $ **6 inches**

   b. $.75(12) = $ **9 inches**

2. $\frac{12}{8} = \frac{9}{6}$

   $72 = 72$

   Yes, the document sizes are similar, and the ratios are equal.

3. The two documents are similar because the length and the width were reduced by the same percent. Therefore, their shape and proportions remained the same.

Finding Missing Dimensions pp. 150–151

Part A

1. $A = lw$

   $\frac{A}{w} = l$

   $\frac{300}{15} = l$

   $20 = l$

   $P = 2l + 2w$

   $P = 2(20) + 2(15)$

   $P = 40 + 30$

   $P = $ **70 centimeters**

2. $6s^2 = 726$

   $s^2 = 121$

   $s = \sqrt{121}$

   $s = $ **11 inches**

3. $V = lwh$ (where $h = $ depth)

   $75 = 15 \cdot 10h$

   $\frac{75}{150} = \frac{150h}{150}$

   $\frac{1}{2}$ **foot** $= h$

4. $V = \pi r^2 h$

   $6,280 = 3.14 \cdot 10^2 h$

   $6,280 = 3.14 \cdot 100h$

   $6,280 = 314h$

   20 feet $= h$

Part B

5. $lw = s^2$

$16w = 12^2$

$16w = 144$

$w = \textbf{9 inches}$

6. $4s = 2l + 2w$

$4(16) = 2l + 2(9)$

$64 = 2l + 18$

$46 = 2l$

$\textbf{23 meters} = l$

7. $lw + lw = 260$

$15(12) + 10w = 260$

$180 + 10w = 260$

$10w = 80$

$w = \textbf{8 feet}$

8. $lwh = s^3$

$8 \cdot 4h = 8^3$

$32h = 512$

$h = \textbf{16 meters}$

Making Connections: Choosing Dimensions p. 151

1.

	length	width	height	volume
Container A	8 ft.	5 ft.	10 ft.	400 ft.^{3}
Container B	8 ft.	6.25 ft.	8 ft.	400 ft.^{3}
Container C	5 ft.	5 ft.	16 ft.	400 ft.^{3}
Container D	20 ft.	4 ft.	5 ft.	400 ft.^{3}
Container E	10 ft.	4 ft.	10 ft.	400 ft.^{3}

2. Containers A, B, and E meet all the requirements. Container C's height is too great. Container D's length is too great.

Equations and Geometric Figures pp. 152–153

Part A

1. $x + 38° + x + 10° = 90°$

$2x + 48° = 90°$

$2x = 42°$

$x = 21°$

$\angle \textbf{c} = \textbf{21}°$

$x + 10° = 21° + 10° = 31°$

$\angle \textbf{d} = \textbf{31}°$

2. $40° + 3x + 4x = 180°$

$40° + 7x = 180°$

$7x = 140°$

$x = 20°$

$3x = 3(20°) = 60°$

$\angle \textbf{a} = \textbf{60}°$

$4x = 4(20°) = 80°$

$\angle \textbf{b} = \textbf{80}°$

Part B

3. Since $P = s_1 + s_2 + s_3$ and the sides are equal, $P = 3s$.

$\frac{1}{3}P = s$

$\frac{1}{3}(102) = s$

$\textbf{34 feet} = s$

4. $A = \frac{1}{2}bh$

$72 = \frac{1}{2}x \cdot x$

$2 \cdot 72 = x^2$

$144 = x^2$

$\sqrt{144} = x$

$\textbf{12 yards} = x$

5. (3)

6. $P = 2l + 2w$

$100 = 2(x + 2) + 2x$

$100 = 2x + 4 + 2x$

$100 = 4x + 4$

$96 = 4x$

$24 \text{ ft.} = x$

$\textbf{width} = \textbf{24 feet}$

$x + 2 = 24 + 2 = 26 \text{ ft.}$

$\textbf{length} = \textbf{26 feet}$

7. $P = 2l + 2w$

$560 = 2(9x) + 2(5x)$

$560 = 18x + 10x$

$560 = 28x$

$20 = x$

$9x = 9(20) = 180 \text{ ft.}$

$\textbf{length} = \textbf{180 feet}$

$5x = 5(20) = 100 \text{ ft.}$

$\textbf{width} = \textbf{100 feet}$

8. $A = lw$

$800 = 40w$

$20 = w$

$l{:}w = 40{:}20 = \textbf{2:1}$

9. a. The enlargements are *not* similar.

b. The enlargements are similar.

Setting Up Solutions pp. 154–155

1. (4) $\frac{1}{2} \cdot 13 \cdot 9$

$A = \frac{1}{2}bh$

$A = \frac{1}{2} \cdot 13 \cdot 9$

2. (2) $\frac{180}{15}$

$A = bh$

$180 = b \cdot 15$

$\frac{180}{15} = b$

3. (2) $\sqrt{10^2 + 6^2}$

$c^2 = a^2 + b^2$

$c^2 = 10^2 + 6^2$

$c = \sqrt{10^2 + 6^2}$

4. (1) $180 - 81$

$x = 180 - 33 - 48$

$x = 180 - 81$

5. (4) $\frac{5 \cdot 20}{7}$

$\frac{5}{7} = \frac{x}{20}$

$7x = 5 \cdot 20$

$\frac{7x}{7} = \frac{5 \cdot 20}{7}$

$x = \frac{5 \cdot 20}{7}$

6. (3) $\frac{360 - 200}{2}$

$P = 2l + 2w$

$360 = 2(100) + 2w$

$360 = 200 + 2w$

$\frac{360 - 200}{2} = \frac{2w}{2}$

$\frac{360 - 200}{2} = w$

Mixed Review pp. 156–157

Part A

1. **Yes.**

Ratio of long sides $= \frac{5}{20} = \frac{1}{4}$

Ratio of short sides $= \frac{4}{16} = \frac{1}{4}$

2. **No.**

Ratio of long sides $= \frac{18}{9} = \frac{2}{1}$

Ratio of short sides $= \frac{11}{4\frac{1}{2}}$

3. **No.**

Ratio of long sides $= \frac{9}{20}$

Ratio of middle sides $= \frac{8}{16} = \frac{1}{2}$

Ratio of short sides $= \frac{6}{14} = \frac{3}{7}$

4. **Yes.**

Ratio of long sides $= \frac{10}{15} = \frac{2}{3}$

Ratio of short sides $= \frac{6}{9} = \frac{2}{3}$

Part B

5. $\frac{8}{11} = \frac{24}{x}$

$8x = 264$

$x = \mathbf{33}$

7. (1) $\frac{10}{2\pi}$

$C = 2\pi r$

$10 = 2\pi r$

$\frac{10}{2\pi} = \frac{2\pi r}{2\pi}$

$\frac{10}{2\pi} = r$

8. (3) $\frac{1,000}{20}$

$V = lwh$

$1,000 = 20 \cdot 10 \cdot h$

$\frac{1,000}{20 \cdot 10} = \frac{20 \cdot 10 h}{20 \cdot 10}$

This form represents choice **(1)**.

In choice **(2)**, the denominator has been multiplied.

In choice **(4)**, the fraction has been simplified by dividing numerator and denominator by 10.

6. $\frac{9}{10} = \frac{x}{24}$

$10x = 216$

$x = \mathbf{21.6\ meters}$

7. $\frac{15}{20} = \frac{x}{3}$

$20x = 45$

$x = \mathbf{2\frac{1}{4}\ feet}$ *or* **2.25 feet**

8. $\frac{9}{x} = \frac{12}{40}$

$12x = 360$

$x = \mathbf{30}$

Part C

9. $\frac{6}{5} = \frac{x}{60}$

$5x = 360$

$x = \mathbf{72\ feet}$

10. $P = 4s$

$96 = 4s$

$24 = s$

$A = s^2$

$A = 24^2$

$A = \mathbf{576\ square\ inches}$

11. $lw = s^2$

$25w = 20^2$

$25w = 400$

$w = \mathbf{16\ yards}$

12. $6s^2 = 384$

$s^2 = 64$

$s = \sqrt{64}$

$s = \mathbf{8\ inches}$

13. $lw + lw = 360$

$12 \cdot 5 + 20w = 360$

$60 + 20w = 360$

$20w = 300$

$w = \mathbf{15\ feet}$

Part D

14. (2)

5x · 3x rectangle

15. a. $P = 2l + 2w$

$90 = 2(5x) + 2(4x)$

$90 = 10x + 8x$

$90 = 18x$

$5 = x$

$l = 5(5) = \mathbf{25\ feet}$

$w = 4(5) = \mathbf{20\ feet}$

b. $A = lw$

$A = 25 \cdot 20 = $ **500 square feet**

c. $\frac{500}{16} = 31.25$

31 students is the maximum.

16. (1) $\sqrt{200}$

$A = s^2$

$200 = s^2$

$\sqrt{200} = s$

17. (3) $\frac{3 \cdot 24}{5}$

$\frac{3}{5} = \frac{x}{24}$

$5x = 3 \cdot 24$

$\frac{5x}{5} = \frac{3 \cdot 24}{5}$

$x = \frac{3 \cdot 24}{5}$

18. (4) $\frac{20-6}{2}$

$P = 2l + 2w$

$20 = 2l + 2(3)$

$20 = 2l + 6$

$\frac{20-6}{2} = \frac{2l}{2}$

$\frac{20-6}{2} = l$

The Coordinate System pp. 158–159

Part A

1. A = (3,4)
2. B = (−2,3)
3. C = (−4,0)
4. D = (−3,−3)
5. E = (0,−4)
6. F = (5,−1)

Part B

7–12.

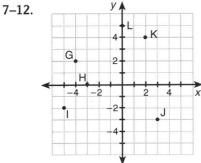

Part C

13. $|-2 - 5| = |-7| = 7$

or

W is 2 units left of the y-axis, and X is 5 units right of the y-axis, and 2 + 5 = **7.**

14. $|3 - (-1)| = |3 + 1| = 4$

or

W is 3 units above the x-axis, and Z is 1 unit below the x-axis, and 3 + 1 = **4.**

Part D

15. $|-2 - 3| = |-5| = 5$

or

K is 2 units left of the y-axis, and M is 3 units right of the y-axis, and 2 + 3 = **5.**

16. $|4 - (-2)| = |4 + 2| = 6$

or

L is 4 units above the x-axis, and M is 2 units below the x-axis, and 4 + 2 = **6.**

Making Connections: Reading Temperatures p. 159

1. $|-4 - (-2)| = |-4 + 2| = |-2| = \mathbf{2°}$

   or $|-2 - (-4)| = |-2 + 4| = |+2| = \mathbf{2°}$

2. The lowest temperature is −5°. The highest temperature is 3°. The difference is $|3 - (-5)| = |3 + 5| = \mathbf{8°}$ or $|-5 - 3| = |-8| = \mathbf{8°.}$

Distances on the Coordinate System pp. 160–161

Part A

1. length = horizontal distance = $|-3 - 5| = |-8| = \mathbf{8}$

2. width = vertical distance = $|-2 - 6| = |-8| = \mathbf{8}$

3. The figure is a square.

4. $P = 4s = 4(8) = \mathbf{32}$

5. $A = s^2 = 8^2 = \mathbf{64}$ **square units**

Part B

6. base = $|-4 - 7| = |-11| = \mathbf{11}$

7. height = $|4 - (-2)| = |4 + 2| = \mathbf{6}$

8. $A = \frac{1}{2}bh = \frac{1}{2} \cdot 11 \cdot 6 = \mathbf{33}$ **square units**

Part C

9. length = $|-2 - 10| = |-12| = \mathbf{12}$

10. width = $|3 - (-2)| = |3 + 2| = \mathbf{5}$

11. $P = 2l + 2w$

   $P = 2(12) + 2(5)$

   $P = 24 + 10$

   $P = \mathbf{34}$

12. $A = lw$

   $A = 12 \cdot 5$

   $A = \mathbf{60}$ **square units**

13. $KM = \sqrt{12^2 + 5^2}$

   $KM = \sqrt{144 + 25}$

   $KM = \sqrt{169}$

   $KM = \mathbf{13}$

Making Connections: Accident Reports p. 161

1. Vertical distance = 7 + 8 = 15 ft.

   Horizontal distance = 8 + 12 = 20 ft.

   $KM = \sqrt{15^2 + 20^2}$

   $KM = \sqrt{225 + 400}$

   $KM = \sqrt{625}$

   $KM = \mathbf{25 \ feet}$

2. 1 foot

Making a Table of Patterns pp. 162–163

Part A

1. a. $y = 3(5) = \mathbf{15}$
   b. $y = 3(1) = \mathbf{3}$
   c. $y = 3(-2) = \mathbf{-6}$

2. a. $y = 2 + 6 = \mathbf{8}$
   b. $y = 0 + 6 = \mathbf{6}$
   c. $y = -4 + 6 = \mathbf{2}$

Part B

3. $2 + 5 = 7$
   $0 + 5 = 5$
   $-3 + 5 = 2$

x	y
2	7
0	5
−3	2

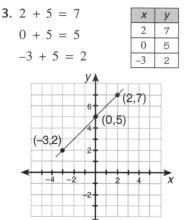

4. $6 - 2 = 4$
   $3 - 2 = 1$
   $-2 - 2 = -4$

x	y
6	4
3	1
−2	−4

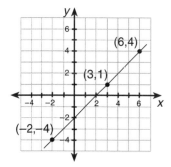

5. $2(3) = 6$
   $2(1) = 2$
   $2(-1) = -2$

x	y
3	6
1	2
−1	−2

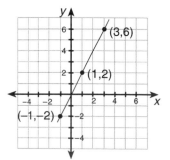

Making Connections: Graphing Complementary Angles p. 163

$90 - 15 = 75$

$90 - 30 = 60$

$90 - 50 = 40$

$90 - 65 = 25$

x°	y°
15	75
30	60
50	40
65	25

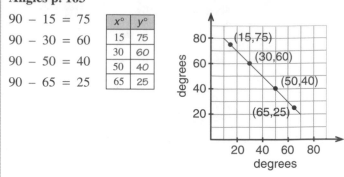

Graphing Multistep Linear Equations pp. 164–165

Part A

1. $2(4) - 5 = 8 - 5 = 3$
   $2(1) - 5 = 2 - 5 = -3$
   $2(-1) - 5 = -2 - 5 = -7$

x	y
4	3
1	−3
−1	−7

2. $4(0) + 1 = 0 + 1 = 1$
   $4(2) + 1 = 8 + 1 = 9$
   $4(-3) + 1 = -12 + 1 = -11$

x	y
0	1
2	9
−3	−11

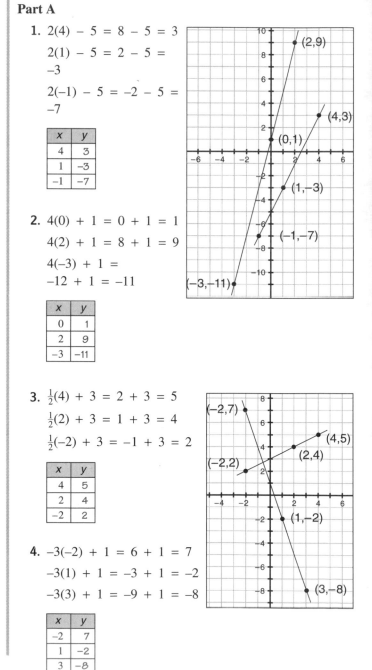

3. $\frac{1}{2}(4) + 3 = 2 + 3 = 5$
   $\frac{1}{2}(2) + 3 = 1 + 3 = 4$
   $\frac{1}{2}(-2) + 3 = -1 + 3 = 2$

x	y
4	5
2	4
−2	2

4. $-3(-2) + 1 = 6 + 1 = 7$
   $-3(1) + 1 = -3 + 1 = -2$
   $-3(3) + 1 = -9 + 1 = -8$

x	y
−2	7
1	−2
3	−8

Part B

5. Yes, when $x = 2$, $y = 6(2) - 1 = 12 - 1 = 11$.

6. Yes, when $x = 5$, $y = 13 - 5 = 8$.

7. No, when $x = 1$, $y = 5(1) + 4 = 5 + 4 = 9$.

Making Connections: Graphing Messenger Rates p. 165

$.75(1) + 2 = .75 + 2 = 2.75$

$.75(2) + 2 = 1.50 + 2 = 3.50$

$.75(3) + 2 = 2.25 + 2 = 4.25$

x	y
1	2.75
2	3.50
3	4.25

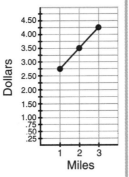

Slope and Intercept pp. 166–167

Part A

1. $\frac{y_2 - y_1}{x_2 - x_1} = \frac{4 - 2}{5 - 1} = \frac{2}{4} = \frac{1}{2}$

2. $\frac{y_2 - y_1}{x_2 - x_1} = \frac{1 - 7}{2 - (-2)} = \frac{-6}{2 + 2} = \frac{-6}{4} = -\frac{3}{2}$

3. $\frac{y_2 - y_1}{x_2 - x_1} = \frac{6 - (-2)}{2 - (-2)} = \frac{6 + 2}{2 + 2} = \frac{8}{4} = 2$

4. $\frac{y_2 - y_1}{x_2 - x_1} = \frac{-4 - 2}{5 - (-3)} = \frac{-6}{5 + 3} = \frac{-6}{8} = -\frac{3}{4}$

5. The roof with a pitch of 9 in 12 has a steeper slope. You could draw a sketch of the two roofs or compare ratios. A larger ratio means a steeper slope. A $\frac{3}{9}$ pitch has a slope of $\frac{3}{9} = \frac{1}{3}$. A $\frac{9}{12}$ pitch has a slope of $\frac{3}{4}$. For every 4 feet of run, the roof rises 3 feet.

Part B

6. $(0,5)$ **7.** $(4,0)$

Part C

8. $y = 2(0) - 1$

$y = 0 - 1$

$y = -1$

y-intercept $= (\mathbf{0,-1})$

$0 = 2x - 1$

$1 = 2x$

$\frac{1}{2} = x$

x-intercept $= \left(\mathbf{\frac{1}{2}, 0}\right)$

9. $2(0) + y = 5$ $2x + 0 = 5$

$0 + y = 5$ $2x = 5$

$y = 5$ $x = \frac{5}{2} = 2\frac{1}{2} = 2.5$

y-intercept $= (\mathbf{0,5})$ x-intercept $= (\mathbf{2.5,0})$

10. $y = \frac{1}{2}(0) + 3$ $0 = \frac{1}{2}x + 3$

$y = 0 + 3$ $-3 = \frac{1}{2}x$

$y = 3$ $-6 = x$

y-intercept $= (\mathbf{0,3})$ x-intercept $= (\mathbf{-6,0})$

Linear Equations and Graphs pp. 168–169

Part A

1.

hours	0	1	2	3	4
distance	0	40	80	120	160

In each case, use the formula $d = rt$.

For 2 hours, $d = 40(2) = 80$ miles.

For 3 hours, $d = 40(3) = 120$ miles.

For 4 hours, $d = 40(4) = 160$ miles.

2. **(2)** $d = 40h$

3. **(1)**

Only choice **(1)** shows the distance increasing from 0 miles.

In choice **(2)**, the distance decreases with time.

In choice **(3)**, the distance stays the same with time.

In choice **(4)**, the distance starts at 40 miles when no time has passed.

4. No, when $h = 5$, $d = 5(40) = 200$.

Part B

5.

w	5	10	15	20	25
l	45	40	35	30	25

6. **(2)**

In this graph, as w gets larger, l gets smaller.

In graph **(1)**, as w gets larger, l also gets larger.

The perimeter could not remain 100.

In graph **(3)**, as w gets larger, l stays the same.

The perimeter could not remain 100.

In graph **(4)**, as w stays the same, l gets larger.

The perimeter could not remain 100.

7. a. The two points are (10,40) and (20,30).

The slope is $\frac{30 - 40}{20 - 10} = \frac{-10}{10} = \mathbf{-1}$

b. The slope is **negative.** It falls from left to right.

8. The graph would cross the vertical axis when $w = 0$ and $l = 50$. This point cannot represent the length and width of a rectangle because the width has no value. A rectangle must have both a length and a width.

Making Connections: Renting Equipment p. 169

1.

hours	2	3	4	5
cost	20	25	30	35

2.

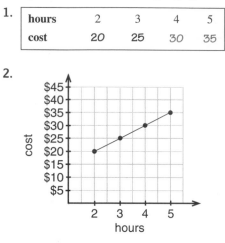

3. **(4)** $c = 5h + 20$

Choice **(1)** leaves out the $20.

Choice **(2)** charges $20 an hour.

Choice **(3)** charges $20 an hour and an additional $5.

4. **No.**

The first 2 hours cost $20. The remaining 6 hours are shown by h in the formula.

$c = 5(6) + 20 = 30 + 20 = \$50$

5. $c = 5(4) + 20 = 20 + 20 = \mathbf{\$40}$

6. positive; as the hours increase, the cost also increases.

Unit 5 Review pp. 170–171

Part A

1. No.

Ratio of long sides $= \frac{12}{16} = \frac{3}{4}$

Ratio of short sides $= \frac{8}{12} = \frac{2}{3}$

2. Yes.

Ratio of long sides $= \frac{12}{20} = \frac{3}{5}$

Ratio of short sides $= \frac{9}{15} = \frac{3}{5}$

Part B

3. $\frac{8}{5} = \frac{4}{x}$

$8x = 20$

$x = 2\frac{1}{2}$

4. $\frac{4}{5} = \frac{x}{10}$

$5x = 40$

$x = \mathbf{8}$

Part C

5. **(2) 30 feet**

$lw + lw = 1,125$

$l \cdot 25 + 25 \cdot 15 = 1,125$

$25l + 375 = 1,125$

$25l = 750$

$l = 30$

6. **(1)** $\frac{30 \cdot 60}{20}$

$\frac{20}{30} = \frac{60}{x}$

$20x = 30 \cdot 60$

$\frac{20x}{20} = \frac{30 \cdot 60}{20}$

Part D

7. A = (−3,4)

8. B = (5,4)

9. C = (5,−2)

10. $\left|-3 - 5\right| = \left|-8\right| = \mathbf{8}$ or Point A is 3 units left of y-axis and Point B is 5 units right. The total is $3 + 5 = \mathbf{8.}$

11. $\left|4 - (-2)\right| = \left|4 + 2\right| = \mathbf{6}$ or Point B is 4 units above the x-axis and Point C is 2 units below. The total is $4 + 2 = \mathbf{6.}$

12. Total horizontal distance from Point A to Point B is 8.

Total vertical distance from Point B to Point C is 6.

$c^2 = a^2 + b^2$

$c = \sqrt{a^2 + b^2}$

$AC = \sqrt{8^2 + 6^2}$

$AC = \sqrt{64 + 36}$

$AC = \sqrt{100}$

$AC = \mathbf{10}$

13. area $= 8 \cdot 6 = \mathbf{48\ square\ units}$

Part E

14. As t increases, d also increases.

15. The slope is positive. The graph rises from left to right.

16. (0,0) The graph intercepts both axes at the origin.

Working Together

Answers will vary.

Glossary

absolute value the distance of a number from zero on the number line (p. 23)

$$|-8| = 8 \text{ "The absolute value of } -8 \text{ is 8."}$$

acute angle an angle measuring less than 90° (p. 91)

60°

adjacent angles two angles that share a side (p. 95)

∠a and ∠b are adjacent.

angle a figure formed when two rays meet at a single point (p. 91)

area the amount of surface on a flat figure; usually in square units (p. 20)

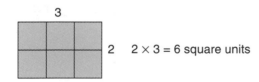

2 × 3 = 6 square units

base a number that is multiplied by itself in a power (p. 16)

exponent

$$3^2 = 3 \cdot 3 = 9$$

base

capacity the amount of liquid (such as milk) or granular substance (such as sugar) that a container can hold (p. 127)

circle a figure whose every point is the same distance from its center (p. 104)

circumference the distance around a circle (p. 104)

complementary angles two angles whose measures add up to 90° (p. 94)

∠c and ∠d are complementary.

coordinate system two perpendicular number lines that intersect at zero (p. 158)

cube a three-dimensional figure whose faces are all squares (p. 125)

degree a unit of measure for an angle (p. 91)

diameter a line segment that passes through the center of a circle and ends on the circle's edge (p. 104)

diameter

distributive property $a(x + y) = ax + ay$ (p. 40)

$$5(3 + 4) = 5 \cdot 3 + 5 \cdot 4$$

equation a statement that two mathematical expressions or amounts are equal (p. 52)

$$x + 7 = 12$$

equilateral triangle a triangle with three equal sides and three equal angles (p. 106)

5 m 60° 5 m
60° 60°
5 m

evaluate to solve (p. 18)

$$3x = 15$$
$$x = 5$$

exponent a number that tells how many times to multiply the base by itself (p. 16)

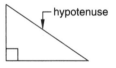

expression a mathematical amount written with symbols (p. 14)

$$9x + 4$$

horizontal running left and right (p. 90)

hypotenuse the side across from the right angle in a right triangle; the longest side of a right triangle (p. 108)

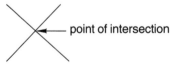

inequality a statement that expressions or amounts are not equal (p. 68)

2 < 5 "2 is less than 5"
8 > –1 "8 is greater than –1"

intersect to cross (p. 90)

point of intersection

inverse operation the opposite operation; the operation that can undo another operation (p. 14)

Subtraction is the inverse of addition.

isosceles a triangle with two equal angles and two equal sides (p. 106)

line a straight path of points that continues in two directions (p. 90)

linear referring to length; for example, linear measurements include inches and meters (p. 96)

linear equation an equation that, when graphed, forms a straight line on the coordinate system (p. 163)

line segment a straight path of points with definite length (p. 90)

negative number a number less than zero (p. 22)

–6 and –125

number line a line with evenly marked spaces to show the order of positive and negative numbers (p. 22)

number series a set of numbers that progress according to a rule (p. 32)

1, 3, 5, 7, . . .

obtuse angle an angle between 90° and 180° (p. 91)

135°

opposite across from (p. 102)

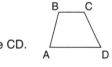

Side AB is opposite side CD.

parallelogram a quadrilateral with equal opposite sides and two pairs of parallel sides (p. 102)

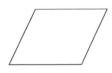

218

perimeter the distance around a flat figure (p. 20)

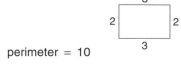

perimeter = 10

perpendicular meeting at right angles (p. 90)

Line AB is perpendicular to CD.

pi (π) the ratio of the circumference of a circle to its diameter, approximately 3.14 or $\frac{22}{7}$ (p. 104)

positive number a number greater than zero (p. 22)

+3 and +250

power a number multiplied by itself (p. 16)

$$5^2 = 5 \cdot 5 = 25$$
$$6^4 = 6 \cdot 6 \cdot 6 \cdot 6 = 1{,}296$$

proportion two equal ratios (p. 82)

$$4{:}6 = 2{:}3$$
$$\frac{4}{6} = \frac{2}{3}$$

Pythagorean theorem a formula that shows the relationship between the sides of a right triangle (p. 108)

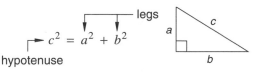

quadrilateral a polygon with four sides. Squares, rectangles, and parallelograms are examples (p. 102).

quotient the answer to a division problem (p. 15)

radius a line segment from the center of a circle to the circle's edge (p. 104)

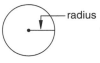

ratio a comparison of numbers by division (p. 80)

$\frac{1}{12}$: The ratio of 1 inch to 1 foot is 1 to 12.

ray a straight path of points that starts at one point and continues infinitely in one direction (p. 90)

rectangle a flat figure with four sides with opposite sides equal and sides meeting at right angles (p. 21)

right angle an angle measuring 90° (p. 91)

90°

right triangle a triangle with one right angle (p. 106)

90°

scientific notation a method of representing large numbers with powers of ten (p. 44)

$$270{,}000 = 2.7 \times 10^5$$

similar having the same shape and same proportions (p. 146)

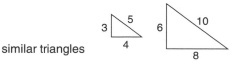

similar triangles

simplify to group variables and numbers in an expression (p. 42)

$$4x + 2 + 5x + 6 = 9x + 8$$

slope the ratio of rise to run of a line (p. 166)

square a flat figure with four equal sides and four right angles (p. 21)

square root the opposite of a squared number. The symbol for square root is $\sqrt{\ }$ (p. 17).

$$\sqrt{64} = 8$$

straight angle an angle measuring 180° (p. 91)

substitute to replace a variable with another value (p. 30)

$$\text{when } x = 5, x + 2 = 5 + 2 = 7$$

supplementary angles two angles that add up to 180° (p. 94)

∠m and ∠n are supplementary.

surface area the sum of the areas of the faces of a solid (p. 128)

symmetry a property that describes balanced shapes (p. 105)

trapezoid a figure with four straight sides and one pair of parallel sides (p. 102)

triangle a figure made up of three line segments (p. 106)

variable a letter or symbol representing an unknown value (p. 28)

vertex a point where two rays or two line segments meet (p. 91)

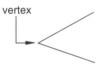

vertical running straight up and down (p. 90)

vertical angles two angles that do not share a side but are opposite each other when two lines intersect. Vertical angles are equal (p. 95).

volume the amount of space taken up or enclosed by a three-dimensional figure (p. 124)

x-axis the horizontal number line on a coordinate graph (p. 158)

y-axis the vertical number line on a coordinate graph (p. 158)

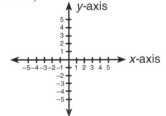

Tool Kit

Powers, Square Roots, and Order of Operations

Finding Powers

A **power** means a number multiplied by itself.

$$\text{base} \longrightarrow 4^2 \longleftarrow \text{exponent}$$

To find a power, write the base the number of times indicated by the exponent and multiply across.

Examples: $4^2 = 4 \cdot 4 = 16$ $\qquad 6^3 = 6 \cdot 6 \cdot 6$

$$36 \cdot 6 = 216$$

A number raised to the second power is called a square. A whole number squared is called a **perfect square.** The table at the right shows some common perfect squares.

Finding Square Roots

The opposite of squaring a number is finding a **square root.** The symbol for this operation is $\sqrt{}$, called a **radical sign.**

Example: Find $\sqrt{64}$.

To find a square root, ask yourself, "What number multiplied by itself would result in this number?" Since $8 \cdot 8 = 64$, $\sqrt{64} = 8$.

Learning the perfect squares listed in the table on this page can help you find some square roots. For large square roots, use a calculator.

Perfect Squares
$2^2 = 4$
$3^2 = 9$
$4^2 = 16$
$5^2 = 25$
$6^2 = 36$
$7^2 = 49$
$8^2 = 64$
$9^2 = 81$
$10^2 = 100$
$11^2 = 121$
$12^2 = 144$
$13^2 = 169$
$14^2 = 196$
$15^2 = 225$
$20^2 = 400$

Order of Operations

To evaluate expressions with two or more operations, perform the operations in the following order:

Example

1 Grouping symbols

$$\frac{(4 + 2)^2}{3} + 5 \cdot 4$$

2 Powers and roots

$$\frac{(6)^2}{3} + 5 \cdot 4$$

3 Multiplication and division

$$\frac{36}{3} + 5 \cdot 4$$

4 Addition and subtraction

$$12 + 20$$

$$\mathbf{32}$$

Within each level, work from left to right.

Tool Kit

Units of Linear Measurement and Rounding

English Units

In the English system, inch (in.), foot (ft.), yard (yd.), and mile (mi.) are the basic units of linear measurement.

The values of these units are shown in the table at the right.

Use substitution to change units.

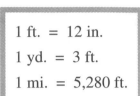

1 ft. = 12 in.

1 yd. = 3 ft.

1 mi. = 5,280 ft.

Metric Units

In the metric system, the meter (m) is the basic unit of linear measurement. The other common units are the millimeter (mm), the centimeter (cm), and the kilometer (km).

The values of these units are shown in the table at the right. Notice that no periods are used with metric abbreviations.

1 mm = 0.001 m

1 cm = 0.01 m

1 m = 1,000 mm = 100 cm

1 km = 1,000 m

Rounding

Rounding is used to find an approximate answer and to make numbers easier to work with.

Examples: Round 4.3 m to the nearest meter.

⌐ less than 5, round down to 4 m

Round 5.6 km to the nearest kilometer.

⌐ 5 or more, round up to 6 km

Tool Kit

Formulas and Calculators

	Shape	Figure	Formula	Description
P E R I M E T E R		Rectangle	$P = 2l + 2w$	l = length w = width
		Square	$P = 4s$	s = side
		Polygon with n sides	$P = s_1 + s_2 + ... + s_n$	s_1, etc. = each side
		Circle	$C = \pi d$ or $C = 2\pi r$	$\pi \approx 3.14$ d = diameter r = radius
A R E A		Rectangle	$A = lw$	l = length w = width
		Square	$A = s^2$	s = side
		Parallelogram	$A = bh$	b = base h = height
		Triangle	$A = \frac{1}{2}bh$	b = base h = height
		Circle	$A = \pi r^2$	$\pi \approx 3.14$ r = radius
V O L U M E		Rectangular solid	$V = lwh$	l = length w = width h = height
		Cube	$V = s^3$	s = side
		Cylinder	$V = \pi r^2 h$	$\pi \approx 3.14$ r = radius h = height

Tool Kit

Other Formulas

	Formula	Description
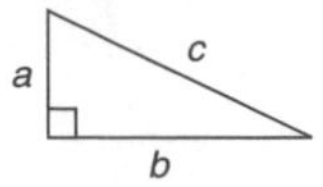 Pythagorean theorem	$a^2 + b^2 = c^2$	c = hypotenuse a and b = legs
Distance	$d = rt$	d = distance, r = rate, t = time
$$$ Cost	$c = nr$	c = cost, n = number of items, r = rate per item
Fahrenheit	$F = \frac{9}{5}C + 32$	F = Fahrenheit temperature C = Celsius temperature
Celsius	$C = \frac{5}{9}(F - 32)$	C = Celsius temperature F = Fahrenheit temperature
Slope	$m = \dfrac{y_2 - y_1}{x_2 - x_1}$	m = slope (x_1, y_1) and (x_2, y_2) are two points on the coordinate system.
Mean (Average)	$\text{mean} = \dfrac{x_1 + x_2 + \ldots x_n}{n}$	$x_1, x_2, \ldots x_n$ = items n = number of items

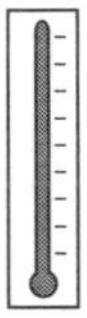

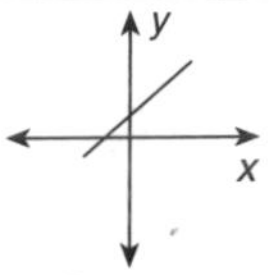

Using a Calculator

A calculator is a tool for solving problems quickly and accurately.

The picture at the right shows a typical calculator.

To evaluate solutions in this book, you will use the number keys (0 to 9), the decimal point key, the four operation keys ($+$, $-$, $\times$, and $\div$), the $=$ key, and the $\sqrt{\ }$ key.

Examples: To find the value of $3m$ when $m = 7$, enter $\boxed{3}$ $\boxed{\times}$ $\boxed{7}$ $\boxed{=}$.

To find $x - y$ when $x = 15$ and $y = 8$, enter $\boxed{1}$ $\boxed{5}$ $\boxed{-}$ $\boxed{8}$ $\boxed{=}$.

To find $\sqrt{289}$, enter $\boxed{2}$ $\boxed{8}$ $\boxed{9}$ $\boxed{\sqrt{\ }}$.